THEORETICAL STRUCTURAL METALLURGY

THEORETICAL STRUCTURAL METALLURGY

By

A. H. COTTRELL
B.Sc., M.A., Ph.D., F.R.S.

Professor of Metallurgy
University of Cambridge

LONDON
EDWARD ARNOLD (PUBLISHERS) LTD.

*First published 1948
Reprinted 1951, 1953
Second Edition 1955
Reprinted 1957, 1959, 1960, 1962*

*Printed in Great Britain by
The Camelot Press Ltd.,
London and Southampton*

PREFACE TO THE FIRST EDITION

THE fundamental concepts of the pure sciences are steadily replacing empirical experimental data as the bases upon which the science of metallurgy is founded, with the result that the numerous and diverse phenomena relating to metals and alloys are gradually being assembled within a common field of explanation. In this process important roles have been played by the sciences of wave mechanics and statistical thermodynamics which, by providing techniques for dealing with atomic structures and for deducing the properties of matter from atomic structure, are ideally suited for application to problems of metals and alloys.

Metallurgists and metallurgical students have very naturally shown a keen desire to study these theoretical advances, but have been hampered because they are usually unable to devote to theoretical physics the considerable time required to comprehend the appropriate research papers. It appeared that an account was needed, written for metallurgical students by a metallurgist, of the ways in which the ideas of atomic mechanics can be applied to problems of metals and alloys, and this has tempted me to prepare the present book.

Throughout the text I have adopted a theoretical outlook and, apart from the briefest of references to X-ray diffraction, there is no discussion of experimental methods. The treatment is mainly descriptive, and mathematics is confined to an elementary level. A certain amount of introductory material, both metallurgical and physical, has been included at appropriate places for the benefit of students previously unacquainted with either physical metallurgy or atomic physics, although no claim is made for comprehensiveness. The selection of topics is centred round the electron theory of metals and the statistical thermodynamics of metals and alloys. If the reader is surprised at the absence of certain subjects, for example, mechanical properties and recrystallisation, I would ask him to remember that, in general, the fields omitted are those of which no adequate theoretical treatment is yet possible. The science of metallurgy still faces many major problems, a fact which is both pleasing and provoking.

A. H. C.

Department of Metallurgy,
University of Birmingham.

PREFACE TO THE SECOND EDITION

ALTHOUGH the organisation in this edition is the same, apart from one new chapter, as that of the first, the tissue has been almost entirely replaced. The compelling reason for this is of course the unparalleled activity in all branches of the science of metals during the past decade. Apart from causing the rewriting of existing sections, the new developments have made it necessary to add accounts of topics such as, for example, the theory of dislocations, surface tensions of grain boundaries, and the physical metallurgy of carbon and nitrogen in ferrite. I had hoped at one time that these changes might be accomplished by means of a limited revision, but in the end it was found that nothing except a complete rewriting of the text would prove satisfactory. Further reasons for this were that I wanted to prevent the book from growing much larger, which meant redrafting existing material in a more economical style, and also wanted to take the opportunity of making a few changes of presentation for purely pedagogical reasons; for example, to delete the account of the old orbital theories of atomic structure, which tend to hinder rather than help the understanding of the modern theory, and to include a fuller explanation of the physical basis of Brillouin zones. The general point of view and purpose of the book are of course exactly the same as in the first edition.

A. H. C.

Department of Physical Metallurgy,
University of Birmingham.
June, 1954.

ACKNOWLEDGEMENTS

During the preparation of the second edition of this book I have had the benefit of useful discussions with several friends and colleagues. Particular thanks are due to Professor F. R. N. Nabarro, Professor G. V. Raynor, and Dr. R. W. Cahn, who have made valuable suggestions on many points of presentation. I am also glad to have this opportunity of acknowledging my great indebtedness to the late Professor D. Hanson, who inspired the teaching of physical metallurgy from the modern atomic standpoint at the University of Birmingham, and who was the first to encourage me to write this book.

Acknowledgement is made to the following for permission to reproduce diagrams: The Council of the Royal Society for Fig. 101; the Council of the Physical Society for Fig. 109; the Council of the Institute of Metals for Fig. 76; the American Institute of Mining and Metallurgical Engineers for Figs. 68 and 93; the American Society for Metals for Fig. 73; the Clarendon Press for Fig. 49; Messrs. Longmans, Green & Co. for Figs. 79, 85, and 86; Messrs. George Bell & Sons for Fig. 5; Messrs. Butterworth's Scientific Publications Ltd., and the Pergamon Press, for Figs. 120, 121, 122, and 125.

CONTENTS

vii

CHAPTER I

THE STRUCTURE OF THE ATOM

1.1 The Atomic Approach to Metallurgy

The first step to take in approaching the science of metals is to decide what is meant by the terms *metal* and *metallic*. The clear difference between metals and other substances is recognised by the layman who confidently names some everyday objects as metallic and others as non-metallic. This difference exists because metals possess certain special and readily observable properties, in particular, high conductivity of heat and electricity, opacity, lustrous appearance, mechanical strength, and ductility.

We might define a metal in terms of these properties; but this would be unsatisfactory for two reasons. In the first place, it cannot easily be made completely discriminative, for there is no obvious property common to metals which is neither shared by an otherwise non-metallic substance nor absent from an otherwise metallic one. If we must define a metal in terms of a special property the best one to choose is the temperature coefficient of resistance, for the metallic state is most sharply characterised by an electrical resistance which increases with increasing temperature. However, this is far from being readily observable in the layman's sense, and one may justifiably feel disappointed if such an unspectacular property is made the final touchstone.

The more important reason why this definition is unsatisfactory is that it does not tell us what a metal is. If we are to explain the metallic state we must seek, not the more obvious bulk properties of metals, but their underlying causes which are inextricably bound up with the ways in which metallic masses are formed from atoms, and hence finally with the structures of the atoms themselves. An atom is the smallest unit of matter which preserves the individuality of a chemical element, and so the differences between the various elements must originate here.

Before attempting a structural definition we should first realise that the term *metallic* is used in two distinct senses. In its *chemical* sense it groups together as *metals* all elements that behave in a certain manner in chemical reactions, forming strongly basic oxides and hydroxides, and combining with acids to form salts. In this case we are really dealing wit the properties of *individual atoms*, since chemical reactions take place by combinations and dissociations among single atoms and molecules. To define a metal in this chemical sense we have to pick out, from the atomic structures of the chemical elements, a feature common to metals and which forms the basis of their chemical behaviour. We shall do this in the present chapter.

When used in its *metallurgical* sense, the term *metallic* is applied to certain macroscopic objects, e.g. a copper wire or a steel ingot. The quite different idea involved here is that certain large aggregates of atoms can exist in a special state, *the metallic state of matter*, in which they possess the physical and mechanical properties mentioned in the first paragraph. These properties are *group* properties, possessed by the aggregate as a whole but not by the atoms in isolation. The white and grey forms of tin show that, for this element at least, identical atoms can exist in two forms of aggregate in which metallic properties are developed to greatly different degrees. Again, it is typical of this second use of the term *metallic* that it is also applied to *alloys*, that is to aggregates of two or more chemical species that possess these properties.

The properties associated with the metallic state are thus not *directly* dependent on the structures of the individual component atoms, and the connection between the chemical and metallurgical definitions is consequently surprisingly remote considering that a single term, *metallic*, can be used successfully to cover the two different senses. It so happens, however, that the same feature of atomic structure which produces metallic behaviour in chemical reactions is also responsible for allowing atoms to exist in the kinds of aggregates which constitute the metallic state.

To define a metal in the metallurgical sense involves two steps: (1) the creation of a theory of the metallic state which explains the unique structure and properties of metallic solids; (2) the explanation of the origin of this structure from the structures of the individual atoms. This has proved a difficult task in theoretical physics, and even to-day some of the questions it raises are still debatable. We shall outline the theory in Chapters IV, V and VI. The theory involves a detailed analysis of the electronic structure of solids, and in many problems of physical metallurgy a simpler picture is usually adequate in which metal atoms are visualised simply as structureless spheres that attract one another and cohere together. This simpler picture, which will be described in Chapter III, is a fair approximation to the detailed one, and in the later chapters of this book it will be used in many problems of crystal structure, thermal behaviour, melting and freezing, alloying, and plastic deformation. Only when faced with problems involving electronic structure, as in Chapters VI and IX, shall we need the deeper approach.

1.2 The Nuclear Atom

In this chapter, and the following one, we outline those parts of atomic theory necessary for the theory of metals. This background knowledge must be presented briefly and dogmatically. The following notes are merely a guide, and for further study the books listed at the end of Chapter II should be consulted.

The starting point for the modern theory is Rutherford's *nuclear atom*, which he suggested to interpret results of experiments on the bombardment of matter with alpha particles. The atom consists of a central *nucleus* around which one or more *electrons* swarm at distances up to about 10^{-8} cm. The nucleus itself is a small cluster, about 10^{-12} cm. across, of *protons* and *neutrons*.

Electrons, protons and neutrons are all *elementary particles*. Each electron is identical in its properties with every other electron, and the same is true for protons and for neutrons. The mass of an electron is $9 \cdot 1 \times 10^{-28}$ gm.; that of a proton or a neutron is about 1840 times greater than this. An elementary particle has a very small radius, believed to be somewhat less than 10^{-12} cm., and it is sufficient for us to picture it as a mathematical point. What is more important than its intrinsic size, particularly for the electron, is the distance at which it exerts strong forces on other particles. A proton possesses a fixed electrostatic charge which is always positive and equal to $e = 4 \cdot 8 \times 10^{-10}$ electrostatic units of charge. An electron possesses a negative charge of the same magnitude, and a neutron is electrically neutral.

The hydrogen nucleus is a single proton, but all other nuclei contain both protons and neutrons in approximately equal proportions. The particles in a nucleus are held together by *nuclear forces*, the nature of which is obscure although another kind of elementary particle, the *meson*, is known to play an important part here. All nuclei belonging to atoms of a given chemical element contain the same number, Z, of protons; this is called the *atomic number* of the element. Each element has its own atomic number and its chemical individuality originates from it. The elements can be arranged in order of increasing atomic number (Table 1), starting with hydrogen (1), helium (2), and continuing with a new element for each integer until the series at present known concludes with uranium (92) and the trans-uranic elements, neptunium (93), plutonium (94), americium (95), curium (96), berkelium (97), californium (98) and others. It is possible for different nuclei to hold the same number of protons (i.e. the same Z) and different numbers of neutrons. These are called *isotopes*, and all belong to the same chemical element associated with that value of Z.

An isolated atom exists usually as an electrically neutral structure. The electrostatic charge on the nucleus is $+Ze$, that on an electron is $-e$, so that the neutral atom possesses Z electrons. It is possible, however, both to remove electrons and to add extra ones to an atom, and this process is known as *ionisation*. Removal of electrons leaves a net positive charge on the atom, which is then called a *positive ion*, and the addition of extra electrons similarly produces a *negative ion*.

The motion of electrons in atoms can be explained satisfactorily only by using ideas which go beyond those of the classical theory of mechanics. At least two experimental observations show the inadequacy of classical mechanics: (1) the stability of atoms, and (2) the sharpness of spectral lines. According to classical theory an atom should not be stable, for its moving electrons should spiral into the nucleus, losing their energy of motion by emitting electromagnetic radiation; but in practice something prevents atoms from shrinking to less than about 10^{-8} cm. across. The difficulty over the spectral lines is that classical mechanics allows an electron to move in any of a continuous series of states of motion, in each of which it has a definite energy, partly kinetic and partly potential. If the electron changes its state of motion, a pulse or *quantum* of electromagnetic radiation (i.e. a *photon* of light or X-rays) is either emitted or absorbed, as the case may be. If the difference in energy between the two states of motion is ΔE, then the frequency of the radiation is ν, where $h\nu = \Delta E$, and h is Planck's constant, $6 \cdot 626 \times 10^{-27}$ erg. seconds. Now if the states of motion form a continuous series any value of ΔE is possible, and so all values of ν should be observed in the spectrum of the atom. The fact that only *discrete* spectral lines are observed, at a few special values of ν, shows again that some restriction, of a non-classical nature, is placed on the motion of the electron. Only certain states of motion are allowed; these are called *stationary states* since they do not change with time (Bohr's theory of the atom).

1.3   Quantum Mechanics

Through the work of de Broglie, Schrödinger, Heisenberg, Dirac, and Born, a new system of mechanics, *quantum mechanics*, or in the form we shall use it, *wave mechanics*, was created, which could deal satisfactorily with the states of motion of electrons. Quantum mechanics is a refinement of ordinary mechanics and is applicable to the motion of all particles, whether these are electrons, protons, atoms, molecules, or billiard balls. Classical mechanics is a simplified approximation to quantum mechanics that is successful when applied to large-scale events, e.g. the movement of a billiard ball on a table, but gives wrong results when applied to small-scale events, e.g. the movement of an electron in an atom. As innumerable experiments have now proved, quantum mechanics gives results in agreement with observation over the whole field of phenomena, except possibly inside the nucleus, and when dealing with large-scale phenomena its results are the same as those of classical mechanics.

Quantum mechanics is often regarded as a difficult subject. Apart from mathematical difficulties, which will not concern us here, the main trouble is due to the depth with which a false notion of classical mechanics is ingrained in our outlook. When thinking of the motion of, say, a billiard ball, the assumption that, at any given instant of time, it has a perfectly precise position and momentum appears so naturally that we do not even stop to recognise that it is an assumption, but go on immediately to apply Newton's laws of motion to this located particle. But this assumption is false. A rigorous analysis shows that it is impossible to determine, even in principle, the position and momentum *simultaneously*. We can measure one of these as accurately as we please, but the experimental refinements needed to make this measuremeut more accurate are of precisely the type that make the other measurement less accurate. This *indeterminacy principle* (Heisenberg) applies to all particles; it is trivial when applied to ones much heavier than atoms, although extremely important when applied to electrons. It can be stated mathematically in various ways depending upon the variables of motion that we decide to study. If these are the position x and momentum p, then the *minimum* uncertainties Δx and Δp possible in them are given by the relation $\Delta x \Delta p = h/2\pi$, where h is Planck's constant. If the energy E and time t are measured, the corresponding relation is $\Delta E \Delta t = h/2\pi$; this version of the principle is important for stationary states, where the same state of motion persists over indefinitely large times, for when Δt is very large, then ΔE can be very small, i.e. electrons in stationary states have sharp values of energy.

If we cannot have sharp values of both position and momentum, it would appear impossible to develop systematically the mechanics of electrons in atoms. This is not so; a complete and exact set of laws of motion can be worked out, which predicts every property that can be reached by experiment, provided that we deal not in the exact values of the position, etc., of the electron, but instead with the *probability* that these values lie in certain ranges. The change in outlook is illustrated in Fig. 1. Suppose that we are trying to locate the position of an electron

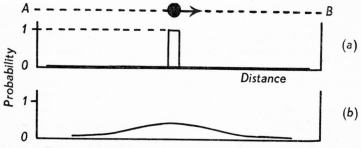

Fig. 1.—The position of an electron moving according to (a) classical mechanics, (b) quantum mechanics.

which is moving along a line AB with a speed lying within some known finite range. We can do this by drawing probability curves, as shown, using the rule that a probability value of 1 expresses certainty of the electron being at that place, a value of 0 certainty that it is not there, and intermediate values give intermediate chances. The upper curve is the classical one, and fixes the position precisely. The lower one is the wave mechanical one, where the electron is most likely to be found at the classical position, but may also be found elsewhere. We mean by this that, if several measurements could be taken of the position of the electron, their results would be scattered according to the distribution curves shown. Experiments of somewhat similar kinds can actually be performed (see Section 1.4) by directing streams of electrons through fixed apparatus and observing the positions at which individual electrons emerge on a scintillation screen.

From such probability curves we can calculate observable properties of electrons in atoms and elsewhere. Wave mechanics does not, however, deal directly with the probability curves. Instead, it calculates what is called the *wave function*, denoted by ψ. The value of ψ varies from place to place, and the rule is, for the problem of Fig. 1, that $\psi^2 dx$ is the probability of finding the electron between the points x and $x+dx$, when the value of ψ at x is used in this expression; alternatively one can regard the value of ψ^2 at the point x as the 'average electrical charge density' at x due to the electron. The advantage of working with ψ instead of with the probability directly is that the equation from which ψ is calculated, known as *Schrödinger's equation*, is a standard *wave* equation of a kind already familiar in many branches of physics. A much more elaborate mathematical system would be needed to calculate the probability directly.

The wave function may have either positive or negative values, or even complex ones,* but must always give, of course, real and positive values for the probability, since this is a measurable property of the physical system. It is also necessary that ψ curves should be 'smooth', in the sense that nowhere along such a curve is there a discontinuity.

1.4 Diffraction of Waves

Because ψ can be both positive and negative it is possible for two sets of ψ curves to overlap so that a crest (positive) in one curve coincides with a trough (negative) in the other. The electron probability at this place is then proportional to the square of the *difference* of the two ψ values at this place. Similarly, if at some place the two ψ values have the same sign (either both positive or both negative) the electron probability there is proportional to the square of their *sum*. This property of the wave function gives rise to many important phenomena, one of the most striking of which is *electron diffraction*.

It is well known that light waves reflected from, or transmitted through, a regularly spaced grating emerge in the form of a *diffraction pattern*; the intensity of the emergent radiation is strong in certain directions and weak in others. This effect occurs because, at each element of the grating, the impinging radiation is *scattered*, in the form of a new wave which spreads out radially from it; the waves from the various elements overlap, in some places with the same signs and in others with opposite signs, so that the phenomenon of interference occurs.

The diffraction phenomenon was used to prove the wave nature of X-rays (von Laue). In X-ray diffraction a *crystal* acts as the diffraction grating, for the atoms in a crystal form a regular pattern (see Chapter

---

* A complex number is denoted by $x+iy$, where x and y are real numbers, and $i=\sqrt{-1}$. If, as is often mathematically convenient, ψ is written in this form, the rule is that the 'square' of ψ in this case is the product $(x+iy)(x-iy)$, which is the real number x^2+y^2.

III) the spacing of which is about the same as the wavelength of X-rays, a condition for good interference phenomena. Although a crystal is a three-dimensional grating, and more complicated than the simple ruled grating of optics, it was shown by (Sir) W. L. Bragg that the law of X-ray diffraction is simple if the X-ray beam is regarded as being reflected from crystal planes. Thus, in Fig. 2 a beam of X-rays, of wavelength λ, is directed on a set of crystal planes, of spacing d, at an angle θ. Reflection occurs from these planes, the angle of reflection being equal to the angle of incidence. The emergent beam can only exist, however, when the path difference between rays reflected from successive planes is a whole number of wavelengths; only then do the waves from successive planes reinforce each other instead of cancelling

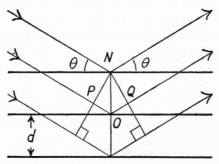

FIG. 2.—X-ray Diffraction.

out. The path difference between rays reflected at N and $O = OP + OQ = ON \sin \theta + ON \sin \theta = 2d \sin \theta$. This must equal an integral number of wavelengths, $n\lambda$, so that the condition for reflection is

$$n\lambda = 2d \sin \theta \quad \ldots \ldots \ldots \ldots (1)$$

where n is an integer defining the 'order of reflection'. This is *Bragg's Law*, and the critical values of θ where it is obeyed are *Bragg angles*.

When wave mechanics had shown that the motion of electrons was governed by the distribution of ψ functions, which in turn obeyed a wave equation, experiments were made by G. P. Thomson, and Davisson and Germer, with beams of *electrons* which showed that these particles could be diffracted by crystals in a manner very similar to that of X-rays. The wavelength λ of the ψ curves, which is used to calculate the directions of the diffracted beams of electrons, depends on the electron velocity v through de Broglie's relation,

$$\lambda = h/mv \quad \ldots \ldots \ldots \ldots \ldots (2)$$

where h is Planck's constant, m is the electron mass, and mv is the electron momentum. Similar experiments have since been made with beams of atomic nuclei, and atoms, which also show diffraction phenomena. They form a striking proof of the idea that the motion of particles of matter is governed by laws generated out of a wave equation.

1.5   Electrons in Atoms

The various stationary states of motion for an electron in an atom are represented by various patterns of the ψ function round the nucleus. Each distinct pattern corresponds to a certain permitted state of motion for the electron. Knowing such a pattern, we can obtain important information about the corresponding motion, e.g. the energy of the electron, the angular momentum, and the magnetic moment. The pattern does not, of course, tell us exactly where the electron is at any instant of time; on the other hand, it tells us the average amount of time spent by the electron in any given region of the atom, since this is proportional to the value of ψ^2 in this region.

In general, ψ is large within a distance of about 10^{-8} cm. from the nucleus, showing that the electron spends most of its time here, and beyond this it falls off rapidly with increasing distance, becoming zero at infinity. The reason for this characteristic dimension of atoms is as follows: the electron is attracted electrostatically to the nucleus; but the smaller we make the region round the nucleus in which ψ is large the shorter are the lengths of the waves that span this region and constitute the ψ function; from equation 2, a small wavelength implies a large momentum, and hence, a large kinetic energy, $\frac{1}{2}mv^2$, for the electron; a balance between falling electrostatic energy and rising kinetic energy is struck at a distance of about 10^{-8} cm.

Within this distance, the pattern of ψ for a particular state of motion is often complicated, so that the electron charge density is high in some places and low in others. The most conspicuous features of these patterns are the *nodes*, places where $\psi=0$, i.e. where no electron is found. These nodes, which are analogous to the nodes in vibrating strings or on the surfaces of sounding drums and are characteristic of all problems involving waves, lie in certain surfaces in the atom, called *nodal surfaces*. If we count also a nodal surface at infinity, in accord with the zero of ψ there, then the total number of nodes belonging to a given state of motion is denoted by n ($=1, 2, 3 \ldots$ etc.) which is called the *principal quantum number* of that state. The more nodes there are for a given state of motion, the greater is the *energy* of an electron in that state. This is because, at each node in the atom, ψ passes through zero, being positive on one side of the node and negative on the other; the more nodes there are the more sharply does the ψ curve have to bend to and fro to accommodate all its crests and troughs within the span of the atom; this sharp curvature implies a short wavelength and, by the argument in the previous paragraph, a large kinetic energy.

The state of motion with the lowest energy, for which $n=1$, is called the *ground* state. In this there are no nodes within the atom, the wave function being zero only at infinity. The wave function for this state is spherically symmetrical, i.e. the same in all directions out of the atom, and falls off exponentially with distance from the centre. The *energy level* of an electron in this ground state is not zero, since the electron has both electrostatic potential energy, due to its separation from the nucleus, and kinetic energy, which is responsible for this separation.

In changing from one state of motion to another, the number of nodes must change by an integral number, since any given node is either present or absent. Thus the energy of the electron can only take one or other from a set of fixed values, the *energy levels*, each of which is associated with a distinct state of motion. This is the wave mechanical explanation of the sharp spectral lines.

States with higher energies than the ground state have nodes inside the atom. These nodal surfaces are of two distinct kinds; *spherical* surfaces centred about the nucleus, and *plane* surfaces passing through the nucleus. The number of *nodal planes* passing through the nucleus is denoted by a second quantum number, l, which can take any value in the set $0, 1, 2 \ldots (n-1)$. States which do not possess nodal planes are called s states, and are spherically symmetrical, since their nodes are all spherical. States having nodal planes are not spherically symmetrical, and the electron density is stronger in some directions out of the atom than others; the *directed bonds* found in some chemical molecules originate from these states. Those with 1, 2, and 3 nodal planes are called p, d, and f states respectively. In this notation, a state symbolised by, say, $3d$, would have three nodes altogether, two plane ones and one spherical one at infinity. This notation, in which the principal quantum number is first stated numerically, followed by a letter representing the second quantum number, is widely used.

Two more quantum numbers are needed to specify a state of motion completely. The first takes account of the fact that nodal planes can exist in several orientations in an atom, and that each permitted orientation belongs to a distinct state of motion. There are three such orientations for the single plane of the p states, one for each of the three cartesian axes x, y, z (which may be defined by, for example, applying a magnetic field) to which the plane may be perpendicular. For the d states there are five orientations and, for the f states, seven. The number of such orientations is represented by a quantum number m_l which can take any integral value from $+l$ to $-l$, including zero. For example, $m_l=0$ for all s states ($l=0$), whereas for d states ($l=2$) it can take any value in the set $+2, +1, 0, -1, -2$.

The fourth number, m_s, is quite different from the others. It is introduced because an electron behaves in some ways as if it were spinning about its own axis, as well as moving about in the atom. Magnetic properties are associated with this spin, and the experimental observations can be satisfied on the basis that two opposite spin directions are possible. These two different states of motion are represented by the two different values, $+\frac{1}{2}$ and $-\frac{1}{2}$, that m_s is allowed to take.

By specifying the particular values of the four quantum numbers, n, l, m_l, and m_s, associated with the state of motion of an electron in an atom, we give all the information defining that *quantum state* uniquely. A quantum state specified by one set of numbers is different from any other specified by a different set.

The laws discussed above define the various allowed states of motion for an electron in an atom. Which of these quantum states does it actually choose to occupy? This is decided by two principles. The first is the general principle that dynamical systems prefer, whenever possible, to settle in those states where they have lowest energy. This principle is also applicable to electrons in atoms at ordinary temperatures.*

We might expect from this that all the electrons in an atom would occupy the two $1s$ states ($n=1$, $l=0$, $m_l=0$, $m_s=\pm\frac{1}{2}$), since these have lowest energy. The fact that this does not occur is expressed by the *Pauli Exclusion Principle*, which states that, in any atom or molecule, there cannot be two electrons in the same quantum state, i.e. with the same four quantum numbers. Often, in stating this principle, the spin quantum number m_s is not counted, and the principle then is that not more than two electrons can occupy a state, and if two are present they must have opposite spins.

With this rule operating, only two electrons are allowed in the $1s$ states, and all others must go into states of higher energy. The situation is analogous to that of a skyscraper block of flats in which all the occupants wish to live as near the ground floor as possible, but only one is allowed to each flat. Thus in an atom at ordinary temperatures the Z quantum states of lowest energy are occupied, with one electron in each, and all higher ones are empty. A distinction should be drawn here between quantum states and *energy levels*. An energy level is the energy of an electron in a quantum state. Different quantum states can belong to the same energy level in certain cases, and they are then described as being *degenerate*. The exclusion principle applies to quantum states, not to energy levels.

It is very difficult to find accurately the wave functions in an atom containing many electrons because of the various interactions which exist between these electrons; an important effect here is *screening*, in which the nucleus is partly shielded from outlying electrons by the electrical charge density of other electrons moving near the nucleus. This alters the energy levels of the quantum states, although the nodal patterns of these states and the rule about the effect of the number of nodes on their energies remain unaltered.

When discussing the occupation of the available quantum states it is convenient to imagine a nucleus of progressively increasing atomic number and to consider which state is chosen by each electron brought in to balance the nuclear charge. The order of choice, which is of course

---

* At very high temperatures, the intense thermal energy available may cause some electrons to jump into quantum states of higher energy. This thermal excitation can be largely discounted at ordinary temperatures, however, for in most cases the energy difference between adjacent levels is much larger than the average thermal energy available to a particle.

TABLE 1.—THE PERIODIC TABLE OF THE ELEMENTS

H 1																	He 2
Li 3	Be 4											B 5	C 6	N 7	O 8	F 9	Ne 10
Na 11	Mg 12											Al 13	Si 14	P 15	S 16	Cl 17	A 18
K 19	Ca 20	Sc 21	Ti 22	V 23	Cr 24	Mn 25	Fe 26	Co 27	Ni 28	Cu 29	Zn 30	Ga 31	Ge 32	As 33	Se 34	Br 35	Kr 36
Rb 37	Sr 38	Y 39	Zr 40	Cb 41	Mo 42	Ma 43	Ru 44	Rh 45	Pd 46	Ag 47	Cd 48	In 49	Sn 50	Sb 51	Te 52	I 53	Xe 54
Cs 55	Ba 56	La* 57	Hf 72	Ta 73	W 74	Re 75	Os 76	Ir 77	Pt 78	Au 79	Hg 80	Tl 81	Pb 82	Bi 83	Po 84	At 85	Rn 86
Fr 87	Ra 88	Ac 89	Th 90	Pa 91	U 92	†											

* The *rare earth* elements are situated between La and Hf.
† The *transuranic* elements follow here; e.g. Np (93), Pu (94), Am (95), Cm (96), Bk (97) and Cf (98).

the order of energy levels, is as follows: $1s$, $2s$, $2p$, $3s$, $3p$, $(4s, 3d)$, $4p$, $(5s, 4d)$, $5p$, $(6s, 5d, 4f)$, $6p$ $(7s, 6d)$. The states enclosed in brackets have almost the same energy levels when they are the highest occupied ones in the atom, and the order of filling them is complicated.

1.6 The Periodic Table

If the chemical elements are arranged in order of increasing atomic number, there is a well-marked periodicity in properties along the series. This is best displayed in a *periodic table* (Table 1), in which the atomic number increases in order from left to right along any row, while groups of chemically similar elements are contained in vertical columns. For example, the alkali metals, lithium, sodium, potassium, etc., all occur in the first column, while the inert gases, helium, neon, argon, etc., occupy the last column and are preceded by the column containing all the halogen elements.

It is instructive to relate this periodicity to the electronic structures of atoms. The first element in the table is hydrogen, the atom of which has one electron, normally contained in one of the two degenerate $1s$ states. The next atom, helium $(Z=2)$, has two electrons of opposite spins in these $1s$ states.

All states in the *first shell*, i.e. the states for which $n=1$, are now full, and the third electron of lithium $(Z=3)$ must take the state of lowest energy in the *second shell* $(n=2)$, which is one of the two $2s$ states. A new shell and a new row of the periodic table both start at lithium. The elements in this row add their electrons to this shell until it is completely filled, at neon. The order of filling is as follows:

Element:		Li	Be	B	C	N	O	F	Ne
Number of electrons in	$1s$	2	2	2	2	2	2	2	2
„ „	$2s$	1	2	2	2	2	2	2	2
„ „	$2p$	0	0	1	2	3	4	5	6

Whenever a new shell starts to form, the element concerned starts a new row of the periodic table. It follows that these elements, the alkali metals, all contain a single electron in their outermost shell. The electronic structure of the sodium atom, for example, which is next after neon, is represented by $(1s)^2 (2s)^2 (2p)^6 (3s)^1$, i.e. it has two electrons in $1s$, two in $2s$, six in $2p$, and one in $3s$. The third shell builds up as follows in the eight elements beginning at sodium:

Element:		Na	Mg	Al	Si	P	S	Cl	A
Number of electrons in	$3s$	1	2	2	2	2	2	2	2
„ „	$3p$	0	0	1	2	3	4	5	6

A new effect appears in the elements following argon. The third shell is not yet full, because the $3d$ states are still empty. However, for these elements, the energy level of the $4s$ states is lower than that of the $3d$ ones, and so the fourth shell begins to form before the third is filled.

The order of filling, which is broadly $4s$ first, then $3d$, then $4p$, is as follows:

Element:	K	Ca	Sc	Ti	V	Cr	Mn	Fe	Co	Ni	Cu	Zn	Ga	Ge	As	Se	Br	Kr
Number of electrons in $3d$	0	0	1	2	3	5	5	6	7	8	10	10	10	10	10	10	10	10
Number of electrons in $4s$	1	2	2	2	2	1	2	2	2	2	1	2	2	2	2	2	2	2
Number of electrons in $4p$	0	0	0	0	0	0	0	0	0	0	0	0	0	1	2	3	4	5	6

This row begins with an alkali metal and an alkaline earth, potassium and calcium, and then follows a set of *transition metals*, between calcium and copper, in which the $3d$ states are filling up. All these metals have only one or two electrons in their outermost ($n=4$) shell.

Similar behaviour occurs in the later rows of the periodic table. The $5s$ states are filled before the $4d$, and the $6s$ before the $5d$, so that more groups of transition metals are formed. An additional complication in the last group is that another group of elements occurs here, the *rare earth metals*, in which the filling of the $5d$ states is interrupted while the fourteen $4f$ states fill up. Because of these effects, most of the chemical elements are metals.

1.7 Electronic Structure and Chemical Behaviour

The above discussion shows that the periodic feature of electronic structure that corresponds to the periodicity of the chemical properties, along the series of elements, is the number of electrons in the *outermost* shell. Metals lie to the left side of the table, where atoms have only one or two such electrons, and non-metals lie to the right, where the number of these electrons rises towards eight. On the other hand, there is no correlation between chemical behaviour and the electron structure of the inner shells (except for the partly filled d states of the transition metals, in which the distinction between outer and inner electron states is less clear). It is the electrons in the s and p states of the outermost shell that mainly determine chemical behaviour; in consequence, these are called *valency electrons*.

A clue to chemical behaviour is provided by the inert gas elements, which show practically no tendency to undergo chemical combination. This suggests that the electronic structure of the outer shell is particularly stable, i.e. has low energy, in these atoms. Much of the chemical behaviour of other atoms can then be interpreted on the idea that they attempt to obtain, when they meet one another, an outer electron structure like that of their nearest inert gas. Sodium, for example, may give away its single valency electron to another atom in order to obtain the electronic structure of neon, the inert gas preceding sodium in the periodic table. Similarly, magnesium would have to give away two valency electrons to do the same thing. Chlorine, on the other hand, has one less electron than argon, so that it prefers to receive an extra electron.

This point of view makes the great chemical affinity between elements such as sodium and chlorine understandable. If two atoms of these elements approach closely, the valency electron of the sodium one may be transferred to the chlorine one, thus satisfying the electronic aspirations of both. This transfer turns the sodium atom into a positive ion and the chlorine atom into a negative ion. These two ions have opposite electrostatic charges and so are pulled together by the electrostatic force between them. They thus form a stable *molecule*. This process occurs in the large class of *ionic* or *heteropolar* compounds.

Elements can therefore be divided into two classes, *electropositive* ones, that give away valency electrons to form stable outer shells, and *electronegative* ones, that accept extra electrons for the same purpose. Metals are electropositive elements, for they possess few valency electrons, usually only one or two, and it is easier for them to lose electrons than to gain extra ones. We have thus arrived at a chemical definition of a metal.

The most typical metals in chemistry have only one valency electron, e.g. the alkali metals, and copper, silver and gold. Transition metals, and alkaline earth metals, are also markedly metallic in chemical properties. With more valency electrons, the chemical behaviour becomes less extreme, and in the case of elements such as aluminium (3 valency electrons), tin (4), and bismuth (5), there is doubt whether they should donate or accept electrons in chemical reactions, so that they exhibit a mixture of chemical properties, some metallic and others non-metallic. When there are six or seven electrons in the outermost shell the electronegative characteristics of the atom predominate, giving typical non-metals such as oxygen, sulphur and chlorine.

CHAPTER II

FORCES BETWEEN ATOMS

In this chapter we consider the origin of interatomic forces. In most metals these forces are strong and bind the atoms together into compact aggregates.

2.1 Aggregates of Atoms

Atoms exist in one or more of three states of aggregation, gas, liquid and solid. In gases the spacing of the atoms or molecules is large, for example about ten atomic diameters in ordinary air, but in liquids and solids each atom is closely confined by the immediate proximity of its neighbours. Liquids and solids are thus called *condensed states*. The state of aggregation selected by a group of atoms depends on the nature and magnitude of the interatomic forces present, and on the pressure and temperature.

The physical interpretation of a chemical affinity between two atoms is that an attractive force is exerted between them. The fact that it is difficult to squeeze atoms together too closely, even when the chemical affinity is strong, shows that a repulsive force is also exerted between the atoms at close distances. This repulsion, the basis of the impenetrability of matter, is a *short-range* force, i.e. it is weaker at large distances, but stronger at small distances, than the attractive force.

The equilibrium spacing of the pair of atoms is that at which these forces are equal. Because the total force on a particle is definable as the rate at which the potential energy varies with its position, this means that the energy of the pair is a minimum at the equilibrium spacing. Quantum mechanics deals directly with energy, and it is usual to treat problems of chemical bonding in terms of energy rather than forces.

Let us bring the two atoms together, starting from infinity and using the standard convention of defining their potential energy of interaction as zero at the starting point. Little change occurs, and the energy stays at zero until the atoms are within a few atomic spacings of each other. As the atoms move closer than this the attractive force becomes stronger (the repulsion still being negligible at this range) and their potential energy falls, to negative values, because work is done *by* the atoms when they move together under the attractive force. Eventually, at still smaller ranges, the repulsive force becomes strong and makes a positive contribution to the potential energy, since work is done *on* the atoms when they move together against its action. At distances where the repulsion exceeds the attraction, the potential energy rises as the atoms move together. The energy is thus a minimum at a certain spacing, the *equilibrium spacing* of the molecule. This behaviour is illustrated in

Fig. 3, which shows the potential energy due to the attractive force (curve *a*), to the repulsive force (curve *b*), and to both forces (curve *c*), as functions of the distance between the two nuclei. The potential energy 'well' or 'trough' is deepest at the equilibrium spacing r, and this extreme value D is equal to the work needed to pull the atoms apart until they are free of one another.

Whether a group of such atoms will exist as a gas or in a condensed state depends not only on D but also on the nature of the forces. Molecular gases can occur even when D is large, e.g. the gaseous forms of hydrogen, oxygen, nitrogen, and carbon dioxide, because in such cases the interatomic forces have the property of *saturation*, a quantum-mechanical effect; here, an atom can form strong bonds with one or two neighbours but, when it joins these, this group then has little

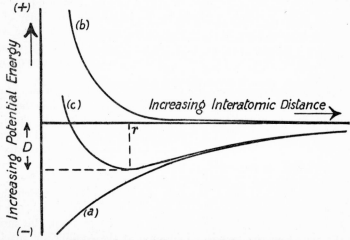

FIG. 3.—Potential Energy of a Pair of Atoms.

residual affinity for other atoms and molecules; the notion of *valency*, i.e. that an atom is able to bond with a definite and small number of other ones, originates here. The residual affinity is not altogether zero, however, and molecular gases can condense at low temperatures into molecular crystals, in which molecules containing strong internal bonds are weakly held together by residual bonds. Many organic substances are of this type. Weak intermolecular bonds are easily disrupted by heat, vaporising the material into a molecular gas, but the molecules themselves can withstand much higher temperatures without dissociating into free atoms.

In another class of substances, saturation does not occur and large strongly-bound aggregates can be built up indefinitely by the continued addition of more atoms. These aggregates can be regarded as giant molecules. Metallic solids and liquids are examples, and here vaporisation is small except at temperatures where their vapours consist mainly of free atoms.

External conditions help to determine the state of aggregation chosen by atoms. An applied pressure reduces the volume. In gases this is done by reducing the free space between the atoms or molecules, but in condensed states the external pressure joins with the attractive force in bringing the atoms closer together. Work is done by the pressure against the repulsive force. A small *compressibility* implies strong interatomic forces, because when a large applied force is necessary to upset the balance significantly the two forces balanced at the equilibrium spacing are also large.

Temperature is a measure of the average kinetic energy of a particle in the system due to its heat motion. If heat is supplied to the two atoms coupled together in the bond of Fig. 3, various effects occur. The molecule as a whole will move about; in a gas it undergoes translational motion and rotation, in a solid and liquid it vibrates and may also in some cases rotate and, to a limited extent, undergo translational motion (cf. Chapter XII). Inside the molecule the atoms vibrate, i.e. their instantaneous spacing oscillates about the equilibrium spacing with a frequency that is very nearly constant, and an amplitude that increases, with increasing temperature.* The bond between the atoms is broken when the vibrational energy exceeds D, the depth of the potential well, for the atoms then fly apart and become free. The stronger the bond, the higher is the temperature needed to do this. Similarly, high boiling points and melting points indicate strong interatomic and intermolecular forces in liquids and solids.

2.2   The Origin of Interatomic Forces

In the *ionic* bond, discussed in Chapter I, the atoms become oppositely charged ions by the transfer of electrons from one to the other and are then pulled together by the electrostatic attraction of opposite charges. The repulsive force which balances this attraction at small distances is due to several effects, the most important of which occurs when the *outermost completely-filled* shells of the ions begin to *overlap* slightly.

To picture overlapping, imagine the atom as a positive charge concentrated on a central point which is enveloped in a 'cloud' of negative electricity. The density of this cloud at any point measures the probability, or proportion of time, that an electron is at that point. Since the cloud thins out gradually at large distances from the atom then, strictly, atoms always overlap. However, overlapping causes strong effects only when dense regions of the clouds overlap so that, for practical purposes, it occurs only when the atoms are within a few Ångstroms of each other.† Forces due to overlapping are therefore *short-range ones*.

---

* For simplicity, we have not mentioned here the quantum restrictions on the motions. Only certain discrete energy levels are allowed. The lowest energy level is not zero, so that the atoms still vibrate at the absolute zero of temperature (*zero-point vibrations*). When the spacing of the levels is large, as in strongly bound molecules, high temperatures are needed to excite the atoms into the higher levels. Vibrations in solids are discussed in Chapter VIII.

† Ångstrom $= 10^{-8}$ cm.

When two shells begin to overlap, an electron in one of them can no longer be regarded as belonging solely to its parent atom; it belongs simultaneously to both atoms, to the molecule as a whole. The motion and energies of the electrons in these shells are still governed by quantum laws. In particular the Pauli exclusion principle must be obeyed. As a result, if the shells are both completely filled the single group of electrons formed by their union is too large for all its members to take quantum states of low energy. Some are *promoted* into higher energy levels. This increase in energy provides the repulsive force. It occurs whenever completely-filled shells overlap, whatever the nature of the attractive force responsible for the overlapping.

Many stable molecules and substances are formed from atoms between which there can be little or no ionic bonding. In such cases as the hydrogen molecule, the chlorine molecule, the carbon atoms in diamond, or those in a piece of copper, for example, the bond exists between chemically identical or similar atoms in which there is little possibility of one atom taking electrons off another. These bonds exist between electrically neutral atoms.

Until overlapping occurs the only force between neutral atoms or molecules is a rather weak attraction, the *van der Waal's* force. This is due to the fact that even a neutral atom exerts a fluctuating electrostatic field caused by the variations, as the electrons move about, in the positions of the negative charges relative to the central positive charge.

The strong forces which can cause chemical binding between neutral atoms do not appear until the electron clouds representing the *valency electrons* begin to overlap. Overlapping occurs at larger distances for valency electrons than others, because their electron clouds spread further from the nuclei, and it does not necessarily cause a repulsion, because valency electrons occupy *partly* filled shells. The repulsion of the filled shells only appears when the electron clouds of the two atoms penetrate each other more deeply.

The attraction that can occur from overlapping valency electron clouds is best explained by considering the hydrogen molecule, the first wave-mechanical theory of which was given by Heitler and London in 1927.

The hydrogen molecule consists of two protons and two electrons. When analysing the motion of the electrons the protons can be considered as stationary because they move so slowly by comparison. By far the strongest force exerted between these particles is the electrostatic one; all others, e.g. magnetic, can be neglected. The electrostatic energy of two charges, each of magnitude e, a distance r apart, is $\pm e^2/r$, positive for charges of the same sign and negative for opposite signs.

If a chemical bond is to be formed from the forces between these particles, the two electrons must spend most of their time in the space between the two nuclei. Although the repulsive force between the electrons themselves will then be large because they are close together, it will on average be outweighed by the four attractive forces which are also strong because of the closeness of both electrons to the two protons they lie between.

A quantum-mechanical treatment of this problem is essential for two reasons. First, we must know the amounts of time the electrons spend at various places in the molecule, in order to calculate the average values of the electrostatic forces between the four particles. If there is a place in the molecule where an electron spends much of its time, the interactions measured from here to the positions of the other particles must be correspondingly strongly-weighted when calculating the average interaction energy.

Secondly, the distribution of the electrons in the molecule is controlled by quantum mechanics. Suppose that the atoms are initially too far apart to affect one another. Each has a single electron in a $1s$ state, and the wave function for this state gives a spherical electron 'cloud' which is centred on the nucleus and thins out rapidly with increasing distance from it. Now bring the atoms together so that these clouds just begin to overlap slightly; two new things have then to be taken into account: (1) *resonance*; each electron can get from one atom to the other: (2) *indistinguishability*; there is no means of knowing which electron is which.

These two effects alter the wave functions. Instead of the two original $1s$ functions, new ones are needed to represent the motion of the electrons in the molecule as a whole. Heitler and London argued that, when the overlap is small, the change in the original $1s$ functions must also be small, so that one might be able to construct a reasonable approximate wave function for the molecule by suitably adding together two undisturbed $1s$ wave functions. They constructed the new function in this way by a process, outlined below, called *exchange*, which takes full account of indistinguishability and almost full account of resonance.*
The resultant force between the atoms is in consequence often called an *exchange* force. This name is a little misleading since it suggests that the force is caused by the mathematical device, i.e. the exchange process, used for constructing the new wave function from the original ones. It must be emphasised that the force between the particles is the ordinary electrostatic one due to the electrical charges they possess, and that the exchange effect is only concerned with the *positions* which the particles take up relative to one another.

Suppose for the moment that nothing happens when the two $1s$ clouds begin to overlap. Then there are two distinct ψ functions of the $1s$ type, i.e. ψ_a centred on nucleus a and ψ_b centred on nucleus b. Denote the

---

* The Heitler-London approximation does not allow for the possibility of states where both electrons are located on one nucleus. These states are of small importance in molecules between like atoms, but should not be entirely neglected. Another approximate treatment, the method of *molecular orbitals*, errs to about the same degree in the opposite direction of overemphasising the importance of these states.

two electrons by the numbers 1 and 2 and if, for example, electron 1 is in the quantum state ψ_a, denote this by writing ψ_{a1}. Thus the value of $\psi_{a1}{}^2$ at some point P in the molecule gives the proportion of time that electron 1 spends at the point P when it is in the 1s state belonging to nucleus a. Similarly, $\psi_{b2}{}^2$ gives the proportion of time that electron 2 spends at some point Q when it is attached to nucleus b. Thus the proportion of time that we find electron 1 at P, *when* 2 is at Q, is given by the product $\psi_{a1}{}^2\psi_{b2}{}^2$. This invites us to regard $\psi_{a1}\psi_{b2}$ as the total wave function for *both* electrons. But we could equally well have arrived at the function $\psi_{a2}\psi_{b1}$ by supposing that it was electron 2 that occupied the wave function ψ_a at the point P and electron 1 that occupied ψ_b at Q.

Clearly, neither function is satisfactory by itself, since each electron can get from one nucleus to the other and we have no means of knowing which electron is which. All we can expect to know is the proportion of time that *one* electron spends at P while the other one is at Q. Hence $\psi_{a1}\psi_{b2}$ and $\psi_{a2}\psi_{b1}$ must have equal status. One of the properties of the wave equation is that we can always construct new solutions of it by adding together already known ones. We can therefore make up the new wave functions ψ_+ and ψ_-:—

$$\psi_+=\psi_{a1}\psi_{b2}+\psi_{a2}\psi_{b1}, \qquad \psi_-=\psi_{a1}\psi_{b2}-\psi_{a2}\psi_{b1},$$

in which no physical change occurs when we interchange the numbers 1 and 2. These are the wave functions used by Heitler and London. The minus sign in ψ_- is admissible since the wave function has to be squared to give the probability of electron positions. The proportion of time that one electron spends at P while the other is at Q is now given by either $\psi_+{}^2$ or $\psi_-{}^2$, i.e. by

$$(\psi_{a1}\psi_{b2})^2+(\psi_{a2}\psi_{b1})^2\pm2\psi_{a1}\psi_{a2}\psi_{b1}\psi_{b2},$$

where the $+$ sign refers to $\psi_+{}^2$ and the $-$ sign to $\psi_-{}^2$.

In the region halfway between the nuclei, the 1s functions ψ_{a1}, ψ_{a2}, ψ_{b1} and ψ_{b2} all have about the same value. It follows that here $\psi_+{}^2$ is particularly large whereas $\psi_-{}^2$ is practically zero. Thus ψ_+ represents a quantum state for the molecule in which the electrons spend most of their time between the nuclei, and pull these together to give a stable molecule; whereas ψ_- represents a state in which the electrons avoid this central region and no bond is formed. The original energy level of the 1s state has split into two levels, as shown in Fig. 4, the lower one belonging to ψ_+ and the upper one to ψ_-. When the electrons have opposite spins, the exclusion principle allows them to enter the ψ_+ state and a stable molecule is formed.

In the hydrogen molecule, of course, there are no filled inner shells to prevent the atoms approaching too closely, and we might imagine that, by a continuous scaling down of all distances in the molecule, we could continue to reduce its energy. However, it must be remembered that if an electron cloud shrinks, the kinetic energy of its electrons increases. If, to avoid this effect, the nuclei continue to move together without the electron cloud shrinking in proportion, the electrostatic repulsion of the positive charges on the nuclei increases faster than the other electrostatic forces and must eventually predominate.

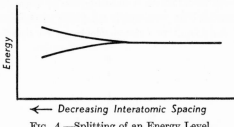

← Decreasing Interatomic Spacing

Fig. 4.—Splitting of an Energy Level.

2.3 Homopolar and Metallic Bonding in Condensed States

When several chemically similar atoms are brought together in a condensed state the valency electron cloud of any one atom overlaps those of all its immediate neighbours, so that, by resonance and exchange, valency electrons are able to move from one atom to another throughout the entire structure. The analysis of the wave functions in such cases shows that the bonds formed by the attractions of the positive ions to the electrons moving between them can be approximated by one or other of two extreme kinds.

In the first, the *homopolar* bond, the valency electrons are shared as *electron pairs*, one such pair joining each pair of neighbouring atoms in the structure. In such cases the number of close neighbours to a given atom is determined by the number of valency electrons it has. With the exception of hydrogen, the homopolar bonds are made from molecular wave functions constructed from both s and p atomic wave functions, and the rule then is that the number of neighbours to which a given atom can join with homopolar bonds is $8-N$, where N is the number of valency electrons it has; the number 8 arises from the number of molecular wave functions that can be created from the valency s and p states. In many materials of this kind the valency bonds stand out from the atom in preferred directions (*directed bonds*). This originates in the fact that p wave functions are not spherically symmetrical but are strong in certain directions out of the atom. An important effect here is *hybridisation*. Out of the original s and p functions it is possible to construct four new functions which stand out strongly in the directions of the corners of a regular tetrahedron. The diamond form of carbon shows these effects well (Fig. 5). The carbon atom has four valency electrons, two $2s$ and two $2p$, and can form electron pairs with four neighbours. In the diamond structure each atom is surrounded by four others symmetrically arranged at the corners of a tetrahedron.

When the number of valency electrons is small, as in metallic solids, this kind of approximation to the electronic structure is unsuitable, for there are then many more molecular wave functions than electrons to fill them, and the resonance of an electron from one bond to another is too important to be neglected. A better approach in this case is to regard the valency electrons as wandering freely throughout the whole of the piece of metal. The cohesion is then due to the attraction of the positive ions to the negative valency electrons passing between them.

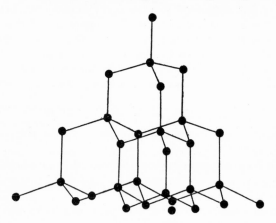

FIG. 5.—Arrangement of Atoms in Diamond.

The idea of free electrons in metals, now generally accepted, originated in the early theories of Drude and Lorentz (1900-1905) to explain the high conductivity of metals. More recent theories, described in Chapters IV, V and VI, have shown that the ability of free electrons to move from atom to atom is not enough to explain the conductivity of metals; additional conditions have to be satisfied. However, the simple picture of a metal as an array of positively-charged spheres held together by a gas or cloud of free electrons is sufficient for explaining many metallurgical phenomena.

2.4 Solids and Liquids

The atoms or molecules in a liquid are packed nearly as closely* as in a solid, but with nothing like so much regularity. It was common at one time to divide solids into two classes, *amorphous*, in which the atoms are packed irregularly, and *crystalline*, in which they are arranged in a regular pattern in space. It is better, however, to regard amorphous materials, such as glass and pitch, as highly viscous liquids. The difference between an ordinary liquid and one of these is one of degree rather than kind; if an amorphous material is heated there is no sharp melting

---

* In a few cases the packing in the liquid is closer than in the solid, e.g. water and ice.

point and the viscosity gradually falls to more familiar values. In crystalline solids, on the other hand, there is a sharp melting point at which many properties change discontinuously. We therefore restrict the use of the term 'solid' to include crystalline substances only.

The important feature of a crystal is the regularity of its atomic arrangement, which originates in the fact that the force exerted by the aggregate on each new atom or molecule added to it is a repetition of that which acted on those added earlier, and so each atom takes up a position of the same kind relative to its neighbours. The external symmetry of many natural crystals is a consequence of this regularity of atomic arrangement and arises when conditions of crystal growth favour the development of flat, regular faces. These conditions are usually absent when metal crystals grow from their liquids, and crystals with irregularly-shaped boundaries, i.e. crystal *grains*, are usually formed.

REFERENCES TO CHAPTERS I and II

Introductions to the theory of atomic structure and chemical binding are given in the following books:

'Electronic Structure and Chemical Binding.' O. K. Rice, McGraw-Hill, 1940.

'Elementary Quantum Mechanics.' R. W. Gurney, Cambridge University Press, 1940.

'Nature of the Chemical Bond.' L. Pauling, Ithaca, N.Y., 1940.

'Elementary Wave Mechanics.' W. Heitler, Clarendon Press, Oxford, 1945.

'Atomic Theory for Students of Metallurgy.' W. Hume-Rothery, The Institute of Metals, 1946.

'The Structure of Matter.' F. O. Rice and E. Teller, Wiley, 1949.

'Elements of Wave Mechanics.' N. F. Mott, Cambridge University Press, 1952.

CHAPTER III

METALLIC CRYSTALS

We shall now examine the ways in which atoms are packed together in metallic crystals. First we look at the main crystal structures of metals and introduce some useful ideas from crystallography and crystal physics. Then we consider the forms of various crystal imperfections and finally discuss the nature of grain boundaries and the influence of these boundaries on the shapes of grains.

3.1 Arrangements of Atoms in Metallic Crystals

In metals the atoms or positive ions are held together by a cloud of free electrons, so that each atom tends to be attracted *equally and indiscriminately* to all its nearest neighbours by the free electrons passing between them. By contrast, in homopolar crystals the number and positions of nearest neighbours are fixed by the directed bonds and by the number of electron-pairs that can be formed. The absence of this restriction in metals enables highly close-packed structures to be formed, of the kinds obtained by packing groups of equal spheres into a minimum total volume. Not every metal forms such a close-packed structure as this, but so many of them do so that it is worth while considering the close packing of spheres.

Most metals crystallise in either the *face-centred cubic* (F.C.C.), the *close-packed hexagonal* (C.P.Hex.), or the *body-centred cubic* (B.C.C.), crystal structures. The first two of these are structures in which equal spheres can be packed together as closely as possible. They are both formed by stacking on top of each other a number of *close-packed* planes. The pattern of (spherical) atoms in a close-packed plane is shown in Fig. 6 (*a*). These atoms lie in three sets of lines which are physically equivalent and inclined at 120° to each other. These planes are called *octahedral* planes in F.C.C. crystals and *basal* planes in C.P.Hex. crystals. In the crystals the planes are stacked on one another so that the *orientation* (i.e. directions of the rows of atoms) and *position* of each plane, relative to the next one below it, conforms to a certain *stacking sequence*.

To see which stacking sequences produce the closest possible packing, suppose in Fig. 6 (*b*) that one layer of atoms has been laid in the positions indicated by the circles of which A is a member, and that a second layer, of which B is a member, is to be placed on top in a position of utmost compactness. By sliding this layer over the first one we see that the spacing between them is least when their orientation is the same and when each B atom rests simultaneously and symmetrically on the three nearest A atoms below it. To add more layers, consider Fig. 6 (*c*). Looking straight down on a stack of close-packed layers, we see that the atoms in different layers can occupy three kinds of position, A, B, and C, relative to neighbouring layers. (For simplicity, the atoms in this diagram are no longer represented by circles in contact.) Any stacking of successive close-packed layers gives the closest possible packing provided that neighbouring layers have different positions. Thus the stacking sequence . . . $ABACABCBA$ . . . is close packed, whereas . . . $ABBACCAAB$ . . . is not.

When the sequence is *regular* the arrangement forms a *crystal structure*.

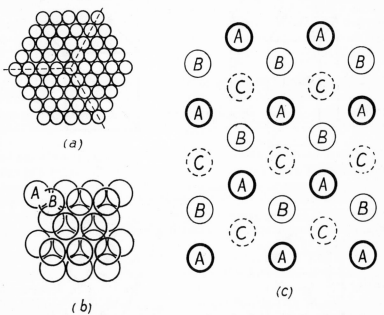

(a)

(b)

(c)

Fig. 6.—(a) Arrangement of Atoms in a Close-Packed Plane, and (b) and (c) in Successive Planes.

Two such sequences are common in metals, . . . $ABABABA$ . . . (or . . . $BCBCB$ . . ., or . . . $CACAC$ . . .), and . . . $ABCABCABC$ . . ., the first being that of the C.P.Hex. structure and the second, the F.C.C. structure. The fact that these regular sequences are common, instead of faulted close-packed sequences (e.g. . . . $ABABCABAC$ . . .), is evidence that forces between atoms other than nearest neighbours are not entirely negligible in metals. The positions of nearest neighbours round any given atom are identical in *all* close-packed sequences, so that if forces between nearest neighbours alone were involved, regular, close-packed sequences would be accidental and rare. In practice, the energy of an atom depends slightly on the positions of distant atoms and this favours regular sequences; even so, *stacking faults* do sometimes occur.

The pattern of atoms in a C.P.Hex. metal is best shown by a *structure cell,* as in Fig. 7 (*a*). The points in this diagram denote *atomic sites,* i.e. the centres of the positions occupied by atoms. The pattern of atomic sites in the complete crystal is generated by mounting a large number of points in space in positions which continue the pattern of the structure cell. This pattern forms a *layer structure* of basal planes. Here the three atomic sites inside the cell belong to one of the basal planes, while those on the top and bottom hexagonal faces of the cell belong to the

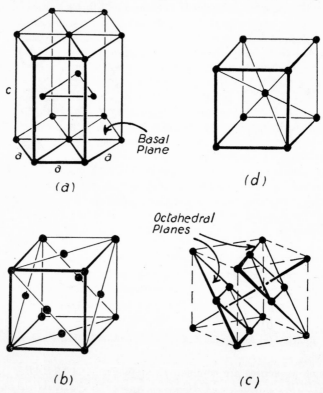

FIG. 7.—Cells of (*a*) Close-Packed Hexagonal Structure, (*b*) and (*c*) Face-Centred Cubic Structure, (*d*) Body-Centred Cubic Structure.

two basal planes neighbouring this one. Any uniqueness of position, suggested by the fact that some sites lie inside the cell and others on its surface, is lost in the crystal, which consists of the alternating sequence of basal planes.

In C.P.Hex. crystals the *axial ratio, c/a,* measures the ratio of the height, *c*, of the structure cell to the distance, *a*, between neighbouring sites in the basal plane. Ideally, when the structure is made from close-packed and equal spheres, $c/a = 1 \cdot 633$; each atom then has twelve equidistant nearest neighbours, which is expressed by saying that the *co-ordination number* of the structure is twelve. In practice, however, a distorted form of the C.P.Hex. structure, in which the axial ratio differs from 1·633, is usually observed. Examples of C.P.Hex. metals are given in Table 2.

The F.C.C. structure, which also has a co-ordination number twelve, is represented by the structure cell of Fig. 7 (b). The atoms occur at the corners and face-centres of a cube. To show the underlying sequence of octahedral planes the F.C.C. cell is given again in Fig. 7 (c), where one set of planes is emphasised. There are four distinct sets of octa-hedral planes, each with its own orientation. One such set is shown in Fig. 7 (c), and the other three are found by rotating the cell 90° about each of the three cube edges. Table 2 gives examples of F.C.C. metals.

The B.C.C. structure is not built from close-packed planes. As a result, it is less closely packed than the C.P.Hex. and F.C.C. structures. Its co-ordination number is only eight, but this is partly compensated by the presence of six next nearest neighbours at distances only a little greater than that of the nearest neighbours. The structure cell given in Fig. 7 (d) shows that the atoms lie at the corners and body-centre of a cube. Table 2 gives examples of B.C.C. metals.

Some metals adopt more than one crystal form, each of the exhibited forms occurring over a certain range of temperature. This phenomenon, called *polymorphism*, is fairly common, particularly amongst transition metals. The familiar example is iron, which is B.C.C. below 910° C. and above 1400° C., and F.C.C. between 910° C. and 1400° C.

3.2 The Transition from Metallic to Homopolar Bonding

The simple crystal structures described above only appear extensively in 'true' metals, i.e. those with one, two, and possibly three, valency electrons. Even here there are exceptions, e.g. manganese and uranium. One form of manganese, for example, has a structure rather like B.C.C. but with a group of twenty-nine atoms at each cube corner and centre.

Less metallic elements, e.g. bismuth, arsenic, and selenium, generally form more complicated structures. This is because the metallic (free electron) bond is replaced to some extent by the homopolar (electron pair) bond. In some of these elements atoms are bound to some of their neighbours by homopolar bonds and to others by metallic bonds. The atoms are then usually assembled into sheets or chains, within which they are linked by homopolar bonds obeying the $(8-N)$ rule, while the sheets or chains themselves are joined together by metallic bonds and van der Waal's forces. These structures are less closely packed than those of true metals because the number of homopolar linkages is limited by the $(8-N)$ rule. In particular, arsenic, antimony, and bismuth form *layer structures*, in each layer of which each atom has three close neighbours.

Some elements of high valency do behave like true metals, however. For example, lead, with four valency electrons per atom, forms an F.C.C. structure which is obviously metallic. The explanation often given in such cases is that the atoms are *incompletely ionised* in the crystals, i.e. some valency electrons are not given to the free electron cloud but are held back in the ions. An interesting case is tin, with four valency electrons per atom. At low temperatures it is fully ionised

TABLE 2.—COMMON CRYSTAL STRUCTURES OF METALS

Element	Crystal Structure	Closest Interatomic Distance (Ångstroms)	Axial Ratio	Temperature of Measurement
Aluminium . . .	F.C.C.	2·862	—	20° C.
Barium	B.C.C.	4·35	—	,,
Beryllium . . .	C.P.Hex.	2·225	1·57	,,
Cadmium . . .	,,	2·979	1·88	,,
Calcium . . .	F.C.C.	3·94	—	,,
Chromium . . .	B.C.C.	2·498	—	,,
Cobalt . . .	{ C.P.Hex.	2·506	1·62	,,
	{ F.C.C.	2·511	—	room
Copper	,,	2·556	—	20° C.
Gold	,,	2·884	—	,,
Iridium	,,	2·714	—	,,
Iron	{ B.C.C.	2·481	—	,,
	{ F.C.C.	2·585	—	950° C.
Lead	,,	3·499	—	20° C.
Lithium . . .	B.C.C.	3·039	—	,,
Magnesium . . .	C.P.Hex.	3·196	1·62	,,
Molybdenum . . .	B.C.C.	2·725	—	,,
Nickel	F.C.C.	2·491	—	,,
Platinum . . .	,,	2·775	—	,,
Potassium . . .	B.C.C.	4·627	—	,,
Rhodium . . .	F.C.C.	2·689	—	,,
Rubidium . . .	B.C.C.	4·88	—	−173° C.
Silver	F.C.C.	2·888	—	20° C.
Sodium . . .	B.C.C.	3·715	—	,,
Strontium . . .	F.C.C.	4·31	—	,,
Tantalum . . .	B.C.C.	2·860	—	,,
Thorium . . .	F.C.C.	3·60	—	,,
Titanium . .	{ C.P.Hex.	2·89	1·60	25° C.
	{ B.C.C.	2·89	—	900° C.
Tungsten . . .	B.C.C.	2·739	—	20° C.
Vanadium . . .	,,	2·632	—	,,
Zinc	C.P.Hex.	2·664	1·86	—
Zirconium . .	{ C.P.Hex.	3·17	1·59	—
	{ B.C.C.	3·13	—	867° C.

and forms a structure of the diamond type (grey tin), but above 13° C. ionisation is incomplete and a body-centred tetragonal structure (white tin) with obvious metallic properties is formed.

3.3 Space Lattices

A clear distinction must be drawn between the ideas of *crystal structure*, *atomic site*, and *structure cell*, introduced in Section 3.1, and the corresponding ideas of the *space lattice*, *lattice point*, and *unit cell*, which are used in crystallography. A crystal is an arrangement of atoms or molecules which follows a certain pattern in space, and the crystal structure is shown in diagrams or models which give the position of each atom relative to its neighbours. In every crystal there is a unit of pattern, or *motif*, and the structure as a whole is created by arranging these motifs in the appropriate pattern. The function of the space lattice is to show this pattern, i.e. to show how the motifs are distributed in space without describing the atomic structure within a motif. In some crystals a single atom constitutes the motif and the diagrams of crystal structure and space lattice are then identical. But in others a group of atoms or a molecule constitutes the motif and the crystal structure then differs from the space lattice. In a perfect crystal of this kind the orientation and grouping of atoms is the same in each motif and the pattern of the motifs is found by taking one point in each motif, selected from the same place in each one, and by marking out the positions of these points in space. This array of points is the *space lattice* of the crystal, and each point is a *lattice point*. The lattice point in general is different

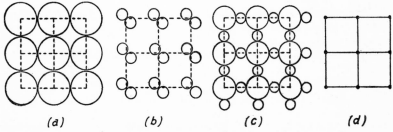

(a)   (b)   (c)   (d)

Fig. 8.—Some Atomic Arrangements (*a*, *b*, and *c*) with the same Space Lattice (*d*).

from an *atomic site*, since the latter is the place occupied by an atom in the crystal, and only in special cases does the array of atomic sites form a space lattice. Thus in Fig. 8 we show some hypothetical crystal structures which have the same space lattice.

The essential feature of a space lattice is that the disposition of neighbouring points is exactly the same round every lattice point. Thus if we determine the vector joining any two lattice points, and then apply this vector to a third point, it will always end at a fourth one. If we test the arrays of Fig. 7 in this way we find that two of them form space lattices, the *F.C.C. lattice* and the *B.C.C. lattice*, respectively, but that the C.P.Hex. array does not. To form a space lattice from the C.P.Hex. structure we have to take two neighbouring atomic sites for the motif, one from each of two neighbouring basal planes, and then mark out the pattern of these motifs.

A result of this feature of a space lattice is that its points delineate three sets of planes, as shown in Fig. 9 (*a*), each point being the place where three planes, one from each set, intersect. All planes in one set are parallel and equally spaced, but in the most general form of lattice the different sets can have different spacings and intersect at arbitrary angles; only in special lattices of high symmetry are the different sets of planes specially related to each other. In this construction the lattice points are connected by the lines of intersection of pairs of planes, and the vectors which join neighbouring points along such lines are called *lattice vectors*. In Fig. 9 (*a*) these vectors are denoted by **a**, **b**, and **c**. It is always possible to move from any initial lattice point to any other one by a path which is a series of translations along such vectors. Thus

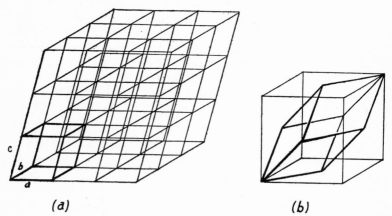

(a)   *(b)*

Fig. 9.—(*a*) A Space Lattice, (*b*) a Unit Cell in the F.C.C. Structure Cell.

a space lattice can be defined mathematically as the array of points generated by the end points of the set of vectors obtained from the formula

$$p\mathbf{a}+q\mathbf{b}+r\mathbf{c} \quad . \quad . \quad . \quad . \quad . \quad . \quad . \quad . \quad . \quad (3)$$

by letting p, q, and r each have, in turn and independently of the others, every value in the whole set of integers.

The intersections of the planes also divide the space into a set of identical *elementary parallelepipeds*, or *unit cells*, as in Fig. 9 (*a*). There is one lattice point to each unit cell, since the cell has eight corners at each of which one lattice point is shared amongst eight adjacent cells. The structure cells of Fig. 7 are not unit cells; thus the B.C.C. structure cell has two lattice points and the F.C.C. cell has four. The difference between a structure cell and a unit cell is illustrated in Fig. 9 (*b*), where a unit cell in the F.C.C. lattice is outlined within a structure cell.

3.4   Indices of Crystal Planes and Directions

We shall now explain the *Miller Index* notation, used for specifying various planes and directions in a crystal. Three axes, X, Y, and Z, are chosen, parallel to the edges of a crystal cell. Sometimes the unit cell is used, but where the structure cell has simpler symmetry, as for example in F.C.C. and B.C.C. crystals, it is more convenient to use this one. Each axis is graduated into divisions equal to the length of the corresponding edge of the cell. For example, in Fig. 10 the axes refer to the unit cell of the lattice in Fig. 9 (a) and are graduated into the corresponding lengths a, b, and c, of this cell. Distances along axes are then measured by the number of edge lengths involved.

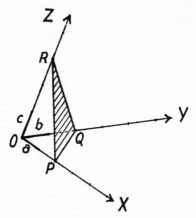

FIG. 10.—Specifying a Crystal Plane.

To specify a given plane in the crystal we count its intercepts on the three axes, then take the reciprocals of these intercepts and divide out their common denominator. Thus the reciprocal intercepts can always be expressed in the form h/n, k/n, and l/n, where n is the common denominator and h, k, and l are integers. These integers are then presented in the form (hkl) and called the Miller indices of the plane. As an example, we shall deduce the indices of the plane in Fig. 10. It makes intercepts $OP=2$, $OQ=2$, $OR=3$, on the X, Y, and Z axes, respectively. The reciprocals are $1/2$, $1/2$, $1/3$, and the common denominator of these is 6. Writing them in the form $3/6$, $3/6$, $2/6$, we identify the plane as (332).

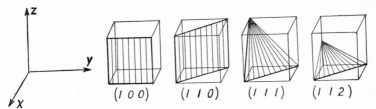

FIG. 11.—Miller Indices of Planes in Cubic Crystals.

For cubic crystals the cube edges of the structure cell are used to define the crystal axes, for the latter are then orthogonal and $a=b=c$. Fig. 11 gives some important planes in cubic crystals. A plane parallel to an axis intercepts that axis at infinity and thus has a zero index for that axis, e.g. the (110) plane in Fig. 11 is parallel to the Z axis. If a plane intersects axes on their negative side this is shown by placing a bar over the indices concerned; e.g. a plane which intercepts X negatively and the other axes positively would be denoted by $(\bar{h}kl)$. The symbol (hkl) represents the whole family of planes parallel to the particular one from which the indices have been determined. Often it is required to specify all planes of a given crystallographic type, irrespective of their orientation, e.g. *all* the octahedral planes of the F.C.C. lattice, not merely all those parallel to (111). This is done by enclosing the indices in different brackets. Thus the class of all octahedral planes is denoted by $\{111\}$, where $\{111\}$ stands for (111), (11$\bar{1}$), (1$\bar{1}$1), and ($\bar{1}$11); these four groups of planes are of course the same as ($\bar{1}\bar{1}\bar{1}$), ($\bar{1}\bar{1}$1), ($\bar{1}$1$\bar{1}$) and (1$\bar{1}\bar{1}$) respectively.

To define a direction we construct a line through the origin in this direction and find the co-ordinates of some other point on the line, using the cell edges as units of length. The indices of the direction are the smallest integers proportional to these co-ordinates. To distinguish them from the indices of planes they are enclosed in square brackets, thus $[uvw]$. For example, if the co-ordinates are $x=3a$, $y=-b$, $z=c/2$, the line is a $[6\bar{2}1]$ direction. In the special case of *cubic* cells, the symmetry is such that directions defined in this way have indices identical with those of planes to which they are perpendicular, e.g. [111] is perpendicular to (111) in cubic crystals. To refer to the class of all directions of a given crystallographic type, irrespective of orientation, different brackets are used. Thus $<111>$ stands for [111], [$\bar{1}\bar{1}\bar{1}$], [11$\bar{1}$], [$\bar{1}$1$\bar{1}$], [1$\bar{1}$1], [$\bar{1}$1$\bar{1}$], [$\bar{1}$11] and [1$\bar{1}\bar{1}$].

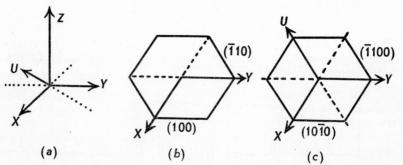

Fig. 12.—(a) Miller-Bravais Axes for Hexagonal Crystals, (b) and (c) Prismatic Planes specified by Miller and Miller-Bravais Indices.

In hexagonal crystals a variant of the notation, the *Miller-Bravais* system, is usually used. Four axes are taken, one of which (Z) is perpendicular to the basal plane, while the other three (X, Y, and U) lie in the basal plane along the three close-packed directions inclined at 120° to one another (Fig. 12 (a)). The intercepts of a plane on the four axes are then measured, in the order X, Y, U, Z, and converted into indices by the same procedure as before. The positive directions of axes are as shown in the diagram. The Miller-Bravais index of the plane is then $(hkil)$, where i is the intercept on U. Actually, the i index is redundant since, by geometry, $i = -(h+k)$, so that the first three indices always sum to zero. The reason for including i is as follows. Suppose, in Fig. 12 (b), we were looking down on the hexagonal prism and wished to give indices of the prism faces in a notation which omitted the U axis. Then one of the faces would be (100) while another one was ($\bar{1}$10). The confusion which would thus arise because planes of the same crystallographic family had different sets of symbols is avoided if the U axis is used. Thus, in Fig. 12 (c), the two planes become (10$\bar{1}$0) and ($\bar{1}$100), which are then obviously members of the general family of prismatic face planes, denoted by {10$\bar{1}$0}.

3.5 Lattice Constants and Atomic Radii

We now pay attention to the size of the crystal cell. To specify a lattice fully, the angles between, and the lengths of, its cell edges must be stated. When the symmetry is high, however, the specification becomes simpler. In a cubic crystal only one *lattice constant* or *lattice parameter*, the length of the cube edge, is needed.

In many simple crystals the lattice constants enable us to determine what may be regarded with limitations as the *atomic radius*. Although a free atom has no atomic radius, since the electron cloud thins out gradually as one moves away from the atom, this rather artificial concept is nevertheless very useful when considering the packing of atoms in crystals. If the atoms in crystals are regarded as spheres in contact with each other then in certain simple crystals it is a straightforward geometrical problem to calculate the radius of a sphere from the lattice constants.

The atomic radius of an element in different crystals varies with the nature of the interatomic forces present. For example, the radius of an ion of a metal in an ionic salt is smaller, often much smaller, than the radius of its atom in a metallic crystal; thus the radius of the sodium ion in salts is 0·98 Å. whereas the radius in the metallic state is 1·85 Å. When using values of atomic radii in different crystals, therefore, one must be sure that they have been obtained from crystals of the same kind. Provided this is done the radius is fairly constant from one crystal to another. Small variations do occur, however, and in particular the radius decreases when the co-ordination number of the crystal structure is lowered. In metals, the reason for this is that the energy of the free electron gas is lowest when the atomic *volume* has a certain value (see section 6.3). When the co-ordination number is reduced more space is left between the atoms and, to compensate partially for the increase in volume that this would otherwise produce, the atomic radius decreases.

In Table 2 is given the *interatomic distance* in some metals, i.e. the distance between the centres of nearest neighbours, or twice the atomic radius. The range of values is fairly narrow, particularly amongst the transition metals. In polymorphic metals the different crystal forms have closely similar spacings. Polymorphism is fairly common in metals, and the reason for this is that it is possible for different crystal structures to have almost the same atomic volumes and hence, in metals, almost the same electron energies. This makes it possible for various minor effects to turn the scales, and so alter the relative stabilities of the crystal structures, in different temperature ranges.

3.6 Directionality in Crystals

Since the atoms in a crystal have a regular pattern we expect that the intensity of certain properties, e.g. electrical conductivity, will depend on the particular *direction* through the crystal along which the measurement is made. This variation with direction is called *anisotropy*. In this section we shall describe the mathematical system which is used for specifying the anisotropic properties of crystals.

Some properties are independent of direction, e.g. mass, volume, density, and temperature. These are called *scalars*. Other properties can be specified only by stating the direction of measurement, as well as the magnitude of the result. Thus, to specify the temperature gradient in a body we must say not only how steep it is but also along what direction the temperature changes. This is best done by stating the three *components* of the gradient measured along three suitable and mutually perpendicular axes. Properties of this kind, with three components, are called *vectors*.

The value of a scalar property at any given point can be specified by *one* number only, but that of a vector property needs *three* numbers to specify it. Thus the temperature at a point can be specified by a statement such as '$T=1000°$', but the temperature gradient at that point would need three statements, e.g. '$dT/dx=10°$, $dT/dy=30°$, $dT/dz=0°$.'

There are other properties which need more than three numbers to specify their values at any given point; they are called *tensor* properties. An example is *strain*. Suppose we deform a cubic structure cell uniformly, so that the strain is constant throughout it. Each face becomes a rectangle or parallelogram. Then to specify this strain fully we should have to state *six* numbers, i.e. the three changes in length undergone by the cell edges and the three changes in angle between these edges.

In a more general use of the term *tensor*, a scalar is called a *zero-order tensor*, a vector is a *first-order tensor*, and all other tensors are of the second, third, and higher, orders. The maximum number of numbers needed to specify the value of an nth order tensor at a point is 3^n. In practice it is often unnecessary to specify the maximum number, for various characteristics of the property itself and of the crystal structure may reduce the number of independent components in the tensor.

Strain, for example, is a second-order tensor but needs only six numbers to specify it.

Many properties of crystals are measured as *coefficients*. We impose some condition on a crystal, e.g. apply a load, a voltage difference, or a temperature difference, and then measure the response of the crystal, i.e. the deformation, or the flow of electricity or heat, to this condition. In many cases the intensity of the response is directly proportional to that of the imposed condition, e.g. as in Hooke's law, Ohm's law, and Fourier's law, and a *coefficient of proportionality* is then defined through a relation of the type, *intensity of response=(coefficient of proportionality)×(intensity of imposed condition)*. Some of the most important properties of matter, e.g. elastic moduli, electrical conductivity, thermal conductivity, coefficients of diffusion and thermal expansion, are defined in this way. Not all properties of crystals are of this simple kind, of course. Plastic strain, for example, is rarely proportional to the applied stress.

Relations where the response is proportional to the imposed condition are called *linear relations*. To express these mathematically, taking account of the tensor character of the properties concerned, *tensor notation* is used. We construct three mutually perpendicular axes in the crystal and label them x_1, x_2, and x_3. In choosing these axes, we take advantage of any symmetry in the crystal, e.g. in a cubic crystal we use the cell edges as axes, and in a hexagonal crystal we take one axis (the *hexad* axis) perpendicular to the basal planes. As an illustration, suppose that we are investigating the conduction of electricity or heat. Let the voltage or temperature at some point be θ. Then the voltage or temperature gradient at this point has components $\partial\theta/\partial x_1$, $\partial\theta/\partial x_2$, and $\partial\theta/\partial x_3$, along the three axes. Let the *current density*, i.e. the amount of electricity or heat crossing unit area perpendicular to the direction of flow in unit time, have components I_1, I_2, and I_3, along the three axes. Then to express the dependence of the current on the gradient, we have to write three equations, one for each component of the current, and in each equation we must make the current proportional to all three components of the gradient. Thus the coefficient of proportionality comprises nine distinct components. The relations are

$$\left.\begin{aligned}
I_1 &= k_{11}\frac{\partial\theta}{\partial x_1} + k_{12}\frac{\partial\theta}{\partial x_2} + k_{13}\frac{\partial\theta}{\partial x_3} \\
I_2 &= k_{21}\frac{\partial\theta}{\partial x_1} + k_{22}\frac{\partial\theta}{\partial x_2} + k_{23}\frac{\partial\theta}{\partial x_3} \\
I_3 &= k_{31}\frac{\partial\theta}{\partial x_1} + k_{32}\frac{\partial\theta}{\partial x_2} + k_{33}\frac{\partial\theta}{\partial x_3}
\end{aligned}\right\} \quad \ldots\ldots (4)$$

The set of nine quantities, $k_{11}, \ldots, k_{33}$, is called the *conductivity tensor*. The quantities can be represented collectively by the symbol k_{ij} where $i=1, 2, 3$, and $j=1, 2, 3$. The equations then become

$$I_1 = \Sigma k_{1j} \frac{\partial \theta}{\partial x_j}, \quad I_2 = \Sigma k_{2j} \frac{\partial \theta}{\partial x_j}, \quad I_3 = \Sigma k_{3j} \frac{\partial \theta}{\partial x_j},$$

where in each case the sum is taken over all the terms generated by substituting the numbers 1, 2, and 3, in turn for the symbol j. The three equations can thus be written collectively as

$$I_i = \Sigma_j k_{ij} \frac{\partial \theta}{\partial x_j}$$

Often the summation sign is omitted, i.e.

$$I_i = k_{ij} \frac{\partial \theta}{\partial x_j} \quad \cdots \cdots \cdots \cdots \quad (5)$$

with the understanding that when a subscript occurs twice on one side of the equation (e.g. j occurs twice in the general term $k_{ij} \partial \theta / \partial x_j$), that term stands for the sum of all terms generated by substituting in turn all the values that the subscript is allowed to have. Equation 5 is thus a compact way of writing the three relations of equation 4.

It will be noticed that the order of the conductivity tensor is higher than that of the tensors it connects. This is a very general effect. For example, the elastic modulus tensor, which connects the second-order stress tensor to the second-order elastic strain tensor, is a fourth-order tensor, with a possible maximum of 81 independent components. Fortunately, crystal symmetry and various other effects usually render many of the components in coefficient tensors either equal to each other, or zero, so that the actual measurement and specification of these properties is usually simpler than one might expect at first sight. For example, in the above conductivity tensor it can be proved that $k_{ij} = k_{ji}$, so this reduces the number of independent terms to six. In addition, in cubic crystals, the symmetry requires that the physical properties of the material shall be the same along the three cubic axes, and the effect of this condition is to make $k_{ij} = k$, a constant, when $i = j$, and $k_{ij} = 0$ when $i \neq j$. This means that the second-order conductivity coefficients reduce to a single term, k, for cubic crystals, i.e. these crystals are *isotropic* for such properties. This extreme simplification does not extend to crystals of other symmetries, however, nor to other kinds of tensor properties in cubic crystals, e.g. the elastic modulus tensor has three components in cubic crystals.

3.7   The Structure of Real Crystals

The perfectly repeating arrays of sections 3.1 and 3.3 apply only to *ideal crystals*, i.e. to idealisations of the much more complicated structures that exist in most real crystals. The first complication is that the atoms in a real crystal do not rest, but vibrate continually about their mean positions. The frequencies of these vibrations are fixed by the interatomic forces, and their amplitudes by the temperature. We shall study them in section 8.1.

There are also many sources of irregularity in the crystal structure which persist when a time-average of the atomic positions is taken. The most familiar of these are atoms of other substances, present in the crystal either intentionally as *alloying elements*, or unintentionally as *impurities*. These foreign atoms may be dispersed as individuals throughout the crystal, when they are said to be in *solid solution*, or they may be grouped together to form particles of *second phases* or *inclusions* in the crystal. The theory of such distributions will be given in Chapters IX to XI.

Many observations have shown that irregularities occur in crystals, quite apart from vibrations and foreign atoms. We call these irregularities *imperfections*; a fuller definition will be given below. Many properties of crystals can be divided into either (i) *structure-insensitive properties*, e.g. specific heat, lattice constants, density, coefficient of thermal expansion, elastic constants, which vary little among different specimens of the same substance, or (ii) *structure-sensitive properties*, e.g. yield strength, breaking strength, magnetic permeability, which can vary greatly among different specimens. While theories based on ideal crystals can usually explain the magnitudes of structure-insensitive properties fairly well, they fail utterly when applied to structure-sensitive ones. Thus the calculated yield strengths and breaking strengths of ideal crystals are some 100 to 10,000 times greater than the actual strengths of most real crystals. This must mean that certain imperfections (i.e. *cracks* and *dislocations*; see Chapter XV) are present which act as centres of weakness and cause premature failure.

The character of X-ray reflections from crystals, and the patterns formed by etching on crystal faces, suggest that many crystals are in fact *mosaics* of smaller crystals, or *crystallites*; the crystal orientation is constant within a crystallite but it varies slightly, of the order of a few minutes of arc, from one crystallite to another. The type of structure envisaged is shown, with exaggeration of the orientation differences, in Fig. 13. The width of the crystallites is often about 1000 to 10,000 atomic diameters, and at their boundaries a region of misfit occurs, called a *small-angle boundary*, due to the small angular difference between the adjoining crystallites. The structures of small-angle boundaries will be discussed in Chapter XV.

The study of phenomena such as diffusion (see Chapter XII) which involve the movement of atoms through crystals has shown that imperfections of an atomic scale of size must exist in crystals. The two kinds mostly considered are (i) *vacant atomic sites* (or simply *vacancies*), i.e. atomic sites which would be occupied by atoms in a perfect crystal but which are in fact unoccupied, and (ii) *interstitial atoms*, i.e. atoms of the ordinary crystal substance that, instead of occupying normal atomic sites, have become misplaced into the *interstices* between atoms in normal sites. We shall see in Chapter VIII that some of these defects must be present in all crystals in equilibrium at ordinary temperatures.

As well as these various imperfections, a crystal may contain *elastic strains* or *internal stresses*. By an elastically strained region of a crystal we mean one in which the actual lattice vectors, defining the position of a lattice point relative to its neighbours, differ from the ideal lattice vectors (equation 3) by an amount which is at least one order of magnitude smaller than these ideal vectors; in practice elastic strains are usually smaller than 1 per cent. An internal stress has two aspects, its *source*, and its *field*. The source is the feature that is responsible for the stress; it may be an externally applied force on the crystal, or some

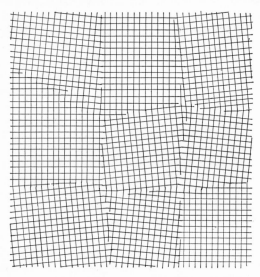

FIG. 13.—Diagram of the Mosaic Structure.

feature, such as an imperfection or a temperature gradient, within the crystal. With all internal sources, which produce *self-stressed* crystals, one can regard the crystal as being composed of two or more parts so joined that each constrains the others to an unnatural size or shape. This may occur, for example, because temperature gradients cause the lattice parameter of one part to differ from another, or because a foreign atom or inclusion is mounted in a hole of the wrong size in the crystal, or because a slice has been taken out of the crystal and the faces exposed by its removal have been forced together and joined. The *field* is the distribution of elastic strain set up in the crystal from the source. A strain field has no independent existence, and disappears if its source is removed.

Most metal crystals are nearly perfect. Even in those that have been severely distorted by cold work usually not more than one atom in a thousand is so grossly misplaced that one cannot recognise the lattice pattern from the positions of its immediate neighbours. Because the basic structure of such crystals is so regular, the imperfections in them must have certain regular and precisely definable forms so that they can be fitted into its regular framework. It is this fact, more than anything else, that has been responsible for the sharpening of our concepts of crystal imperfections from their vague early forms, such as 'amorphous regions', 'crystalline debris' and 'crystal fragmentation', into the present clearly-defined ones such as 'vacant sites', 'dislocations', and 'small-angle' and 'large-angle boundaries'.

The concept of a crystal imperfection involves ideas of an essentially *topological nature*. If the structure in a piece of distorted crystal can be rendered perfect by the application of a *purely elastic field*, no matter how complicated this field may be, then we say that that piece contains no imperfections. But if this cannot be done, i.e. if the crystal contains irregularities that persist through all *elastic* deformations, even though the forms of these irregularities may be greatly altered by the deformations, then we say that it contains some crystal imperfections. This topological approach to imperfections is particularly useful when defining dislocations, as in Chapter XV.

3.8 Grain Boundaries

Most metals in commercial use are *polycrystalline*, i.e. the mass as a whole is made up of a large number of small interlocking crystals, or *grains*. Each grain within the mass is joined to its neighbours at all points on its surface by a *grain boundary*, the shape of which generally bears no relation to the internal symmetry of the crystal. The packing of atoms in the boundaries is almost as compact as that within the grains themselves so that the density of a polycrystal is hardly different from that of the corresponding single crystal. The orientations of the crystal axes in the different grains are often distributed randomly, so that most of the grain boundaries are *large-angle boundaries*, separating grains which are some 20° or more apart in orientation. In many cases, however, the orientations are grouped closely about a mean value; this is called a *preferred orientation* or a *texture*.

The process of melting, casting, and freezing, in a mould, by which many metals are prepared, favours the formation of polycrystalline aggregates. Solidification occurs by *nucleation* and *growth*, i.e. small crystals form in the melt, and then grow at the expense of the surrounding liquid until all is solid. At the rates of cooling usual in castings many nuclei are formed and these grow into a mass of fine grains. Often the nuclei grow rapidly along certain crystallographic directions, and slowly along others, which results in the formation of long branching arms, called *dendrites*, extending out from each nucleus. Eventually the outward growth of each dendrite is obstructed by the mesh of dendrites from neighbouring nuclei, and the remaining liquid freezes in the spaces between the branches. A grain boundary is formed at every point where neighbouring crystals growing in the melt make contact. This is why the grains in a metal often have irregular and uncrystallographic outlines; flat crystal faces cannot form when each grain must take up a shape dictated by the configuration of neighbouring dendrites.

The nature of the grain boundary has long been a favourite problem in physical metallurgy. For many years the *amorphous cement theory* was accepted, in which the grains were considered to be separated by a layer of roughly about 100 atoms thickness, consisting of an irregular arrangement of atoms resembling the structure of a liquid rather than a crystal. The main evidence for this view was the fact that, at high temperatures, polycrystalline metals behave mechanically as if the grains in them were bounded by thin films of a viscous liquid.* However, although such observations proved the existence of boundaries across which the interatomic bonds were irregularly arranged, they did not establish the thickness of such films, and it was not generally realised until much later that these mechanical properties would still be possessed if the boundaries were only one or two atoms thick.

The view most widely held at present is the *transition lattice theory*, proposed by Hargreaves and Hills,† in which the boundary is considered as a narrow transition region, about two atoms thick, across which the atoms change over from the set of sites of the one crystal

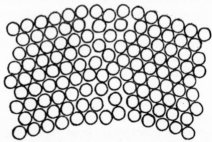

Fig. 14.—Suggested Form of the Boundary between Grains.

to that of the other. A diagram of such a boundary is given in Fig. 14. The arguments and evidence for this theory are as follows:—

(1) The forces causing atoms to crystallise at the freezing-point should also be exerted on atoms at the boundaries between grains. If a thick amorphous layer existed here, crystallisation ought to occur on the two adjoining grains until the layer became so thin that all remaining atoms in it were within range of the interatomic forces from *both* crystals. These remaining atoms would then take up positions which are a compromise between those required by the rival crystals. Since interatomic forces are short-ranged, inappreciable beyond a few atomic diameters, the boundary layer ought to be only one or two atoms thick.

(2) Several properties of grain boundaries, e.g. their energy, their

* W. Rosenhain and D. Ewen, *J. Inst. Metals*, 1912, **8**, 149; 1913, **10**, 119.
† F. Hargreaves and R. J. Hills, *J. Inst. Metals*, 1929, **41**, 257.

etching behaviour, their ability to nucleate precipitates of second phases (see Chapter XIV), are known to depend on the relative orientations of the adjoining grains. This is consistent with the idea that, on the transition lattice theory, more atoms in a boundary can fit simultaneously on to both adjoining grains when these have similar orientations than otherwise.

(3) Measurements have now been made of the energies of grain boundaries.* Large-angle boundaries in copper, for example, have an energy of 550 ergs per sq. cm. The latent heat of melting is of order 10^{-13} ergs per atom, and, since the disorder in a boundary is comparable with that in a liquid, we expect the energy of an atom in a boundary to exceed that of one in the crystal by about the same amount. Suppose the thickness of the boundary is d cm. Then the number of atoms in 1 sq. cm. of boundary is about $10^{23}d$. The energy of this boundary should thus be about $10^{-13} \times 10^{23}d = 10^{10}d$ ergs per sq. cm. Equating this to the experimental value, 550, shows that d is about two atoms thickness.

(4) Comparison of the viscosity of grain boundaries in aluminium, deduced by Kê† from his measurements of their mechanical properties, with the known viscosity of molten aluminium, shows that, for the viscosities to be the same, the boundary must be about 4 Å. thick.

3.9 The Shapes of Metal Grains

We have seen that the shapes of grains in cast metals are fixed by the mutual obstruction of the growing crystals and so bear little relation to the properties of the grain boundaries. However, by plastic

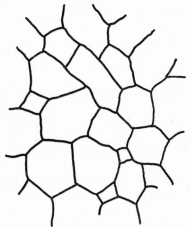

Fig. 15.—Illustrating a Polygonal Grain Structure.

working and annealing at high temperatures it is usually possible to replace the original grains by a new set (*recrystallisation*), formed through

* For a review, see the article by J. C. Fisher and C. G. Dunn in 'Imperfections in Nearly Perfect Crystals' (Ed. W. Shockley), Wiley, 1952.
† T. S. Kê, *Phys. Rev.*, 1947, **71**, 533; 1947, **72**, 41.

atomic rearrangements in the solid state. The shapes of these new grains are determined largely by the properties of their boundaries, and a much more regular polyhedral grain structure is formed, as illustrated in Fig. 15. The striking resemblance that this bears to the cell structures in soap bubble froths is due to the fact that, in both cases, *surface tension* in the boundaries is the governing factor.*

A grain boundary has surface tension because its atoms have higher energy (strictly, higher *free energy*; see Chapter VII) than those within the grains. To reduce its energy as much as possible a polycrystal will tend to reduce the area of its grain boundaries, and this is possible when the material is held at temperatures high enough for atoms to be able to leave one crystal to join its neighbour. For example, at such temperatures a curved boundary will gradually contract until it is as straight as the surrounding configuration of boundaries will allow. The effect is as if the boundary were a stretched skin under a constant tension.

In a liquid-gas boundary, e.g. a soap film, the surface tension T is equal to the force per unit length that must be applied along the periphery of the boundary to prevent the film from shrinking. It then

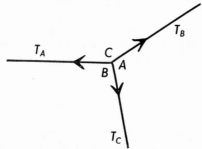

FIG. 16.—Relation between Surface Tensions and Angles.

follows from the relation *force* $\times$ *displacement=work=energy* that $T=\gamma$, where γ is the surface (free) energy per unit area. The concept of surface tension allows the angles at which three boundaries meet to be deduced from a direct application of the triangle of forces. Thus, in Fig. 16, the angles A, B, and C, at which the boundaries meet will adjust themselves until the three surface tension forces, T_A, T_B, and T_C, applied to the meeting point, are in static equilibrium. From elementary statics, the condition for this is that they should form a triangle of forces, in which case

$$T_A/\sin A = T_B/\sin B = T_C/\sin C \quad \text{. . . . . . . (6)}$$

This equation can be applied to grain boundaries in polycrystals on the assumption that the grain boundary energy does not depend on the orientation of the boundary with respect to the crystal axes of its

---

* The modern interest in the shapes of grains is due largely to an outstanding paper by C. S. Smith, *Trans. Amer. Inst. Min. Met. Eng.*, 1948, **175**, 15.

adjoining grains. For the usual boundaries in random polycrystals this assumption proves to be reasonable. A more general formula, which does not make the assumption, has been given by Herring.*

The dependence of the energy of a grain boundary on the crystal orientation of one adjoining grain, relative to that of its neighbour, is only marked for small-angle boundaries. It is a fair approximation to regard the energies of large-angle boundaries as independent of orientation. This approximation means that for a random aggregate of grains, $T_A = T_B = T_C$ so that $A = B = C = 120°$. Smith† has pointed out that this limitation upon the grain boundary angles set by the surface tension generally conflicts with topological requirements for the numbers of sides and faces on grains. For example, in two dimensions, where the grains can be represented as polygons, only a six-sided polygon can have straight sides and 120° angles at its corners. All polygons with either more or less sides than this cannot be in equilibrium. They must have either curved sides or angles different from 120°. At temperatures where the atoms are mobile a curved grain boundary is unstable and tends to straighten out. Likewise a corner where the angles are not 120° tends to move in an attempt to restore the correct angles. As a result, polygons with less than six sides tend to contract, those with more than six sides tend to grow. This instability in a random array of grains is one cause of the phenomenon of *grain growth*, observed in plastically worked and annealed metals at high temperatures.

Important metallurgical applications of these surface tension ideas arise when second phases are present in the polycrystal. These will be discussed in Chapter 10.

SUGGESTIONS FOR FURTHER READING

'The Crystalline State.' W. H. and W. L. Bragg, G. Bell and Sons, 1933.
'Structure of Metals.' 2nd Edition. C. S. Barrett, McGraw-Hill, 1952.
'An Introduction to X-ray Metallography.' A. Taylor, Chapman and Hall, 1945.
'An Introduction to the Physics of Metals and Alloys.' W. Boas, Wiley, 1947.
'Crystal Physics.' W. A. Wooster, Cambridge University Press, 1938.
'Imperfections in Nearly Perfect Crystals.' Ed. W. Shockley, Wiley, 1952.
'The Structure of Metals and Alloys.' 5th Reprint Revised. W. Hume-Rothery and G. V. Raynor, Institute of Metals, London, 1954.

* C. Herring, Chapter 8 in 'The Physics of Powder Metallurgy' (Ed. W. E. Kingston), McGraw-Hill, 1950.
† C. S. Smith, *Amer. Soc. Metals*, Symposium on Metal Interfaces, October, 1951.

CHAPTER IV

THE FREE ELECTRON THEORY OF METALS

The electron theory of metals aims to explain the structures and properties of metals and alloys from atomic theory. At first it dealt only with the electrical and thermal conductivities of metals, but in recent years it has developed far more widely. Besides explaining numerous features of the metallic state it is now the basis of a general theory applicable to *all* solids.

The theory has developed in three main stages: (1) the *classical free electron theory* (1900) of Drude and Lorentz, which assumed that metals contain free electrons obeying the laws of classical mechanics; (2) the *quantum free electron theory* (1928) of Sommerfeld, in which the free electrons obey quantum laws; and (3) the *zone theory*, started by Bloch in 1928, in which the electrons move in a periodic field provided by the lattice.* Although the theory is now very extensive it still deals mainly with structure-insensitive properties and has found few applications to the study of imperfections. This is partly because the complexity of the atomic arrangement at even the simplest of imperfections makes a full quantum-mechanical treatment forbiddingly difficult, and partly because most of the important questions so far asked about imperfections can be answered without going far into details of electronic structure.†

4.1 The Classical Free Electron Theory

Drude and Lorentz pictured a metal as an array of spheres (the atoms) permeated by a gas of free electrons. These electrons wander freely everywhere in the metal and in their movements obey the laws of classical mechanics, in particular those of the classical kinetic theory of gases. Normally they stream randomly in all directions, but in an electric field they are attracted towards the positive end of the field, producing an electrical current in the metal. Collisions with atoms prevent the electrons from accelerating indefinitely and for a fixed voltage gradient a fixed velocity is reached, giving a steady current proportional to voltage (*Ohm's Law*).

The theory was bold. The electrons were supposed to behave towards each other as uncharged particles, in spite of their electrostatic repulsion. The periodic lattice field of the positively charged ions was smoothed out into a uniform potential, i.e. the electrons were really *free* in the strictest sense and not merely dissociated from their parent atoms; the

---

* References to further reading are given at the end of Chapter VI.

† Recent work has however shown that dislocations play an important part in determining the electrical properties of germanium (see W. T. Read, *Phil. Mag.*, 1954, 45, 775).

assumption that an electron could jump from one atom to another was thus taken in its stride by this more general one of the uniform potential inside a metal.

In spite of these assumptions the theory proved highly successful, partly because some of them prove to be much better, when the quantum behaviour of the electrons is taken into account, than first appears, but mainly because in its idea of electrons that can move through the metal as a whole the theory had found the key to the metallic state. The main successes were as follows:—

(a) *Conductivity.* The high electrical and thermal conductivities of metals could be explained directly in terms of the ease with which the free electrons could move.

(b) *Wiedemann-Franz Law.* The theory showed that the ratio of the electrical and thermal conductivities, at the same temperature, should be the same for all metals, in agreement with experiment.

(c) *Optical Properties.* The free electrons could oscillate in the alternating electromagnetic field which constitutes an incident beam of light, absorbing energy from it at all wavelengths and so making the metal opaque. Conversely, an electron excited by its interaction with radiation could fall back to a level of lower energy and emit radiation. In this way a beam of light is almost totally reflected by a metal, and *metallic lustre* is observed.

(d) *Tolman Effect.* A direct though delicate experiment to prove the existence of free electrons has been successful. A piece of metal is accelerated sharply and the free electrons, by their inertia, are thrown to the rear end of the piece, producing a detectable electric field. Measurements of this have shown that the charge-mass ratio for the particles that produce the field is the same, so far as experimental difficulties allow, as that of electrons.

One of the main difficulties in the theory concerned the specific heat of the free electrons which, on the classical kinetic gas laws, should be $3k/2$ per particle, where k ($=1\cdot38\times10^{-16}$ erg per degree) is Boltzmann's constant. But measurements showed that, for non-transition metals at least, the free electron gas absorbs only about one-hundredth of this amount. The difficulty could not be resolved by assuming that the number of free electrons is far smaller than the number of atoms, because conductivity and other measurements show that in many metals all the valency electrons are free. The only conclusion is that the free electrons do not absorb heat like a gas obeying the classical laws. As in other branches of atomic physics, where the use of classical mechanics led to wrong values of the specific heat, the problem was solved only when quantum laws were applied.

4.2 The Quantum Free Electron Theory in One Dimension

Suppose that a free electron is moving in a *one-dimensional* metal, e.g. up and down a wire, of length L. The Schrödinger equation for this case is

$$\frac{d^2\psi}{dx^2}+\frac{8\pi^2m}{h^2}(E-V)\psi=0 \quad \ldots \ldots \ldots \quad (7)$$

where the square of the wave function ψ at a point x on the wire gives the amount of time the electron spends there, and h is Planck's constant, and E and V are respectively the total and potential energies of the electron. It is useful to notice that by rearrangement the equation becomes

$$\frac{1}{\psi}\frac{d^2\psi}{dx^2}=\text{constant }(V-E),$$

so that if V is greater than E the right-hand side is positive, and therefore $d^2\psi/dx^2$ is positive when ψ is positive and vice versa. Since $d^2\psi/dx^2$ is the *curvature* of the curve of ψ against x, then for this case where $V>E$ the curve always appears convex when viewed from points on the x axis; Fig. 17 (a) and (b). Conversely, when $V<E$ the curve is always concave when viewed from the x axis; Fig. 17 (c) and (d). A *point of inflection*, i.e. $d^2\psi/dx^2=0$, occurs either when $\psi=0$, as in Fig. 17 (b) and (d), or when $V=E$ as in Fig. 17 (e).

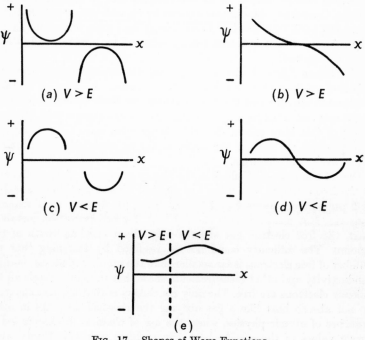

FIG. 17.—Shapes of Wave Functions.

Turning now to the one-dimensional metal with free electrons, we represent the metal by the potential energy curve of Fig. 18. Inside the metal V is constant and, because only *relative* values of potential energy are significant, we can choose the value $V=0$ here. Outside the metal V has some constant and higher value V_m. Electrons with so much energy that $E > V_m$ can escape from the metal entirely, as in *thermionic emission*, but we are interested in those for which $E < V_m$.

Any solution of a second-order differential equation, such as equation 7, contains two arbitrary constants whose values we are free to fix to suit the problem in mind. We shall therefore choose a value of ψ at the boundary of the metal where $x=0$, so fixing one constant, and then choose the *slope* of ψ, i.e. $d\psi/dx$, at this point so that ψ diminishes to zero as x approaches $-\infty$, so fixing the other constant. The ψ curve thus begins as in Fig. 19 (a). If the total energy E of the electron is E'

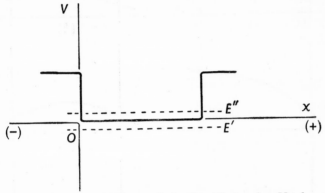

Fig. 18.—Potential Energy V of a Free Electron in a Metal.

(Fig. 18), then $(V-E)$ is positive and ψ must always be convex to the x axis, as in Fig. 19 (b). Since our interpretation of ψ^2 as the electron density does not make sense if ψ rises unceasingly, we conclude that the energy E' is forbidden to the electron.

If $E=E''$ (Fig. 18) there are points of inflection at $x=0$ and $x=L$, and between them ψ is concave to the x axis. If E'' is only slightly greater than V inside the metal, the *kinetic energy*, $E-V$, of the electron is small, and the associated wavelength λ is long (see equation 2). The situation in Fig. 19 (c) then occurs, where the ψ curve does not fall to zero as $x \to +\infty$ but eventually rises indefinitely; i.e. $\psi \to +\infty$ as $x \to +\infty$. This solution is again unacceptable, so that the free electron in the metal cannot have an *arbitrarily small* kinetic energy. It can never stand still, but must always move at a finite speed. This is contrary to what is predicted by the classical free electron theory, where the electrons should come to rest at $0°$ K.

If E is increased slightly the wavelength of ψ in the metal can be shortened until a solution is eventually reached of the kind shown in Fig. 19 (d), where $\psi \to 0$ as $x \to \pm\infty$. This is the first solution that behaves sensibly and is acceptable. It represents the *ground state* for the electron, i.e. the state of lowest permitted energy. Call this energy E_0.

By increasing E beyond E_0, solutions such as that of Fig. 19 (e) are obtained. These are unacceptable since $\psi \to -\infty$ as $x \to +\infty$. The next acceptable one is that of Fig. 19 (*f*) with a node at $x = L/2$. Call the energy of this one E_1. The next acceptable solution has two nodes, and an energy E_2, and so on. The free electron must therefore move in one or other of a set of discrete states of motion, each with a distinct energy

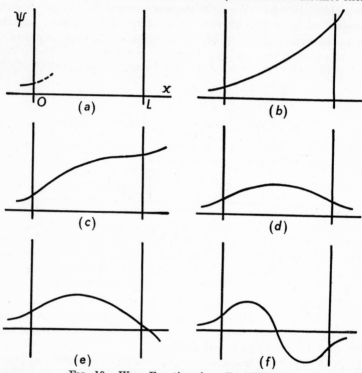

Fig. 19.—Wave Functions for a Free Electron.

E_0, E_1, E_2, etc. As in the free atom (section 1.5), states of higher energies have more nodes in their wave functions.

To calculate E_0, E_1, etc., we assume that V_m is extremely high. This assumption hardly affects the levels in the metal but simplifies the calculation, because ψ then falls to zero so rapidly beyond the boundaries of the metal that we can set $\psi = 0$ at these boundaries. Because $E = \frac{1}{2}mv^2$, where v is the velocity, and $\lambda = h/mv$, then

$$E = h^2/2m\lambda^2 \quad \ldots \ldots \ldots \ldots \ldots \quad (8)$$

Substituting this in equation 7 and remembering that $V = 0$ in the metal, the wave equation becomes

$$\frac{d^2\psi}{dx^2} + \left(\frac{2\pi}{\lambda}\right)^2 \psi = 0,$$

which has the solution

$$\psi = A \cos (2\pi x/\lambda) + B \sin (2\pi x/\lambda) \quad \ldots \ldots \quad (9)$$

where A and B are the disposable constants mentioned earlier. Since $\cos 0 = 1$, $\sin 0 = 0$, and since $\psi = 0$ at $x = 0$, then we must have $A = 0$. To determine B we note that the chance of finding the free electron *somewhere* in the metal must be unity, i.e.

$$\int_0^L \psi^2 dx = 1$$

The application of this condition to equation 9, which gives $B = \sqrt{2/L}$, is an example of what is called *normalising* the wave function. To find the energy levels we note that $\psi = 0$ at $x = L$, i.e. $\sin(2\pi L/\lambda) = 0$. From the properties of the sine function this means that the permissible wavelengths are given by

$$\lambda = 2L, \ 2L/2, \ 2L/3, \ \ldots, \ 2L/n, \ \ldots, \ \text{etc.} \ \ldots \ (10)$$

where $n \ (=1, 2, 3, \ldots, \text{etc.})$ is a *quantum number*. The corresponding energy levels are, from equation 8, given by

$$E = n^2 h^2 / 8mL^2 \ \ldots \ldots \ldots \ldots \ (11)$$

4.3 Generalisation to Three Dimensions

In a three dimensional metal the electrons move in all directions so that three quantum numbers, n_x, n_y, and n_z, are needed, corresponding to the resolution of the motion into components along three perpendicular axes, x, y, and z. With a cubically shaped block of metal, of sides L, the application of equation 11 to each axis gives the permitted levels as

$$E = \frac{h^2}{8mL^2}(n_x^2 + n_y^2 + n_z^2) \ \ldots \ldots \ldots \ (12)$$

where n_x, n_y, and n_z can each take any number from the set 1, 2, 3, ..., etc., irrespective of what numbers the others take.

Which of these levels do the electrons occupy? As in the filling of atomic quantum states, the electrons occupy the states of lowest energy (at 0° K.) with two of opposite spins in each state. Each quantum state is defined by three particular numbers for n_x, n_y, and n_z. At 0° K. all quantum states in the energy levels up to a certain limiting value, E_{max}, are filled and all those above are empty. The value of E_{max} depends on how many free electrons there are.

This is usually represented by a *Fermi distribution curve*, as in Fig. 20, which gives the probability that a quantum state of given energy is occupied. Unit probability means that the state is always full, zero probability means that it is always empty, and a fractional probability means that it is full for part of the time. Although only discrete energy levels are allowed we draw a continuous curve in Fig. 20 because in an ordinary sized piece of metal the allowed levels are too close together and too numerous to mark separately on a diagram. The energy spectrum is said to be *quasi-continuous* in such cases.

Fig. 20 (a) shows that at 0° K. the electrons move about with kinetic energies of all values up to E_{max}, whereas according to the classical kinetic gas laws they ought to be at rest. We shall show at the end of the chapter that

$$E_{max} = \frac{h^2}{8m}\left(\frac{3N}{\pi V}\right)^{2/3} \quad \ldots \ldots \ldots \quad (13)$$

where N is the number of free electrons in a metal of volume V. For a monovalent metal V/N is the volume per atom.* Substituting a numerical value for this and taking $h = 6 \cdot 63 \times 10^{-27}$ erg seconds and $m = 9 \cdot 10 \times 10^{-28}$ gm., we can find the value in ergs of the kinetic energy of a single electron in the highest occupied level. It is convenient to measure this energy not in ergs but in *electron volts* (eV). An electron volt is the kinetic energy an electron acquires in falling freely through

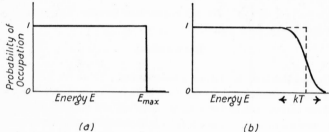

(a)   (b)

FIG. 20.—The Fermi Distribution Curve, (a) at 0° K., (b) at $T°$ K., where $T > 0$.

a potential difference of 1 volt ($1eV = 1 \cdot 59 \times 10^{-12}$ erg; $1eV$ per particle $= 23,050$ calories per gm. mol. of particles). Values of E_{max} for monovalent metals are as follows:

	Li	Na	K	Cu	Ag	Au
E_{max} (eV)	4·7	3·2	2·1	7·1	5·5	5·6

The specific heat per particle of an ordinary gas is $3k/2$, where k is Boltzmann's constant. At room temperature $kT = 1/40 eV$. Thus in copper the electrons in the level E_{max} move about at 0° K. with kinetic energies equivalent to those of the particles of an ordinary gas at a temperature of about 50,000° K. It is no wonder that the classical theory of specific heats cannot be applied to the free electron gas.

At temperatures above 0° K. some electrons absorb thermal energy and move into higher quantum states. The Pauli principle rules that an electron can only enter an empty state, so that the thermally excited ones must go into states above E_{max}. Thermodynamics shows that the average allowance of thermal energy to a particle in a system at a temperature $T°$ K. is of order kT, so that only electrons within an energy interval kT from E_{max}, approximately, can take up thermal energy. Those further down the Fermi distribution are prevented from

* Note that in this section V stands for volume, not potential energy.

doing so by the fact that very rarely is there a vacant quantum state in the energy levels within kT above their own level. At room temperature kT is only $10^{-2}E_{max}$, or less, so that only something like 1 per cent. of the electrons can take up their allowance. This is why the specific heat of the electron gas is much smaller than the classical theory predicts. At ordinary temperatures, e.g. up to the melting-point of the metal, the Fermi curve is hardly altered by temperature. The effect of temperature is shown with some exaggeration in Fig. 20 (b).

The number of thermally excited electrons is of order kT/E_{max}, and each absorbs an energy of order kT. Hence their total thermal energy is proportional to $(kT)^2/E_{max}$, so that the electronic specific heat is proportional to k^2T/E_{max}. This linear dependence on temperature has been verified by experiments at low temperatures where the lattice specific

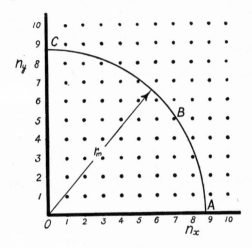

FIG. 21.

heat (see section 8.1) practically vanishes, so enabling the small electronic contribution to be measured.

To conclude this chapter we shall now calculate E_{max}. Let the number of free electrons be N and consider first a two-dimensional metal, for which

$$E=\frac{h^2}{8mL^2}(n_x^2+n_y^2) \quad \ldots \ldots \ldots \quad (14)$$

The quantum states defined by the various numbers given to n_x and n_y can be represented by points in a diagram, as in Fig. 21.

With a suitable scale we can assign unit area to each point. The distance of a point from the origin is r, where $r^2=n_x^2+n_y^2$, and all states with energies up to E in equation 14 are represented by points within the quadrant $OABC$ of radius r_m, where

$$r_m=(8mL^2E/h^2)^{1/2}$$

The area of the quadrant is $\pi r_m^2/4$. Since each point has unit area and there are $N/2$ occupied quantum states up to E_{max}, then

$$\frac{N}{2} = \frac{\pi r_m^2}{4} = \frac{\pi}{4}\left(\frac{8mL^2E_{max}}{h^2}\right),$$

from which we can find E_{max}. In three dimensions we must use equation 12 for E and replace the quadrant by an octant ($\frac{1}{8}$th part of a sphere) whose volume is $\pi r_m^3/6$. Then, as above,

$$\frac{N}{2} = \frac{\pi r_m^3}{6} = \frac{\pi}{6}\left(\frac{8mL^2E_{max}}{h^2}\right)^{3/2},$$

which gives

$$E_{max} = \frac{h^2}{8m}\left(\frac{3N}{\pi L^3}\right)^{2/3}$$

Writing $V = L^3$, for the volume, we obtain equation 13 for E_{max}. Notice that E_{max} depends on N/V, i.e. on the number of free electrons per unit volume in the metal; thus it does not alter when we join together two pieces of the same metal.

It will be useful later to know the value of λ_{min}, the smallest wavelength a free electron will have. From equation 8

$$\lambda^2_{min} = h^2/2mE_{max},$$

and substituting for E_{max}, we find

$$\lambda_{min} = 2(\pi V/3N)^{1/3} \quad \ldots \ldots \ldots \ldots \quad (15)$$

In a monovalent metal $(\pi V/3N)^{1/3}$ is practically equal to the interatomic spacing, so that λ_{min} is about two spacings.

CHAPTER V

THE ZONE THEORY OF METALS

In this chapter we consider the effect of the *periodic* lattice field on the motion of the electrons. This will lead us to the *zone* or *band* theory of solids, which is of the greatest importance for understanding the structures and properties of metals, alloys, and non-metallic solids. We shall use the theory to understand the difference between metallic and non-metallic solids, but other applications of the theory will not be made until the next chapter.

5.1 Running Waves for Free Electrons

As a preliminary, we shall go a little further into the free electron theory to find solutions of the wave equation most suitable for generalising when the periodic field is taken into account. The general solution for a constant potential was given in equation 9. The wave equation is satisfied whatever values—whether positive, negative, or even complex (see section 1.3)—we give to the disposable constants A and B in this solution. In the last chapter we considered a situation that led us to take A as zero and B as a real number, i.e. that led us to use a wave function $\sin(2\pi x/\lambda)$.

This particular form of the solution is very useful for finding the energy levels of the electrons. But it has disadvantages. It leads to the rather mysterious conclusion that the electron density varies periodically through the metal even though the potential is *constant*, whereas physical intuition suggests that there should be an equal chance of finding an electron anywhere, except near the surface. The difficulty springs from the fact that this solution gives *standing waves*, i.e. waves that do not alter their position with time. In terms of electron movements a standing wave means that we are ignorant of the *direction* that the electron is moving along the x axis, e.g. of whether it is moving up or down the wire.

To deal with a current of electrons that we know is going one way along the wire, *running waves* that move along in time have to be used. We might consider $\sin 2\pi[(x/\lambda)-\nu t]$ for these, where ν is the frequency of the wave. Then, as the time t increases, x must also increase to keep up with a given point on the wave, i.e. the wave moves towards increasing values of x with a speed $c=\lambda\nu$. A wave going in the opposite direction would be represented by $\sin 2\pi[(x/\lambda)+\nu t]$.

The trouble with these functions is that they do not satisfy the boundary conditions ($\psi=0$ at $x=0$ and $x=L$) except at special values of t. To satisfy these conditions for all t more elaborate solutions would have to be developed, which showed how the electron approaches the surface of the metal and is then reflected back in the opposite direction.

To overcome the difficulty with the least effort two steps are usually taken. First we bend the wire into a circle and join its ends, forming a closed ring (Fig. 22). This allows us to consider an electron going round and round the ring without meeting a free surface. The quantum conditions that lead to the formula 10 then no longer apply. Instead, the ψ curve round the ring must join up smoothly at its ends, forming a single smooth closed curve. If the circumference is L the allowed wavelengths must be given by

$$\lambda = L/n \quad \ldots \ldots \ldots \ldots \quad (16)$$

where $n = 1, 2, 3, \ldots$, etc., i.e. a whole number of wavelengths must fit round the ring.

It should be noticed that although equation 16 generates only half as many energy levels as equation 10, the overall energy of the electron gas does not change; for there are now twice as many quantum states per

Fig. 22.—A Cyclic Metal.

level since an electron moving clockwise is in a different state from one moving anticlockwise. If this were not so, joining the ends of a piece of wire together would have spectacular consequences.

The second step is to admit imaginary numbers when choosing the values of A and B in equation 9. This can be done because when ψ is a complex number, e.g. $\psi = x + iy$ where $i = \sqrt{-1}$ and x and y are real numbers, the 'square of ψ' is the product $(x + iy)(x - iy)$, which is always the real number $x^2 + y^2$. We try taking $B = iA$ in equation 9, i.e.

$$\psi = A\,(\cos\theta + i\sin\theta) = Ae^{i\theta} \quad \ldots \ldots \quad (17)$$

where $\theta = 2\pi x/\lambda$ or, with the time factor in, $= 2\pi[(x/\lambda) - \nu t]$. The 'square of ψ' is then $A^2(\cos\theta + i\sin\theta)(\cos\theta - i\sin\theta) = A^2(\cos^2\theta + \sin^2\theta) = A^2$, with the welcome result that the electron density is the same all round the ring. The value of A has to be fixed by normalising, i.e. the total probability of finding the electron somewhere in the ring (which equals A^2L) must equal unity.

Having found a successful function we shall no longer need to refer explicitly to time in it, and so we shall take as our function for the moving free electron

$$\psi = Ae^{ikx}, \text{ or } Ae^{-ikx} \quad \ldots \ldots \ldots \quad (18)$$

according as the electron moves in the direction of $+x$ or $-x$. The symbol k is given by

$$k = 2\pi/\lambda \quad (= \pm 2\pi n/L) \quad \ldots \ldots \ldots \quad (19)$$

and is called the *wave number*; it counts the number of wave crests over a distance 2π. In three dimensions k is a vector, the *wave vector*, which gives the direction of propagation of the waves, as well as the wavelength. It can be resolved into components k_x, k_y, and k_z, along perpendicular axes, x, y, and z. Since the *momentum mv* of a free electron of mass m and speed v is given by $\lambda = h/mv$ (equation 2), then for free electrons

$$k = mv(2\pi/h) \quad \ldots \ldots \ldots \ldots \quad (20)$$

so that k can be regarded as a measure of the momentum or velocity of the particle. This simple interpretation of k is not always applicable to an electron in a periodic field, however. In the zone theory we shall be much concerned with how the energy E of an electron varies with its wave number. For free electrons, where $E = \frac{1}{2}mv^2$, this (E, k) relation is a simple parabola,

$$E = h^2k^2/8\pi^2m \quad \ldots \ldots \ldots \ldots \quad (21)$$

as shown in Fig. 23. Here the wave number is positive or negative according as the electron moves clockwise or anticlockwise.

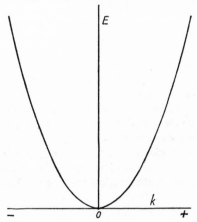

FIG. 23.—Relation between Energy E and Wave Number k for a Free Electron.

5.2 Electrons in a Periodic Field

We now take up the case where the potential V in equation 7 varies periodically with x, due to the periodic atomic structure of the crystal. Through the centres of a line of atoms V varies as in Fig. 24 (a), and through a parallel line not through the centres it varies as in Fig. 24 (b). To make the problem as simple as possible we shall deal with *nearly free* electrons, for which V is nearly constant (e.g. Fig. 24 (b) and (c)), since these ought to behave to a first approximation like free electrons. We shall take the average value of V as zero, so that in the limit where V becomes constant the results established in Chapter IV must hold.

We shall find that for most values of k the wave function is virtually the same as that for a free electron, equation 17. The electron density is then uniform throughout the lattice, i.e. the nearly free electron spends as much time on the crests of V as in the troughs, and so its energy is practically unaffected by the periodic variation of V. Thus equation 21 is still applicable. However, *at certain values of k this similarity to free electrons breaks down completely, even when the periodic part of V is extremely small*; the nearly free electron moves more slowly, its speed actually becoming zero at a critical value of k, and its energy differs from that of a free electron. Some of the most important properties of metals, alloys, and other solids originate in this effect.

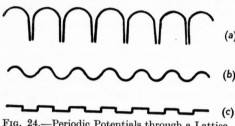

(a)

(b)

(c)

FIG. 24.—Periodic Potentials through a Lattice.

The diffraction of electrons (and X-rays) by crystals, discussed in section 1.4, shows that something of the kind must happen. For an electron shot into a crystal from outside experiences the same lattice field as a native one, once inside; and we know from experiment that for certain speeds and angles of incidence such electrons are rejected by the crystal. They are reflected off the lattice planes, obeying Bragg's law (equation 1). Evidently there cannot also be any native electrons in the crystal moving so as to satisfy the Bragg equation.

This connection with electron and X-ray diffraction provides a useful approach to the physical basis of the zone theory, and we shall make use of it below. Formal mathematical treatments, based directly on the solution of the wave equation for a periodic V, may be found in the books listed at the end of Chapter VI.

Consider the case shown in Fig. 25, where an incident wave, denoted by $A_0 e^{ikx}$ is moving in the $+x$ direction perpendicularly to a set of lattice planes. As this wave undulates across each row of atoms some of it is scattered into wavelets that spread out equally from each atom, as shown for the middle row in the figure. These wavelets correspond to the Huygens wavelets in optics that spread out from the lines of a diffraction grating. All wavelets from one row of atoms are in phase, since they are all generated simultaneously from the same crest or trough of the incident wave. As a result they interfere constructively and build up into two waves the same type as the incident wave (i.e. *plane waves*). One of these resultant waves goes forward in phase with the incident wave and cannot be identified apart from it. The other goes backward, and can be denoted by the wave function $A_1 e^{-ikx}$. This backward wave has the physical meaning that there is a chance of the electron whose motion is represented by this system of waves being reflected back by the row of atoms. The amplitude A_1 of the reflected wave depends on how effectively the atoms can scatter, i.e. it increases with increase in the amplitude of V.

The important question now is what happens when the backward waves from different rows interfere with each other. In general, for an

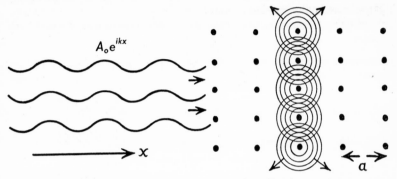

FIG. 25.—Scattering of a Wave by a Lattice.

arbitrary value of k, they are out of phase with each other and interfere destructively, cancelling out. Thus for these cases A_1 is zero for the whole system of reflected waves, which means that the electron with this k travels through the lattice without being deflected or disturbed in any way in its motion. Since there is no significant contribution to the wave function except for the 'free electron' term, $A_0 e^{ikx}$, this electron behaves practically as a free electron.

We now turn to the critical values of k where the electron behaves differently. The argument that leads to Bragg's Law (section 1.4) has now to be used. If k has a value such that the path difference, $2a$, for rays reflected from successive rows equals a whole number, $n\lambda$, of wavelengths, successive reflected waves interfere constructively and add together to make a strong reflected beam. In terms of k, this Bragg reflection condition is

$$k = \pm \pi n / a \quad \ldots \ldots \ldots \ldots \quad (22)$$

where $n = 1, 2, 3$, etc. These are the critical values of k. Although the individual reflected waves are weak when V is nearly constant, a sufficient number of them can always add together to give a total reflected beam nearly as strong as the incident one, so that the latter will eventually be substantially reflected, no matter how far it enters the lattice. This means that when k satisfies equation 22, the wave function is no longer represented even approximately by a single function e^{ikx} representing an electron going in one definite direction. We need functions in which incident and reflected waves are equally strong. Since the reflected beam is e^{-ikx}, these functions are

$$e^{ikx}+e^{-ikx} \quad (=2\cos kx) \quad \cdots \cdots \cdots \quad (23)$$

and
$$e^{ikx}-e^{-ikx} \quad (=2i\sin kx).$$

However, as we saw in section 5.1, these functions represent *standing waves*. This means that for the critical values of k:—

    (*a*) the electron has a zero overall velocity through the lattice, since it is continually reflected to and fro;

    (*b*) the electron density *really does* vary periodically through the lattice.

This second point is important for the energy of the electron. The two functions, sine and cosine, of formula 23 give two forms for the periodic

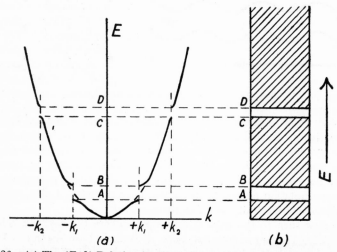

Fig. 26.—(*a*) The (E, k) Relation for Electrons moving in a Particular Direction through a Crystal, and (*b*) the Energy Bands for this Direction.

variation of electron density through the lattice. The sine function has its nodes at the places where the cosine has its maxima, and vice versa. As a result, one of the standing wave functions gives the greatest electron density in the troughs of V, in which case the electron energy is lower than for a free electron, and the other gives the greatest density at the crests of V, in which case the energy is higher. The effect of the periodic field is that, at each critical value of k the free electron level is split into two distinct levels, e.g. A and B in the (E, k) diagram of Fig. 26, separated by a range of energy in which there is no allowed state of motion for the electron. Clearly the energy gap between A and B depends on the amplitude of the periodic part of V, and vanishes when V is constant, as in Fig. 23.

Fig. 26 shows how the (E, k) relation follows the free electron parabola (Fig. 23) for most values of k, and how it deviates from this near the critical values, $\pm k_1$, $\pm k_2$, etc. Here it flattens off, producing the discontinuities A to B, C to D, and at higher energies not shown on the diagram. This means that there are certain ranges of energy *forbidden* to electrons moving in this direction through the crystal. Thus, if we gradually increased the wave number of an electron, starting at the bottom of the curve, the energy would increase steadily until the value A was reached; at this point the smallest further increase in k would necessitate a jump in the energy of the electron to the value B. These forbidden ranges divide the energy spectrum into alternating *bands* of allowed and forbidden regions, as in Fig. 26 (*b*). In conductors these allowed bands are often called *conduction bands*. When presented in a different form of diagram, discussed in section 5.3, the allowed regions are called *Brillouin zones*, or simply *zones*. In each Brillouin zone the energy levels are closely spaced, forming a quasi-continuous spectrum. The *first zone* contains all levels up to the first discontinuity, the *second zone* all those between the first and second discontinuities, and so on.

Fig. 26 shows that the free electron approximation breaks down not only at the exact critical values of k but also at neighbouring values. The reason for this can be seen physically as follows. Near a critical k value the scattered waves from neighbouring lattice rows are nearly in phase with each other and interfere constructively. Only those waves arriving from more distant rows are so far out of phase as to interfere destructively. Suppose that we are dealing with values of k near to k_1. The corresponding critical wavelength is then $2a$ (equation 22). The path difference for rays reflected from atoms m spacings away is $2ma$. Since k is the number of wavelengths in a distance 2π, the number over the path $2ma$ is $k(2ma/2\pi)$. When k is precisely k_1 this is simply equal to m. The interference is certainly destructive when k differs from k_1 sufficiently that the actual number of wavelengths differs from m by $\pm\frac{1}{2}$, i.e. when $kma/\pi = m \pm \frac{1}{2}$, or

$$k = \frac{\pi}{a}\left(1 \pm \frac{1}{2m}\right) = k_1\left(1 \pm \frac{1}{2m}\right) \quad \ldots \ldots \quad (24)$$

This gives the order of magnitude of m, the number of atom rows that can reflect coherently for a given value of k. The nearer that k is to k_1 the bigger is this number and the greater is the intensity of the reflected beam. When m becomes so large that the reflected beam approaches the incident one in intensity, the electron behaves differently from a free one in both its velocity, which is reduced on account of reflections, and its energy, which is altered because its wave function takes on some of the character of a standing wave. The number of atomic rows needed to build up a strong reflected beam depends on the scattering power of the individual atoms, i.e. on the amplitude of the periodic part of V. Increasing this amplitude thus not only widens the gap AB, but also widens the range of k, about the critical value, where the (E, k) curve deviates from the free electron parabola.

5.3   k-Space and Brillouin Zones

The generalisation of the zone theory to two- or three-dimensional crystals is straightforward because the critical values of k are determined quite simply by Bragg's Law. Suppose we are dealing with a two-dimensional square lattice of lattice constant a, as in Fig. 27, and consider those electrons moving at an angle θ across the planes of atoms

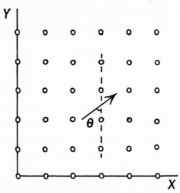

Fig. 27.—Electrons moving in a Square Lattice.

parallel to the Y axis. Then, from Bragg's Law, reflection occurs at wavelengths given by $\lambda = (2a \sin \theta)/n$, i.e. at wave numbers

$$k = \pm n\pi/a \sin \theta \quad \ldots \ldots \ldots \ldots \quad (25)$$

The 'boundary of the first Brillouin zone', i.e. the position of the first discontinuity in the (E, k) curve for this general direction of motion, is then given by

$$k = \pm \pi/a \sin \theta.$$

This result can be expressed more simply by resolving the vector k into components, k_x along the X axis and k_y along the Y axis. The component of k perpendicular to the reflecting planes we are considering is k_x, and since $k_x = k \sin \theta$, the above result for the first discontinuity becomes

$$k_x = \pm \pi/a.$$

Thus a discontinuity occurs, due to reflection from these planes, for *all* electrons which have a resolved component of the wave number, perpendicular to the planes, equal to $\pm \pi/a$; this result holds whatever the value of the other component, k_y. By a repetition of the argument the general condition for reflection from the planes of atoms parallel to the X axis is $k_y = \pm \pi/a$.

The best way of expressing these results in a diagram is by using *k-space*. For three-dimensional crystals k-space is three-dimensional, but in the present case, where we have only two wave number components,

k_x and k_y, to deal with, k-space is two-dimensional. We construct axes in the X and Y directions along which k_x and k_y are measured, as in Fig. 28. Then any point in the diagram has particular values of k_x and k_y, and so represents a particular state of motion for the electron in the lattice. The discontinuities are shown by marking in those values of k_x and k_y at which they occur. The first discontinuity occurs when at least one of the following conditions is fulfilled,

$$k_x = +\pi/a, \quad k_x = -\pi/a, \quad k_y = +\pi/a, \quad k_y = -\pi/a,$$

and so occurs at all points on the square, $ABCD$, in Fig. 28. This square is therefore the boundary of the first Brillouin zone for this lattice.

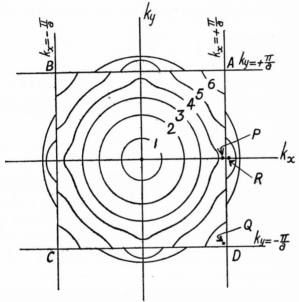

FIG. 28.—The First Brillouin Zone for the Two-Dimensional Square Lattice.

Boundaries of higher zones can be found by taking higher values of n in equation 25 and by considering other lattice planes for reflection. It will be noticed that the boundaries of the zone in Fig. 28 are parallel to the planes in the crystal that give rise to this zone. This is a general property of zone boundaries which follows directly from Bragg's Law.

The usefulness of Brillouin zone diagrams is greatly increased by marking in *energy contours*, i.e. those values of k for which the electrons all have the same energy. By forming (E, k) curves for several different directions through the crystal, all the k values for these directions which correspond to the same selected energy level can be found, and then marked in the k-space diagram. A typical set of contours for nearly free electrons is shown in Fig. 28. The low energy contours, 1, 2, and 3, which do not approach the boundary closely are circles centred on the origin. This follows because electrons with wave numbers well away from the critical values resemble free electrons, and these behave the same whatever direction they move since there is no periodic field to give them directionality. Further out from the origin in k-space, however, the contours are no longer circular (e.g. contour 4), but bulge out towards the nearest parts of the zone boundaries. This occurs because, near these boundaries, the (E, k) relation deviates below the free electron parabola, and E rises abnormally slowly with k. In these regions of k-space, then, the rise in energy from one contour to the next involves an exceptionally large increase in k. Higher energy contours, such as 5 and 6, intercept the zone boundaries, showing that the only electronic states in the zone that have energies in this range lie in the corners of the zone.

The energy contours do not continue across the zone boundary because of the discontinuity in energy there. Thinking of Fig. 28 geographically as a contour map of a more or less parabolically shaped hollow (height corresponding to energy), the boundary of the zone represents a vertical cliff. The energies of the contours in the second zone, the first few of which are shown in the diagram, depend on the height of this cliff. It is important to know whether the two zones *overlap*, i.e. whether the *lowest* levels in the second zone are *lower* than the *highest* levels in the first zone. Consider the two following cases:

(1) Where the discontinuity at the zone boundary is large, so that the zones do not overlap. For example, suppose in Fig. 28 that $P=4\cdot5$, $Q=6\cdot5$, and that the height of the cliff from P to R is 4, so that R is $8\cdot5$. Then the lowest level, R, in the second zone is higher than the highest level, Q, in the first one, and the band structure of Fig. 29 is obtained.

(2) Where the discontinuity is small so that the zones overlap. Thus if the cliff from P to R is 1, R is $5\cdot5$, and the energy levels at the bottom of the second zone are lower than those at the top of the first one. The conclusion is that, although there are *always* forbidden ranges in individual (E, k) curves for particular directions of motion through a crystal, the energy spectrum for *all* directions of motion in two- and three-dimensional lattices may or may not have forbidden ranges.

In actual metals the Brillouin zones are polyhedra, the plane surfaces of which are parallel to the appropriate reflecting planes in the crystal. These planes are the same as give rise to X-ray diffraction spectra, and the intensity of a diffracted X-ray line is an indication of the reflecting power of the planes from which it comes, and therefore of the height of the energy cliff for the zone boundary caused by these planes. Fig. 30 shows the first Brillouin zone for the F.C.C. lattice. X-ray analysis shows that reflections in this lattice occur first from the {111} and {200} planes, so that the boundaries of the first zone are parallel to these.

We now enquire how these zones are filled by electrons, i.e. which of the various electronic states are actually used. This involves first finding how many quantum states belong to a zone. The increase in

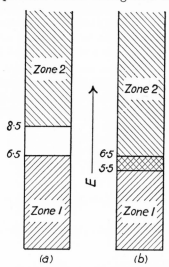

FIG. 29.—Energy Bands for (a) Large Discontinuities and (b) Small Discontinuities.

the value of k from one state to the next, in the one-dimensional problem, is seen from equation 19 to be $2\pi/L$, where L is the length of the crystal in this dimension. In three dimensions, then, the volume given

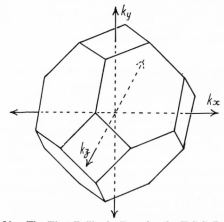

FIG. 30.—The First Brillouin Zone for the F.C.C. Lattice.

to each quantum state in k-space is $8\pi^3/V$, where V is the volume of the crystal. The volume of the cube representing the first zone in a simple cubic lattice, of which Fig. 28 could be regarded as a section in the plane $k_z=0$, is $(2\pi/a)^3$, where a is the lattice constant. Thus the number of quantum states in this zone is $(8\pi^3/a^3)/(8\pi^3/V)$, i.e. V/a^3, and therefore exactly equals the number of lattice points in the crystal. Since two electrons with opposite spins can enter each quantum state, the zone can hold twice as many electrons as there are lattice points.

The number of quantum states in a Brillouin zone is thus found by measuring the volume of the zone in k-space and dividing this by the volume allotted to one quantum state. For F.C.C. and B.C.C. lattices the result is the same as above; each zone in these lattices holds precisely one quantum state (or two electrons with opposite spins) for each lattice point in the crystal. In C.P.Hex. structures the Brillouin zones do not contain a simple integral number of quantum states. The actual number depends on the axial ratio and, for the first zone, is generally slightly smaller than for a zone in the cubic lattices. For example, zinc, with an axial ratio of 1·856, has room for only 1·792 electrons in its first zone.

The same rules apply as before for the occupation of quantum states by electrons. The electrons fill the states of lowest energy (at 0° K.), with

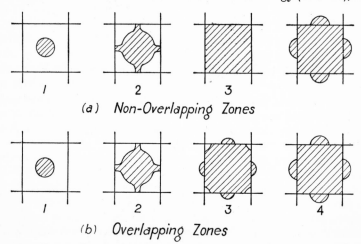

Fig. 31.—Various Stages (1, 2, 3, and 4) in the Occupation of Brillouin Zones by Electrons.

two of opposite spins in each. Thus for monovalent metals, such as the alkalies and copper, silver, and gold, the $N/2$ quantum states of lowest energy are filled, where N is the number of atoms in the metal. With one atom to each lattice point this means that the first zone is half filled.

For elements of higher valency the occupation of the Brillouin zones depends on whether they overlap. In Fig. 31 we imagine that the first zone of the square lattice (Fig. 28) is being 'filled up' as more and more electrons are added to the crystal. Diagrams 1, 2, 3, and 4 show the various stages of filling for both overlapping and non-overlapping zones, the occupied regions being shaded in each case. The condition that the electrons as a whole should have as little kinetic energy as possible requires that the energy at the limit of the occupied region (called the *Fermi surface*) must be the same at all points. For, if at some place on the Fermi surface electrons had higher energy than at other places, they could lower their energy by moving into empty quantum states just above the Fermi surface at these other places. The application of this condition to overlapping zones means that it is impossible to complete the filling of one zone without also starting to fill the next one, as in Fig. 31 (*b*), diagram 3. In crystals of this kind there are *always* partly filled zones, whatever the electron concentration. When the zones do not overlap, on the other hand, it is possible to avoid partly filled zones by choosing an electron concentration that fills some completely and leaves others completely empty.

5.4 Metals and Insulators

While it is obvious that free electrons can move about through the entire region where their potential energy is constant, it is less obvious that electrons moving in a periodic field can also do the same. If two regions *A* and *B* of low potential energy are separated by a third region where the potential energy is higher than the total energy of the electron, then on classical laws one would suppose that the electron could not move from *A* to *B*, or vice versa. Quantum mechanics shows that this view is wrong. There is a definite chance that the electron will cross the barrier even when its kinetic energy is *smaller* than the height of the barrier. The effect cannot be understood on classical ideas, and one must imagine that the electron in some way 'tunnels' through the barrier; hence the name *tunnel effect*.

The effect arises because the wave function representing the electron does not fall sharply to zero when the barrier is reached, but becomes gradually weaker the further it penetrates into the barrier. If it has not fallen to zero by the time that the far side of the barrier is reached, then the wave function can spread out again in the region beyond the barrier. A somewhat similar effect can be produced with light waves. If two parallel glass plates are placed about a wavelength apart, then part of a light beam can be transmitted from one plate into the other, thereby jumping the gap between them, even when the angle of incidence of the light is set to produce total internal reflection.

In the tunnel effect, the frequency with which an electron jumps the barrier decreases very sharply as either the width or the height of the barrier is increased. There is almost no chance of electrons jumping from one atom to another in a gas, except when these atoms collide with each other. In a solid, on the other hand, the atoms are all 'in contact' with each other, and the comparatively small potential barriers between them offer little resistance to valency electrons. The inner core electrons, on the other hand, have lower kinetic energies than the valency electrons, and to them the barriers between atoms in crystals are virtually impenetrable.

Because of the tunnel effect, then, the valency electrons in *all* solids can move from atom to atom. This justifies the first assumption underlying the whole electron theory—that electrons can move about inside metals. But why limit the argument? If the valency electrons in all solids are mobile, why are only some solids metals? Why is the electrical resistance of insulators such as quartz or diamond as much as 10^{24} times as great as that of metals? A difference as great as this cannot be explained merely by arguing that the potential barriers between atoms are higher for some substances than others. An entirely new principle is needed to distinguish between metals and insulators. We shall take up this problem immediately.

Consider a direction $+X$ through a crystal along which an electric field will be applied. Before this is applied no current flows along this direction; for every electron moving with a certain speed in the direction $+X$ there is another moving with the same speed in the opposite

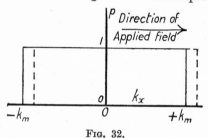

FIG. 32.

direction. This follows because, in the absence of a field, the occupied states are distributed symmetrically about the origin in k-space. We can represent this state of affairs by a diagram, like a Fermi distribution curve, which gives the probability, p, of occupation of a state as a function of its wave number k. The distribution (at 0° K.) is represented by the full curve of Fig. 32, which is symmetrical about $k_x=0$, all states up to $\pm k_m$ (k_m is the value of k_x at E_{max}) being full and all others empty, so that there is no net flow of current. When the field is applied the electrons accelerate in the $+X$ direction and the whole distribution curve is moved sideways, to the position shown by the broken curve of Fig. 32. Most of the electrons in this displaced distribution still do not give a current through the metal, since for an electron with wave number $+k_x$ there is also one with $-k_x$, excepting only those near $+k_m$. Only here, where there are none with $-k_m$ to balance the flow, do those moving in the $+X$ direction constitute a flow of current through the metal. This means that, while all the electrons are accelerated by the field, only those at the top of the Fermi distribution, i.e. with energies near E_{max}, produce a current.

Suppose now that a Brillouin zone is completely filled, and that there is no overlapping, as in Fig. 33 (*a*). Here the Fermi distribution cannot be displaced except by lifting some electrons up the energy cliff at the zone boundary into the next zone. In general the electrons can only acquire enough energy from the field to do this if the latter is some thousands of volts. But so long as all the electrons stay in the filled zone there can be no current, since the distribution remains symmetrical about $k=0$. *Substances with zone structures like that of Fig. 33 (a) are therefore insulators, not metals.*

When the Brillouin zones are partly filled, as in Fig. 33 (*b*), Fig. 31

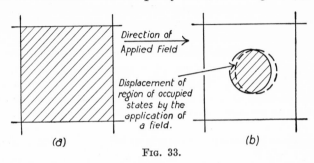

Direction of Applied Field

Displacement of region of occupied states by the application of a field.

(*a*)   (*b*)

FIG. 33.

(*a*), diagrams 1, 2, and 4, and Fig. 31 (*b*), diagrams 1, 2, 3, and 4, the distribution can be displaced sideways by moving electrons into adjacent states within the same zone. Because the energy levels of these states are very close together, the lifting of electrons into adjacent levels can be accomplished by arbitrarily small voltages. This condition is necessary for large-scale electronic conduction, and therefore *metals are solids with partly-filled zones.*

In a third class of substances, called *semi-conductors*, a feeble electronic conductivity occurs. This happens when the zones do not overlap but the energy gaps between them are small, or when impurities or lattice irregularities are present which either add a few electrons to an empty zone or remove a few from a full zone.*

There are two ways in which partly-filled zones can occur:

(1) When the number of electrons is not such as to fill some zones completely and leave others empty.

(2) When the zones overlap, so that it is impossible to complete the filling of one zone without starting to fill the next.

In metallic crystals the zones generally overlap. This must happen in, say, the divalent alkaline earth metals; otherwise these would be insulators because their first zone would be exactly filled by the valency electrons (2 per atom) in them. In copper, silver, gold, aluminium, and the alkali metals, on the other hand, partly-filled zones occur both because of overlapping and because there is an odd number of electrons per atom whereas the zones hold an even number (2) per atom.

* The semi-conducting properties of impure germanium and silicon find an important practical application in the electronic device known as the *transistor*; see, for example, W. Shockley, *Trans. Amer. Inst. Min. Met. Eng.*, 1952, **194**, 829.

For many years it was thought that all solids with partly-filled zones must *necessarily* be metals. Mott* has recently questioned this view. He points out that one must also consider the distribution of the electrons in ordinary space, as well as in k-space. If conditions are such that, although the electrons can move from atom to atom, there must always be one (assuming a monovalent substance) on each atom, then all that is possible is that the electrons on neighbouring atoms can exchange places with each other. There is no net flow of electronic charge in such a process and no current flows. The substance is an insulator. The condition for a current is that an electron can jump to another atom without the electron on that atom having to make the reverse jump; this produces some atoms (temporarily) without electrons and others with extra electrons. When these extra electrons can, by jumping from atom to atom, get well away from the positively charged atoms without electrons, they can accelerate in an applied field and produce an electronic current.

Mott believes that materials such as nickel oxide, which have partly-filled zones, are in fact insulators because the electrons must remain distributed equally on all molecules. Presumably this is also the reason why some liquids, e.g. paraffins, and fused salts, are insulators in spite of the fact that the irregular distribution of the molecules in the liquid state must largely preclude a zone structure (see section 6.4).

5.5 The Density of States

It is important to know how many electrons have energies in each range of the energy spectrum. For example, in some crystals, it might happen that most of the levels occur at the low end of the spectrum, whereas in others there might be few levels there. This raises the possibility of different crystal structures having different energies and, since the stable one has lowest energy, of deciding whether one structure is more stable than another.

We have to find the number of quantum states in each range of energy, i.e. the *density of states*. This density of states is defined as $N(E)$, where $N(E)dE$ is the number of states per unit volume of crystal with energies in the range E to $E+dE$. For free electrons, with no complications due to zone boundaries, it is easy to calculate $N(E)$. We recall that the maximum energy of a free electron in a crystal of volume V with N electrons is given by

$$E=(h^2/8m)(3N/\pi V)^{2/3}.$$

The number n, of occupied quantum states per unit volume, is $N/2V$, so that, from the above formula,

$$n=(4\pi/3h^3)(2m)^{3/2}E^{3/2}.$$

Differentiation gives

$$dn=(2\pi/h^3)(2m)^{3/2}E^{1/2}dE,$$

* N. F. Mott, *Proc. Phys. Soc.*, 1949, **62**, 416; also Chapter 3 in 'Progress in Metal Physics, III' (Ed. B. Chalmers), Pergamon Press, 1952.

and this is the number of quantum states per unit volume with energies in the range E to $E+dE$. But this by definition is $N(E)dE$, so that the density of states is

$$N(E) = (2\pi/h^3)(2m)^{3/2}E^{1/2} \qquad \ldots \ldots \ldots \ldots \quad (26)$$

Thus the density of states for free electrons varies parabolically with energy, as in Fig. 34 (a).

In crystals this curve is modified by the Brillouin zones. Fig. 34 (b) shows the type of $N(E)$ curve obtained in a Brillouin zone. To understand the shape of this, suppose that we are adding electrons to an initially empty zone. While only the low energy states are being filled the free electron relations are followed and the $N(E)$ curve in this range (OA) agrees with the parabolic, free electron, $N(E)$ curve. As the expanding sphere in k-space, which represents the occupied states, approaches

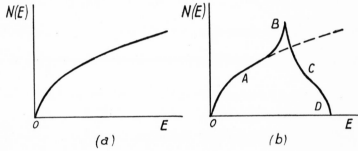

FIG. 34.—Density of States (a) for Free Electrons and (b) as modified by the Zone Structure.

the nearest points on the zone boundary the (E, k) relation for these states deviates from the (E, k) parabola (Fig. 26). The energy E rises slowly as a zone boundary is approached, and so the density of states becomes high. The $N(E)$ curve climbs above the parabola in this range (AB in Fig. 34). It reaches a peak, B, when the expanding sphere, by now rather distorted, touches the zone boundaries at the nearest points. Beyond this stage only the corners of the zone remain to be filled and the density of states falls, because of the limited numbers of states in these regions, eventually becoming zero when the zone is completely filled. The shape taken by the $N(E)$ curve in this range is often of the form given by BCD in Fig. 34.

When Brillouin zones overlap the total $N(E)$ curve is obtained by superposing the individual $N(E)$ curves of the zones on each other and adding together the densities of states in the overlapping ranges. An illustration is given in Fig. 35. Because of these superpositions the total $N(E)$ curves of crystals are generally very complicated in high energy ranges.

It is possible to determine the occupied regions of $N(E)$ curves experimentally by a technique known as *soft X-ray spectroscopy*.* Here the

* See H. W. B. Skinner, *Phil. Trans. Roy. Soc.*, 1940 A, **239**, 95.

metal is made the anticathode in an X-ray tube and is bombarded by electrons. This causes electrons in the inner shells of some of the atoms to be ejected, and electrons may drop back from the conduction band to fill the gaps which have thus been formed in the inner shells. The energy lost by these electrons, when they drop back, is emitted as X-radiation and can be measured from the frequency of the latter. From the intensity of the radiation emitted at a given frequency it is possible to find the density of states in the part of the conduction band

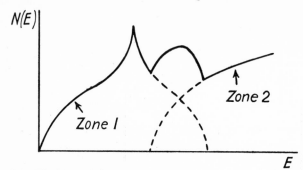

FIG. 35.—The Total $N(E)$ Curve (Full Line) obtained from the Sum of Individual $N(E)$ Curves (Broken Lines) of Overlapping Zones.

responsible for this frequency. This is a powerful technique for studying the electronic structure of metals and alloys.

5.6   Energy Bands and Atomic Energy Levels

We have developed the idea of energy bands by first considering free electrons and then going on to nearly free electrons. The alternative method of approach we shall now discuss, which also predicts energy bands, starts at the other extreme, completely bound electrons, and then goes on to consider nearly bound electrons. It is very useful for showing the relation of the energy levels of free atoms to the energy bands of the solid.

The method is essentially the same as that in Chapter II (section 2.2), where we deduced the splitting of atomic energy levels when two atoms are brought together. We consider a crystal with all its atoms correctly placed but with an interatomic spacing so large that the atoms do not affect each other. Each atom has its electrons arranged in its own characteristic energy levels. We then examine how these levels change as the interatomic spacing is progressively decreased to the normal value of the crystal. As in the two-atom problem of Chapter II, an energy level splits when electron clouds belonging to that level begin to overlap. The number of levels (or, more strictly, quantum states) into which this level splits is equal to the number of atoms participating. For the two-atom problem only two levels are produced (Fig. 4), but in a crystal each original atomic energy level gives a quasi-continuous band of levels.

As the spacing is further reduced, so that the overlapping becomes more extensive, the width of the band increases. The splitting and broadening occur first for the valency electrons, since these are found mostly in the outer regions of the atom, and the levels of the inner electrons do not split until the atoms approach much nearer. The effect is illustrated in Fig. 36. In metals the broadening of the valency levels, and higher ones, at the equilibrium lattice spacing is sufficient to produce much overlapping of the energy bands.

This approach to the electronic structure of metals thus leads to general conclusions very similar to those reached by the zone theory.

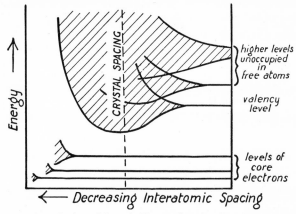

FIG. 36.—Broadening of Atomic Energy Levels when Atoms approach to form a Crystal.

The two methods are complementary. The zone theory is most appropriate when the valency electrons are nearly free, as is the case with s electrons in the alkali metals and copper, silver, and gold. This other method is most appropriate when the electrons are more tightly bound to their parent atoms, as is the case with d electrons in transition metals; in fact, it is usually called the *method of tight binding*.

5.7 The Electronic Structure of Transition Metals

The special feature to which these metals owe their unique properties is the partly filled d shell below the valency electrons. In the crystal the energy levels of the d shell broaden out into partly filled bands. Fig. 37 (a), which follows the method of the previous section, shows in a highly simplified way how the bands broaden in a crystal of a metal such as iron. The diagram shows only the most general features; not the detailed shapes and positions of the bands, which vary from metal to metal.

The 4s band is relatively very broad in the crystal and, because it is derived from an atomic s state which holds only two electrons per atom, the density of states in the band is low. This is shown by the $N(E)$

curves of Fig. 37 (*b*) and (*c*). These curves are highly idealised, but their precise shapes are not important in the present discussion. The 3*d* band, however, is quite narrow. Also, it is made up of five superposed bands from each of the five 3*d* states in the atom, so that it can hold a total of ten electrons per atom. The density of states in the band is thus extremely high, as shown in Fig. 37.

To fill the 3*d* band completely, between ten and eleven electrons per atom from the 3*d* and 4*s* levels are needed, because this band cannot be filled without also filling the overlapping part of the 4*s* band up to the same level. In nickel and copper this part of the 4*s* band holds about 0·6 electrons per atom. Thus in transition metals the 3*d* band is only partly filled in the solid state, as shown (e.g. for nickel) by the shaded region of Fig. 37 (*b*). But in copper, with eleven electrons per atom of the

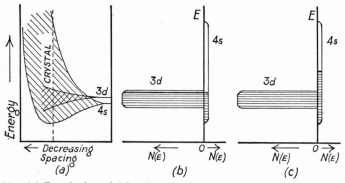

FIG. 37.—(*a*) Broadening of 3*d* and 4*s* Bands in Transition Metals of the Iron Group, (*b*) Filling of Levels in a Transition Metal, and (*c*) Filling of Levels in Copper.

3*d* and 4*s* type, the 3*d* band fills completely and the remaining one electron per atom fills the lower half of the 4*s* band. This is shown in Fig. 37 (*c*).

The partly filled *d* band is the source of many of the properties of transition metals. It produces the ferromagnetism of iron, cobalt, and nickel, and is responsible for the great strength, high melting point, and poor electrical conductivity, that one associates with a transition metal. One consequence of this band can be dealt with here. The high density of states in the *d* band means that, in a transition metal, there are many more electrons than usual at the top of the Fermi distribution. It will be recalled that only those electrons within a range of about kT from E_{max} can contribute to the specific heat of a metal at a temperature T. The unusually large number of electrons in this range in transition metals means that there is a substantially larger electronic specific heat in these than in other metals, which is observed experimentally. Thermal excitation in the 3*d* band cannot occur in, say, copper, however, because there are no empty levels at the top of the band into which electrons can be excited.

CHAPTER VI

APPLICATIONS OF THE ELECTRON THEORY

We shall now discuss some important physical properties of metals in terms of the electron theory. The subjects considered are electrical conductivity, ferromagnetism, cohesion, elasticity, and crystal structure. Specific heat and thermal properties will be discussed in Chapter VIII.

6.1 Electrical Conductivity

Given that a metal has partly filled Brillouin zones, what determines its electrical conductivity? This is the general question we shall consider in this section. When an electric field is applied to a metal the conduction electrons are accelerated towards the electropositive end. Since experiment shows that the flow of current has a steady value for a steady applied voltage, we deduce that the electrons meet some *resistance* to their passage through the metal, which counteracts the accelerating effect of the field and causes a steady mean rate of flow to be set up. It is usual to start the theory by assuming that the resistance is caused by collisions of the electrons with the lattice ions, the extra velocity acquired by any electron during the interval between successive collisions being lost at each collision. The *mean free path, l,* is defined as the average distance travelled between collisions, and it can be shown that the resistivity of the metal is given by

$$R = mv/ne^2l \qquad \qquad \ldots \qquad (27)$$

where n=number of conduction electrons per unit volume, v=velocity of the conducting electrons, m=electron mass, and e=electron charge.

It is well known that the resistivity of a metal decreases with decreasing temperature. How does this fact fit in with the above formula? We know that only electrons near E_{max} can take part in conduction, so that n and v refer to these electrons only. Also, at all temperatures up to the melting point, the Fermi distribution is hardly affected by temperature, so that n and v should be nearly constant. Since m and e are constants, we must attribute the observed temperature dependence almost entirely to a change in l, the mean free path. For pure metals the resistance-temperature relation is generally of the form shown in Fig. 38.

Above about 100° K., R is proportional to T, the absolute temperature, but at low temperatures it behaves differently, becoming proportional to T^5 and reaching zero at 0° K. The mean free path can be calculated from such observations; for a good conductor, e.g. copper or silver, it is about 100 atomic spacings at room temperature and increases rapidly with decreasing temperature, becoming infinite at

0° K. At low temperatures it can be measured directly by comparing the resistivity of thin sheets or wires with that of thick specimens.* As the temperature is lowered the mean free path increases so much that the electrons can traverse the width of a thin specimen without a collision occurring. Below this range of temperature the mean free path is essentially fixed by this width, since the electrons are reflected at the free surface, with the result that a thin specimen has a higher resistance than a thick one. The effect is similar to that which makes

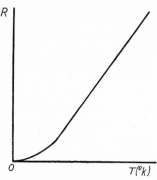

FIG. 38.—Variation of Resistance with Temperature.

it difficult to evacuate a gas through a pipe of diameter smaller than the mean free path of its molecules.

The long mean free path of the electrons, and its dependence on temperature, cannot be explained by picturing the collisions between electrons and lattice ions simply as the 'bumping of particles against each other', for if this were the case the path ought to be of the same order of magnitude as the atomic spacing. To obtain a sensible answer one must calculate the scattering of the ψ waves and deduce the movements of the electrons from this scattering. The results of section 5.2 are important here. We have seen that, when a train of waves moves through a perfect lattice, the individual wavelets scattered at each lattice point reinforce one another coherently, so that the incident beam continues through the crystal without disturbance. In other words, the electron travels through a perfect lattice without being deflected or disturbed in any way during its motion. It can be shown that this conclusion also holds for a lattice which is in its lowest state of natural vibration. Thus, according to the theory, the resistance of a pure crystal should approach zero as the temperature approaches 0° K.

Resistance is due to incoherent scattering of the waves, which occurs at places where the periodicity of the lattice is disturbed, for an incoherently scattered wave implies that there is a chance that the electron will be deflected at the place concerned. Irregularities on an atomic scale of magnitude are particularly effective, whereas long-range features

* References to further reading are given at the end of this chapter.

such as slowly varying elastic strains cause little scattering. When a crystal is heated the thermal vibrations throw the atoms out of alignment with one another and this causes scattering. At low temperatures the amplitude of the vibrations is small, giving little scattering and low resistance. As the temperature is raised the increasing disorder of the array causes more scattering and higher resistance. A quantitative explanation of the variation of resistivity with temperature can be given along these lines. The fact that the resistance of a metal generally increases on melting is also explained, since the extra irregularity of arrangement in the liquid state causes further scattering.

Irregularities such as foreign atoms in the crystal, dislocations, vacant atomic sites, and grain boundaries, also cause resistance. It is well-known that certain alloys (*random* solid solutions*) in which two or more different kinds of atoms are distributed randomly in the array of atomic sites have much higher resistances than pure metals. This is because the electric charges on, and sizes of, the atoms are then not all the same, so that the periodicity of the lattice field is disturbed at randomly distributed places. It is noteworthy that when alloys of this type are converted, by suitable heat-treatment, into a condition where the different kinds of atoms are arranged in a periodic pattern through the lattice (*ordered* solid solutions), the resistance is greatly reduced. This effect provides good evidence for the wave theory of electron scattering, since in such heat-treatments neither the species nor the numbers of the different atoms are changed, only the regularity of their distribution on a common lattice, and it is difficult to think of anything but a diffraction effect which could be so sensitive to the distribution.

Certain metals (e.g. lead, tin, mercury), which at ordinary temperatures are not particularly good conductors, show the phenomenon of *superconductivity*. When cooled below a certain critical temperature, which is different for each substance but is always within a few degrees of absolute zero, they suddenly lose their electrical resistance completely. The change is reversible and as soon as they are heated above their critical temperatures again their resistance sharply reappears. The explanation of superconductivity has been regarded for many years as the main unsolved problem in the electron theory of metals. Recent experiments have shown that different isotopes of mercury have different critical temperatures, the latter being proportional to $M^{-1/2}$, where M is the atomic mass of the isotope concerned. This result has also been verified for isotopes of tin. Now it is known that the amplitude of lattice vibrations in a crystal is also proportional to $M^{-1/2}$, and this strongly suggests that superconductivity is caused by an interaction of the electrons with the lattice vibrations. Theories based on this idea have been proposed recently.† The nature of the interaction can be

---

* See Chapter IX.

† H. Fröhlich, *Proc. Phys. Soc.*, 1950, **63**, A, 778; J. Bardeen, *Phys. Rev.*, 1950, **79**, 167.

appreciated by realising that the electrons will be attracted to places where the positive ions are close together by the high density of positive charge there. Conversely they will tend to spread out from places where the ions are far apart. We thus expect the energy of the electrons to be reduced if they move so that their density fluctuates, from place to place, in accord with the fluctuations in ionic spacing caused by the thermal motion of the lattice. There are reasons for believing that super-conductivity has its origin in this effect.

We turn now to a different question. Why are some metals better conductors than others? In Table 3, column 2, the conductivities of typical metals at 0° C. are given. These show little regularity apart from the notably high values for copper, silver and gold. To clarify matters it is usual to compare, as in column 3, the conductivities under

TABLE 3.—ELECTRICAL CONDUCTIVITY OF METALS*

Metal				Conductivity at 0° C. $(ohm^{-1} cm.^{-1} \times 10^{-4})$	Relative Conductivities, Corrected for Thermal Vibrations
Li	.	.	.	11·8	12·9
Na	.	.	.	23	24
K	.	.	.	15·9	15·3
Cu	.	.	.	64·5	9·1
Ag	.	.	.	66·7	12·4
Au	.	.	.	49	8·1
Be	.	.	.	18	2·0
Mg	.	.	.	25	8·1
Ca	.	.	.	23·5	11·1
Ba	.	.	.	1·7	1·0
Zn	.	.	.	18·1	6·1
Cd	.	.	.	15	4·5
Ti	.	.	.	1·2	0·21
Cr	.	.	.	6·5	0·51
Fe	.	.	.	11·2	1·14
Co	.	.	.	16	1·7
Ni	.	.	.	16	1·9
Al	.	.	.	40	9·5
Sn	.	.	.	10	1·2
Pb	.	.	.	5·2	3·4
Bi	.	.	.	1·0	0·5

conditions in which the contribution of the thermal vibrations is standardised. At a given temperature different metals have different amplitudes of thermal vibration, and this leads to differences in the thermal scattering of the electrons. From the theory of specific heats (see Chapter VIII) it is possible to deduce correction factors which enable

* Data taken from Mott and Jones, 'The Theory of the Properties of Metals and Alloys', Oxford, 1936, pp. 246-7.

one to compare the conductivities under conditions in which the amplitude of vibration is constant. These modified values are given in column 3. We notice that the monovalent non-transition metals as a group are better conductors than either the alkaline earths or the transition metals.

These effects can be explained by the zone theory. When a zone is nearly empty the conductivity is low because there are few electrons to carry the current. As more electrons are put in the zone the top of the Fermi distribution moves forward into the central part of the zone where the density of states is higher (see Fig. 34 (b)); more electrons are then available to carry the current and the conductivity increases. However, when the zone becomes nearly full, the conductivity decreases again, becoming zero when it is completely full. As well as the reduction in the density of states near the zone boundary, there is another effect which reduces the 'effective number of conduction electrons' in such cases. Electrons whose representative points lie near a zone boundary are liable to undergo Bragg reflections during their motion (see section 5.2); the result of this is that they are not accelerated so much by a given applied field as is a free electron. They behave as if they had a large 'effective mass'.

It follows that the monovalent non-transition metals should be good conductors since they have half-filled zones, whereas the divalent alkaline earth metals should have lower conductivities since they have one nearly-filled zone with a small 'overflow' of electrons into the second zone; neither of these zones provides good conduction. Bismuth is interesting, for it is a poor conductor and has a particularly small overlap between its filled and empty zones. There is a small overflow, just sufficient to provide a small conductivity. It is noteworthy that when bismuth is melted, its resistance *decreases*. This is because the zone structure is partly destroyed when the lattice breaks up on melting. Moreover, additions of tellurium, which increase the number of electrons that overflow into the second zone, also decrease the resistance of bismuth.

The low conductivities of the transition metals are due to the smallness of the mean free paths of their electrons. The deflection of an electron by an irregularity in the metal causes the electron to jump into a different quantum state, and it can be shown that the more vacant quantum states there are available in the same range of energy, the more likely it is that the electron will be deflected at a given irregularity. The high density of states in the partly filled d bands of the transition metals provides opportunities for the deflection of the electrons by transitions into vacant d states, so that irregularities which normally cause little scattering are effective in these metals.

6.2 Ferromagnetism

If an object is placed in a magnetic field a force is exerted on it, and it is said to have become magnetised. The *intensity of its magnetisation*,

J, is measured by the intensity of the force, and its relation to the *magnetic field strength*, H, depends on the *susceptibility*, κ, which is a property of the material in the object. The relation is

$$\kappa = J/H \quad . \quad . \quad . \quad . \quad . \quad . \quad . \quad . \quad . \quad . \quad . \quad (28)$$

The susceptibility varies greatly from one material to another. The three main classes are:—

(1) *Diamagnetic materials*, for which κ is small and negative. These are weakly repelled by the field. Examples are copper, silver, gold, bismuth.

(2) *Paramagnetic materials*, for which κ is small and positive. These are weakly attracted. Most metals fall into this class, e.g. the alkalies, the alkaline earths, transition metals, ferromagnetic metals above their Curie points.

(3) *Ferromagnetic materials*, for which κ is large and positive. These are strongly attracted. Examples are iron, cobalt, nickel, gadolinium. Several alloys and compounds containing either these metals or manganese or chromium are also ferromagnetic. An important feature of ferromagnetic materials is that they can retain their magnetisation after the field has been removed, i.e. they can become permanent magnets.

Experiments have shown that the source of ferromagnetism is the spin of the electron. Each electron behaves like a very small bar magnet which, in a magnetic field, can align itself either with the field or against it, according to its spin. Although a physical picture of the effect is strictly not possible, one is often tempted to think of the electron as a small electrically charged sphere which spins about an axis through its centre, the rotation of the charge producing a magnetic field aligned along the axis of spin.

For an object to be magnetised it is necessary for more of its electrons to spin one way than the other, so that an excess of elementary magnets points in one direction. If equal numbers are aligned in the two opposing directions their magnetic fields cancel and the group as a whole shows no magnetisation. An applied field pulls some spins round into its own direction and, by upsetting the balance in this way, produces a magnetisation of the object proportional to the number of excess spins aligned with the field. In ferromagnetic materials the magnetisation can be permanent, which means that in these there is an inherent tendency for electrons to align in one direction.

What kind of interaction between spinning electrons can cause their spins to align in parallel? Since they behave like bar magnets there is of course a magnetic force between them, but this turns out to be far too small to maintain the alignment. Heisenberg[*] first pointed out that the *exchange interaction* could provide forces of sufficient strength, and

[*] W. Heisenberg, *Zeit. Physik*, 1928, **49**, 619.

this idea has become basic to all later theories of ferromagnetism. It will be recalled from section 2.2 that, when wave functions are constructed which allow for the exchange of electrons between two quantum states, the resulting electron distribution differs somewhat from that obtained by superposing the distributions belonging to the two states independently. The electrostatic interactions of the electrons with one another, and with the atomic nuclei, are altered in magnitude by this exchange effect, since these interactions depend on the average distances between these charged particles. Some of them (i.e. electron-electron, proton-proton) raise the electrostatic energy of the system, while others (electron-proton) lower it, so that the final result depends upon the precise distribution of the charges in the system. In the case of the hydrogen molecule discussed in section 2.2, the overall exchange interaction is negative, which means that the energy is lowered if the electrons have opposite spins. It cannot be taken for granted, however, that the same conclusion holds for all other types of electron distributions in atoms, and Heisenberg suggested that, for the electrons which cause ferromagnetism, the overall exchange interaction might be positive, so that the exchange energy would be lowered if the electrons had parallel spins. The types of electron distribution that favour a positive exchange interaction can be deduced by considering how different distributions will affect the relative magnitudes of the various electrostatic interactions between the particles. It is found that the interatomic distance should be larger than the ionic radius, and that the atomic wave functions should be comparatively small near the nuclei. Electrons in d and f states appear to be particularly suitable.

Even if the exchange interaction is favourable, it does not necessarily follow that the electrons will adopt parallel spins. Opposing the alignment is the exclusion principle. If the spins are all parallel only one electron can occupy each quantum state, whereas if the spins are opposed there can be two in each state. To align the spins, then, many of the electrons have to be promoted into states of higher kinetic energy. We arrive at two conditions for ferromagnetism:—

(1) Electrons giving ferromagnetism must originate from partly filled shells in the free atoms, in order that the energy bands formed from these shells have vacant quantum states available for occupation when the electrons align their spins.

(2) The density of states must be high so that the increase in kinetic energy, due to the promotion of electrons when these align their spins, shall be smaller than the decrease in energy due to the exchange interaction.

Electrons in the atomic cores cannot take part in ferromagnetism because they occupy filled shells. The outer, valency electrons also cannot take part because their density of states is not sufficiently high. In the transition metals, however, there are also the partly filled d bands, which have a high density of states. Conditions are favourable here, and transition metals are either ferromagnetic or strongly paramagnetic. The atomic spacing is critical. If the atoms are too far apart the exchange interaction is too weak to resist thermal agitation.* If they are too close together, the kinetic energy factor is dominant. Conditions appear to be most favourable when the atomic radius is 1·5 to 2 times greater than the radius of the atomic d shell. Thus in the iron group of metals the ratio falls in this range for iron, cobalt, and nickel:—

Ratio of Atomic Radius to Radius of d Shell

Metal	.	.	Ti	Cr	Mn	Fe	Co	Ni
Ratio	.	.	1·12	1·18	1·47	1·63	1·82	1·98

Objections have been raised to the Heisenberg theory of ferromagnetism. The theory *assumes* that the exchange interaction between d shells becomes positive when the overlap between them is small, and this has never actually been proved. Secondly, the theory is based on the Heitler-London method, which allows electrons to change places but not to move about independently through the crystal. In the energy band method (see section 5.7) the electrons move through the lattice as a whole, and this, rather than the Heitler-London method, is the appropriate one for applying to solids which are electronic conductors. This second point has led Stoner† to develop a band theory of ferromagnetism in which the force aligning the spins in the d band is introduced as an empirical constant. Recently, Zener‡ has suggested that the exchange interaction between adjacent d shells always retains the same sign as in the hydrogen molecule, and is not responsible for ferromagnetism. He proposes instead that it is the exchange interaction between the d electrons and the electrons in the overlapping s band which causes the d spins to align in parallel, and he shows that the aligning force produced by this interaction is of the right order of magnitude.

It is interesting to compare the saturation magnetisations of various ferromagnetic metals and alloys with the numbers of electrons in their d bands. The saturation magnetisation is obtained when as many electrons as possible in the d band spin in parallel. There are five quantum states per atom in, say, the $3d$ band and each of these can hold two electrons of opposite spins. We can thus imagine the band as two half-bands, each holding all the states with only one of the two spin directions. In substances where the $3d$ band is more than one-half filled the saturation magnetisation occurs when one half-band is completely filled, leaving the minimum number of electrons for the other half-band. Suppose that the total number of $3d$ and $4s$ electrons per atom in the substance is n, distributed so that there are x and $n-x$ per atom in the $4s$ and $3d$ bands respectively. Measured in units of electron spin

* See Chapter VIII.
† E. C. Stoner, *Reports on Progress in Physics*, 1948, **11**, 43.
‡ C. Zener, *Phys. Rev.*, 1950, **81**, 440.

per atom, the saturation magnetisation is then $5-(n-x-5)$, i.e. $10+x-n$. In nickel the experimental evidence shows that $x=0\cdot6$, and as a first approximation we can use this value for the transition metals near nickel. Thus we expect that, for these substances, the saturation magnetisation is $10\cdot6-n$ electron spins per atom. An experimental curve can be obtained by varying n through a series of ferromagnetic alloys of iron, cobalt, nickel, and other substances. In Fig. 39 we compare the theoretical relation, ABC, with the experimentally derived one, ABD. In the range A to B the agreement is satisfactory but, below the point B, corresponding to $n=8\cdot3$ approximately, the saturation magnetisation in practice decreases steadily. This means that, for some reason, it is not possible to have the one half-band completely filled if the other half-band is more than about half empty. As the electron

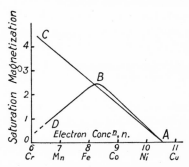

FIG. 39.—The Saturation Magnetisation per Atom of Ferromagnetic Alloys as a Function of the Total Number of Electrons per Atom in the $3d$ and $4s$ Bands.

concentration is reduced below $8\cdot3$ the filled half-band begins to empty and continues to do so until the two half-bands have equal numbers of electrons, at about $n=5\cdot6$. We shall consider the theoretical interpretation of this effect in section 6.4.

The idea that electron spins are spontaneously aligned in a ferromagnetic material might appear at first inconsistent with the well-known fact that a bar of iron can exist in an unmagnetised state. The explanation is that the material contains what is called a *domain structure*. Each domain is a region of the material in which the electron spins are parallel, and so it is permanently in a fully magnetised state.* The direction of magnetisation is different in different domains, however, and the mutual cancellation of the opposite magnetic fields of oppositely oriented domains is such that the substance as a whole appears unmagnetised. When an external magnetic field is applied, the magnetic energy of domains oriented in the direction of the field is lowered and that of those oriented against the field is raised. The favourably oriented

---

* The demagnetisation caused by heat will be discussed in Chapter VIII. In the present discussion we suppose that the temperature is low enough to allow full magnetisation.

domains grow at the expense of the others by the migration of boundaries (called *Bloch walls*) between them. It is also possible at high field strengths for unfavourably oriented domains to jump suddenly into better orientations. The general result is that the volume of material aligned in one direction increases at the expense of the rest and so the specimen as a whole appears magnetised.

This domain structure is quite distinct from the grain structure in the material, and in fact a single crystal of a ferromagnetic metal generally contains many domains. A striking technique for revealing the domain structure in crystals has been developed which involves studying the patterns (called *Bitter patterns*) formed by colloidal mag- netite spread on the surface of the specimen.* This material acts like 'iron filings' of submicroscopic size and reveals very clearly the traces of the Bloch walls emerging at the surface.

It is important to notice that a crystal exists naturally in the form of a domain structure. The reason for this can be seen by considering

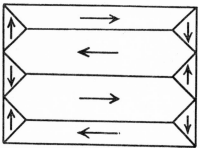

Fig. 40.—Illustrating a Simple Domain Structure of the Type found in Silicon-Iron. The arrows show the direction of magnetisation in the domains.

two bar magnets. If these are placed north against south they attract each other. This means that the magnetic energy is lowered when they have this arrangement, in which there are no free poles, i.e. in which every pole is attached to one of opposite sign. The same effect exists in a magnetised crystal. If this consisted of a single domain it would have two free poles, and to avoid these it prefers to form a domain structure, in which each pole of every domain is joined to opposite poles of neigh- bouring domains. As a result, Bitter patterns of great regularity are often formed in unstrained crystals, of the type shown in Fig. 40.

The width of the domains depends on the magnetic properties of the material, and in silicon-iron (4 per cent. Si) is typically about 0·1 mm. A lower limit to the domain size is set by the surface energy of the Bloch walls. This energy is positive, and if the domains exist on a suffi- ciently fine scale the total surface energy, which increases as the number of domain boundaries increases, can increase the overall energy of the crystal above that which it would have at larger domain sizes.

* F. Bitter, *Phys. Rev.*, 1931, **38**, 1903.

The way in which the direction of magnetisation changes from one side of a domain boundary to the other is shown in Fig. 41 for the case where the orientation changes by 180°. The positive surface energy of the boundary is due to two effects. The exchange energy does not reach such a low value in the boundary as elsewhere, since the alignment of the electron spins in neighbouring atoms through the boundary is not quite parallel. These neighbouring spins become more nearly parallel as the thickness of the boundary increases, and so the effect of the exchange energy is to increase this thickness.

Opposing this is the effect of *magnetic anisotropy*. It is observed experimentally that full magnetisation can be achieved by smaller

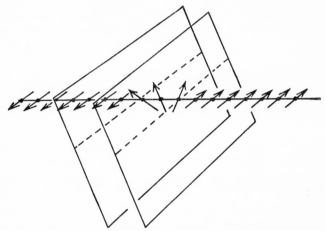

FIG. 41.—Change in Direction of Magnetisation across a 180° Bloch Wall.

applied fields in certain crystallographic directions than in others, and that the spontaneous magnetisation within the domains occurs along these *directions of easy magnetisation*. In iron they are <100>, and in nickel, <111>. As one passes through a domain boundary the direction of magnetisation is forced to rotate away from one easy direction, passing through a series of unfavourable directions before it reaches another easy direction again. To minimise the number of spins not aligned along easy directions the boundary should be as thin as possible. This effect opposes that of the exchange energy and a balance is struck when the thickness of the boundary is (in iron) about 300 atoms. The surface energy of a 180° boundary parallel to {100} in iron is 1·8 erg. cm.$^{-2}$.

The existence of directions of easy magnetisation is utilised in transformer steels, the laminae of which are prepared, by rolling and critical annealing, in a state of preferred orientation arranged so that a direction of easy magnetisation is aligned with the direction of the electromagnetic field. In this way magnetic 'softness' is obtained and hysteresis losses are reduced.

The ease of magnetisation also depends on the state of internal strain in the material and on the presence of impurities; for this reason it is common to remove non-metallic impurities from transformer iron by annealing in hydrogen. Internal strains affect the magnetic 'hardness' through the phenomenon of *magnetostriction*; the lattice constants are slightly altered by the magnetisation and, in consequence, a pattern of internal strains in the specimen tends to fix the pattern of magnetic domains.

The main sources of *coercivity* in a magnet, according to Néel,* are the local magnetic fields which form on non-magnetic inclusions or holes in the metal. Free magnetic poles must form on the surfaces of these features and magnetic energy is associated with them. But these poles can be eliminated, and the magnetic energy reduced, if the inclusions are contained in a Bloch wall, for then a domain structure of the type shown in Fig. 42 can be formed. There is thus an attraction between

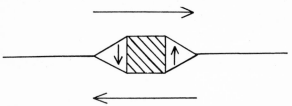

FIG. 42.—Domains Round a Non-Metallic Inclusion (shaded region) in a Bloch Wall. The arrows show the direction of magnetisation.

magnetic cavities and Bloch walls, and the latter will tend to be anchored by the cavities to which they are joined. When the walls are hard to move it is difficult to magnetise the material as a whole, but once magnetised, it is equally difficult to demagnetise and so is a good permanent magnet.

6.3 Cohesion

The technological value of metals is almost entirely due to the nature of the cohesive forces between metal atoms. High cohesive forces produce large elastic constants, high melting-points, and small coefficients of thermal expansion. Differences in cohesive energy between one crystal structure and another are responsible for the crystalline forms exhibited in the solid state. The fact that metal atoms tend to bond with as many neighbours as can be packed round themselves (see section 3.1) leads to the simple crystal structures possessing slip planes suitable for plastic deformation.

The mechanical strength and plastic properties of metals depend in a more subtle manner upon cohesion. For the observed yield strengths and breaking strengths of metal crystals are much smaller (e.g. by a factor 10^{-4}) than the forces required to slide atoms past one another, or to pull them apart. This is because in practice cracks and dislocations are present which cause premature failure (section 3.7). However, it is

* L. Néel, *Ann. Univ. Grenoble*, 1946, **22**, 299.

a fact that metals with high cohesive forces are also, in general, the ones with greatest mechanical strength, and this is recognised in all theories of yield strength and fracture, which always give their calculated strengths as proportional to the elastic constants of the material. The fact that there is little or no *directionality* in the bond between metal atoms (see section 3.1) is extremely important. For it means that atoms can slide past one another by large amounts without the bond becoming broken, and this, together with the simple crystal structures possessed by most metals, is responsible for the ability of metals to undergo plastic deformation without breaking. The more refined analysis of this effect shows that, when the bonds have this non-directional character, *dislocations* in the crystal can adopt a form in which the cohesive forces offer almost no resistance to their motion (see Chapter XV), and plastic flow occurs through the gliding of these dislocations along slip planes.

The simplest metals to understand are the alkalies, for they have only one valency electron per atom, and these valency electrons behave very like free electrons in the solid state. Moreover, the ratio of ionic radius to atomic radius (i.e. one-half the interatomic distance) is small in these metals, as the following comparison with copper, silver, and gold shows:—

	Li	Na	K	Cu	Ag	Au
Ratio	0·39	0·51	0·58	0·75	0·88	0·95

This means that, pictorially, the ions in an alkali metal are not 'in contact with each other'. We say that these are *open metals*, whereas copper, silver, and gold are *full metals*. In open metals the complicated interactions between overlapping ionic charge distributions, called *ion-ion interactions*, are very small.

For the alkali metals, then, we can use the free electron theory and picture the metal as an array of positively charged spheres, separated from each other and floating in a uniform 'sea' of negative charge, representing the free electrons. The bonding force is provided by the electrostatic attraction between the positive ions and the negative free electrons. Electrostatics shows that the potential energy of an electron at a distance r from a positive ion, measured from the centre, is $-e^2/r$, where $+e$ and $-e$ are the ionic and electronic charges respectively. If we take r to be the average distance of an electron from a neighbouring positive ion in the metal, which is proportional to the atomic spacing, we can write the potential energy of the crystal as $-A/r$, where A is a constant and r is the atomic radius.

In an alkali metal the balancing repulsive force is not due to ion-ion interactions since these are very small. Instead, it is due to the kinetic energy of the electrons, which increases as the lattice is contracted. The most important contribution to this kinetic energy comes from the Fermi distribution (section 4.3). There is also another contribution, which is small at the equilibrium spacing; we shall discuss it below. To find the average kinetic energy per electron due to the Fermi distribution (or the *mean Fermi energy*, as it is called) we note that the total Fermi energy of all free electrons in a solid of volume V is given by the formula

$$\int_0^{E_{max}} 2VEN(E)dE \qquad \dots \dots \dots \quad (29)$$

where $N(E)$ is the density of states. Substituting for $N(E)$ from equation 26, integrating, and making use of equation 13 for E_{max}, we find that the mean Fermi energy is $\frac{3}{5}E_{max}$. Since E_{max} is proportional to $(N/V)^{2/3}$ (see equation 13), i.e. to r^{-2}, we can express the Fermi energy in the form Br^{-2}, where B is a constant. The total energy U of the crystal is therefore given by

$$U = Br^{-2} - Ar^{-1} \qquad \dots \dots \dots \dots \quad (30)$$

which gives a curve of the form shown in Fig. 43. At large distances the potential energy term predominates and the atoms attract, but at small distances the kinetic energy increases so much that the atoms repel.

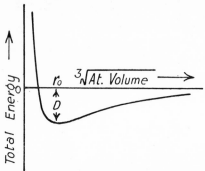

FIG. 43.—The Total Energy of a Metal Crystal as a Function of the Lattice Spacing.

A minimum occurs at a critical atomic volume corresponding to the stable atomic radius, r_0. The depth D of the energy well equals the work needed to expand the crystal at 0° K. into a gas of positive ions and free electrons. If we subtract from D the *ionisation potential*, i.e. the work needed to decompose gaseous atoms into positive ions and free electrons, we then obtain the work required to convert the crystal at 0° K. into a gas of neutral free atoms. This is the *heat of sublimation*, a quantity which can be found from experiment.

Knowing the energy U in terms of the spacing r, we can find the elastic *compressibility* of the material. At the equilibrium spacing r_0 the energy is $U(r_0)$. A small volumetric strain which changes r_0 to r_0+dr_0 also changes $U(r_0)$ to $U(r_0+dr_0)$. Using Taylor's series expansion, we have

$$U(r_0+dr_0) = U(r_0) + \frac{dU}{dr}dr_0 + \frac{1}{2}\frac{d^2U}{dr^2}(dr_0)^2 + higher\ terms.$$

If the strains are small we can neglect the higher terms. Also, the condition of equilibrium is $dU/dr=0$ at $r=r_0$, so that we can write

$$dU = U(r_0+dr_0) - U(r_0) = \frac{1}{2}\frac{d^2U}{dr^2}(dr_0)^2,$$

where the differential is taken at $r=r_0$. Hence

$$F = \frac{dU}{dr} = \frac{1}{2}\frac{d^2U}{dr^2}dr \quad . . . . (31)$$

where F is the force needed to produce the strain. We see that for small strains $\left(\frac{dr}{r} \ll 1\right)$ the force and strain are proportional, with the factor d^2U/dr^2 serving as an elastic constant, i.e. Hooke's Law is obeyed. Using equation 30, we have

$$\frac{dU}{dr} = -2Br^{-3} + Ar^{-2}$$

Since $dU/dr=0$ at $r=r_0$, then $A=2B/r_0$. The resistance of the lattice to compression (or expansion) is then given by

$$\frac{1}{2}\frac{d^2U}{dr^2} = 3Br^{-4} - Ar^{-3} = 3Br_0^{-4} - 2Br_0^{-4} \quad . . . . (32)$$

The important thing to notice here is that the repulsive term in equation 30, i.e. Br^{-2}, makes a bigger contribution to the elastic constant than the attractive term Ar^{-1}. This is an example of a very general result which arises essentially because repulsive forces have shorter ranges than attractive ones. When calculating elastic constants the important interatomic forces to take into account are the short-range repulsive ones.

Although it illustrates the physical principles in the cohesion of alkali metals, equation 30 is not nearly accurate enough for actually calculating cohesive energies. The usual treatment is to use Schrödinger's equation to find the energy of an electron in the ground state of the Fermi distribution as a function of atomic volume (*method of Wigner and Seitz*[*]). This replaces the term $-Ar^{-1}$ in equation 30 by a term which is approximately $-Ar^{-1}+Cr^{-3}$, where Cr^{-3} represents a kinetic energy (not Fermi energy) and is small at the equilibrium spacing. The potential energy $-Ar^{-1}$ is mainly responsible for the cohesion. Certain small additional terms have also to be included, the most important of which are due to the tendency of the electrons to keep out of each other's way. These detailed calculations give results in excellent agreement with experiment;[†] the calculated binding energy of lithium, for example, is 36·0 kcal/gm. atom and the observed value is 36·5 kcal/gm. atom.

The next metals to consider are copper, silver, and gold, which differ

[*] E. Wigner and F. Seitz, *Phys. Rev.*, 1933. **43**, 804; 1934, **46**, 509.
[†] C. Herring, *Phys. Rev.*, 1951, **82**, 282.

from the alkali metals in that they have filled d shells and their ions are much larger in comparison with the atomic spacing. In fact, the charge distributions of neighbouring ions overlap sufficiently at the equilibrium spacing that the mutual repulsion of the filled d shells (see section 2.2) is mainly responsible for fixing the distance between neighbours. One can regard such metals as hard spheres (the ions) held in contact by their electrostatic attraction to the valency electrons moving between them. Now we have seen that elastic constants are proportional to d^2U/dr^2. Hard spheres are those for which d^2U/dr^2 is large at the equilibrium spacing; for *completely rigid* spheres the energy sharply rises to infinity as soon as one tries to compress them, and hence for these d^2U/dr^2 is infinite at $r=r_0$. Large values of d^2U/dr^2 mean that the elastic constants are also large.

Because the atomic spacing in copper, silver, and gold is fixed mainly by the ionic radius, the spacing at which the free electrons have lowest energy is smaller than the equilibrium one. However, the energy of the free electrons does not depend *directly* upon atomic spacing but upon atomic volume. For a fixed atomic spacing the volume can be minimised by assembling the ions, in contact with one another, into a pattern of closest packing. This explains why copper, silver, and gold (and also the transition metals cobalt and nickel, rhodium and palladium, iridium and platinum, which lie next to them in the periodic table) all crystallise in close-packed structures.

For calculating elastic constants other than the compressibility it is convenient, following Mott and Jones,[*] to consider two basic ways of distorting a cubic crystal without changing its volume:—

(1) Equal contraction and expansion, respectively, along two crystallographic cube edges, the volume being kept constant (see Fig. 44). If the length of the cube edge after distortion is $(1+\epsilon)a$, where a is the lattice parameter, we define a parameter

$$A=1/2 \; \partial^2U/\partial\epsilon^2$$

to measure the resistance of the lattice to this distortion. The distortion is equivalent to a shear on (110) type planes in the $[1\bar{1}0]$ direction.

(2) Shear in a plane parallel to a cube face (Fig. 44). If γ is the angle of shear we define the parameter

$$B=1/2 \; \partial^2U/\partial\gamma^2.$$

The shear occurs on (100) type planes in the [010] direction.

Fuchs[†] has calculated A and B for a few simple metals. The change in energy due to distortions which do not change the volume depends on the following factors:—

(1) The electrostatic energy of the valency electrons in the field of the positive ions.

* 'Theory of the Properties of Metals and Alloys', p. 147.
† K. Fuchs, *Proc. Roy. Soc.*, 1936, **153**, 622.

(2) The ion-ion interactions in full metals.

(3) Small changes in Fermi energy in metals where part of the Fermi surface lies in the vicinity of a Brillouin zone boundary; these make minor contributions to the cohesive energy but are important in determining the elastic constants of some metals and in deciding the crystal structures of certain alloys (see Chapter IX).

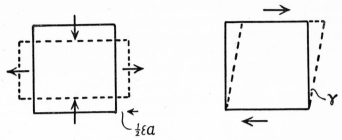

FIG. 44.—Distortions of a Cubic Crystal.

The ion-ion repulsion is important in copper, silver, gold, and the transition metals. Exchange forces are so short-ranged that only the interactions of neighbouring ions need be considered. These interactions act along the line joining the centres of the ions (*central forces*). Let $W(r)$ be the exchange energy of a pair of neighbouring ions when the distance between them is r. Then a calculation for the distortions of Fig. 44, similar to the one we have made for the compressibility, shows that the ion-ion interactions make the following contributions to A and B:—

	Face-centred Cubic	Body-centred Cubic
A	$\dfrac{1}{2}r^2\dfrac{d^2W}{dr^2}+\dfrac{7}{2}r\dfrac{dW}{dr}$	$\dfrac{8}{3}r\dfrac{dW}{dr}$
B	$\dfrac{1}{4}r^2\dfrac{d^2W}{dr^2}+\dfrac{3}{4}r\dfrac{dW}{dr}$	$\dfrac{2}{9}r^2\dfrac{d^2W}{dr^2}+\dfrac{4}{9}r\dfrac{dW}{dr}$

Zener* has emphasised an important consequence of these formulae. Where the observed atomic spacing is fixed by the contact of the ionic shells, the ions behave like hard spheres. For hard spheres the term d^2W/dr^2 is extremely large (approaching infinity for rigid spheres) and outweighs all other contributions. In extreme cases, then, we shall have $A/B\rightarrow2$ for the face centred cubic lattice and $A/B\rightarrow0$ for the body centred one. In other words a body centred cubic lattice composed of hard spheres is mechanically unstable with respect to a $[1\bar{1}0]$ shear on a (110) plane; the lattice should shear spontaneously into a close-packed structure. One does not expect, therefore, body centred cubic structures in full metals, and in fact they are only found in metals not too near

* C. Zener, 'Elasticity and Anelasticity of Metals', Chicago: University Press' 1948.

copper, silver, and gold in the periodic table. The nearest case to an exception is β-brass, the body-centred cubic alloy of copper and zinc (equal amounts of each), and here it is found experimentally that the elastic constant for the (110) [1$\bar{1}$0] type of shear is extremely small, only one-eighteenth that of the (100) [010] shear.

It is much more difficult to identify the sources of cohesion in metals other than the alkalies. The very strong binding of the transition metals is shown by the way the melting points and interatomic spacing vary across the first group:—

	K	Ca	Sc	Ti	V	Cr	Mn	Fe	Co	Ni	Cu	Zn
Melting-point (° C.)	63	810	1400	1800	1710	1830	1260	1535	1490	1452	1083	419
Atomic spacing (Å.)	4·62	3·93	3·20	2·93	2·63	2·49	2·24	2·48	2·51	2·49	2·55	2·66
			3·30				2·71	2·96				2·91

While there is general agreement that this strong cohesion is due in some way to the d band, the detailed mechanism is still obscure. One suggestion is that when the d band is partly full most of the electrons lie in the lower half of the band and only a minority are in the high energy levels. Thus the average energy is low, which implies a strong binding. This effect is reasonable but it is difficult to see how it could explain the strong binding in, say, cobalt, nickel, and copper, where the d bands are practically or entirely full. It is probable that in these elements there is a strong van der Waal's attractive force between the d shells.*

6.4 Pauling's Theory

A different approach to the cohesive properties of metals has been pioneered by Pauling.† The metallic bond in, say, lithium is thought to originate in homopolar bonds formed by valency electrons between neighbouring atoms. Since there are 14 close neighbours to an atom in the B.C.C. lattice (8 nearest and 6 next nearest neighbours), there are not enough valency electrons to form homopolar bonds between all neighbours. If the available bonds are distributed randomly, with every atom participating in precisely one bond, a large number of such distributions is possible; according to Pauling there should be $(3·14)^N$ such distributions in a crystal of $2N$ atoms if the bonds are restricted to the 8 nearest neighbours. The *resonance* of the electrons amongst these bonds lowers the electronic energy and raises the stability of the crystal (see section 2.2).

However, electrical conductivity is not possible if the resonance is purely of this synchronised kind, since there can be no flow of charge when electrons on neighbouring atoms can only change places with one

* N. F. Mott, Chapter 3 in 'Progress in Metal Physics, III' (Ed. B. Chalmers) Pergamon Press, 1952.

† L. Pauling, *Phys. Rev.*, 1938, **54**, 899; *J. Amer. Chem. Soc.*, 1947, **69**, 542; *Proc. Roy. Soc.*, 1949, **A196**, 343.

another (see section 5.4). The essential requirement for conductivity is the existence of *non-uniform* distributions in which atoms can become (temporarily) *ionised*, i.e. some gain extra bonding electrons at the expense of others.

Pauling emphasises that the metallic state is characterised by these non-uniform distributions. The number of such distributions is extremely large, even by comparison with the uniform distributions in which there are no ionised atoms; thus, for the example quoted above, Pauling deduces that there are $(2 \cdot 32 \times 3 \cdot 14)^N$ non-uniform distributions. In consequence, they have a correspondingly favourable resonance energy. Counteracting this, however, is the fact that the accumulation of electronic charge on one atom and its depletion on another atom, such as occurs with ionised states, involves an increase of energy. In metallic substances this increase is smaller than the decrease due to resonance. The necessary condition is that the free atom of the substance concerned must possess empty quantum states (e.g. the $2p$ states in lithium) whose energy levels are only a little higher (e.g. two electron volts) than those of the filled valency states (e.g. the $2s$ states in lithium). When such atoms are brought together to form a metallic aggregate, these empty states give rise to extra bonding states on the atoms which in turn make it possible to have resonating non-uniform distributions of lower energy than resonating uniform distributions. Pauling calls these extra bonding states *metallic orbitals*.

In atoms of transition metals the d states with energy levels near those of the valency electrons provide a large number of metallic orbitals and Pauling attributes the strong cohesion in such metals to the resonance of bonding electrons amongst these orbitals. This strong cohesion persists to a large degree in the noble metals copper, silver, and gold, and this is accounted for by invoking p states in these metallic orbitals. Thus the orbitals used by Pauling for explaining the bonding of the transition and noble metals are *hybridised* quantum states (see section 2.3) created from mixtures of s, p and d states.

In the free copper atom there are 11 outer electrons; one in a $4s$ state and the rest in $3d$ states. Separating the five $3d$ states from one another, we describe the outer electron structure of this atom as

$$(3d)^2 \ (3d)^2 \ (3d)^2 \ (3d)^2 \ (3d)^2 \ (4s) \quad ,$$

in the notation of section 1.6. Pauling supposes that in the metallic state some of the electrons in the $3d$ states are promoted into $4p$ states, and that the unpaired s, p, and d electrons thus obtained resonate among the metallic orbitals created from the hybridised s, p, and d states. Two promoted configurations are considered,

$$(3d)^2 \ (3d)^2 \ (3d)^2 \ (3d) \ (3d) \ (4s) \ (4p) \ (4p) \quad ,$$

and

$$(3d)^2 \ (3d)^2 \ (3d) \ (3d) \ (3d) \ (4s) \ (4p) \ (4p) \quad ,$$

the first of which provides five unpaired electrons, and the second of which provides seven, suitable for bonding by resonance in metallic orbitals. In practice, a mixture of the two configurations is to be expected, a given atom in the metal existing sometimes in the one and sometimes in the other. Consideration of various pieces of evidence, especially the length of the metallic bond as determined by the interatomic spacing, leads to the conclusion that on average 5·44 bonding electrons per atom are formed in metallic copper. Pauling thus regards copper as having a 'valency' of 5·44 in the metallic state.

Pauling points out that in the transition metals iron, cobalt, and nickel, immediately preceding copper in the periodic table, the cohesion is fairly constant. Consideration of interatomic spacings leads in this case to the conclusion that 5·8 electrons per atom take part in cohesion. Since there are in iron, for example, 8 outer electrons altogether, there must be $8-5·8=2·2d$ electrons per atom which do not take part in cohesion but remain localised within their parent atoms. It is these electrons which, according to Pauling, align their spins in parallel and give rise to ferromagnetism, with a saturation magnetisation of 2·2 per atom (see Fig. 39).

Interpreted in terms of the band theory (section 6.2), Pauling's theory thus leads to the idea that the d band can be divided into two parts, one of which holds a maximum of 4·8 electrons per atom and gives ferromagnetism, while the quantum states in the other part join with the $4s$ and $4p$ states to form bonding states responsible for cohesion. Moving across the row from potassium to copper, the bonding states fill up first, so that the cohesion steadily increases until chromium is reached. Beyond chromium the extra electrons enter the atomic states and align their spins, giving ferromagnetism. The maximum alignment occurs between iron and cobalt (26 per cent. cobalt), and beyond iron the pairing of electron spins in this part of the band reduces the saturation magnetisation, the latter reaching zero at a composition between nickel and copper (60 per cent. copper).

Pauling's theory is more intuitive and empirical than the strict zone theory of metals. Its strength lies in the fact that, by making use of concepts such as bonding states and valency, it can attack the problem of cohesion more directly than can the zone theory, and is able to correlate neatly several observed features of cohesion, magnetisation, and interatomic spacing, which are otherwise not easily reconcilable with one another. The zone theory, on the other hand, is much better for explaining the electrical properties of metals; it also makes fewer assumptions.

The detailed quantitative features of Pauling's theory have aroused much controversy, centred particularly on the 'valencies' used by Pauling in the metallic state. In one alternative theory,* valencies between 3 and 2 have been suggested for iron, cobalt, and nickel. Another

---

* W. Hume-Rothery, H. M. Irving, and R. J. P. Williams, *Proc. Roy. Soc.*, 1951, **A208**, 431.

view is that the concept of regarding d states as contributing to homo-polar bonds, while reasonable for metals such as titanium on the left hand side of the transition group, where the d shells are large compared with the s shells, is less reasonable for the right hand side because here the d shells do not overlap enough. Instead, couplings between electron spins are thought to provide a strong interaction in some of these metals.*

Clearly, it is too early yet for a firm opinion to have formed about the best description, in physical terms, of the nature of the cohesive forces in transition metals.

FURTHER READING ON ELECTRON THEORY

General Reading
'The Electronic Structure of Metals.' J. C. Slater, *Reviews of Modern Physics*, 1934, **6**, 209.
'Semi-Conductors and Metals.' A. H. Wilson, Cambridge University Press, 1939.
'The Theory of the Properties of Metals and Alloys.' N. F. Mott and H. Jones, Oxford, 1936.
'The Theory of Metals.' A. H. Wilson, Cambridge University Press, 1953.
'Modern Theory of Solids.' F. Seitz, McGraw-Hill, 1940.
'Magnetism and Matter.' E. C. Stoner, Methuen, 1934.
'Atomic Theory for Students of Metallurgy.' W. Hume-Rothery, The Institute of Metals, 1946.
'Valence.' C. A. Coulson, Clarendon Press, Oxford, 1952.
'The Theory of Cohesion.' M. A. Jaswon, Pergamon Press, 1954.

Recent Reviews
'The Band Theory of Metals.' G. V. Raynor, Reports on Progress in Physics, 1951.
'Recent Advances in the Electron Theory of Metals.' N. F. Mott, Progress in Metal Physics, III, Pergamon Press, 1952.
'Ferromagnetism.' E. C. Stoner, Reports on Progress in Physics, 1948 and 1950.
'The Mean Free Path of Electrons in Metals.' E. H. Sondheimer, *Advances in Physics*, 1952, **1**, 1.
'The Transition Metals and their Alloys.' W. Hume-Rothery and B. R. Coles, *Advances in Physics*, 1954, **3**, 149.

* C. Zener, *Phys. Rev.*, 1951, **81**, 440; **82**, 403; **83**, 299; 1952, **85**, 324.

CHAPTER VII

EQUILIBRIUM AND THE RATE OF APPROACH TO EQUILIBRIUM

We shall be much concerned in later chapters with equilibrium structures in metals and alloys and with the rates at which these structures are formed. To solve problems in these fields we have to use thermodynamics and the theory of reactions. In this chapter we shall outline some of the main features of these subjects that are relevant to our task.

7.1 Equilibrium

The idea of equilibrium is basic in physics and chemistry. Purely mechanical systems are in equilibrium when all the bodies taking part are at rest and occupy positions where their potential energy is at a minimum; a stone rolling down a hillside reaches equilibrium when it comes to rest at the bottom of a hollow. Thermal equilibrium is reached between two bodies in close thermal contact when heat no longer passes between them. Chemical equilibrium is reached when the concentrations of all the substances taking part in a chemical reaction no longer change.

Is it possible to go beyond these separate notions of equilibrium, different for different situations, to reach more general properties of physical and chemical systems, common to all, in terms of which a universal criterion of equilibrium can be stated? A criterion of this kind is in fact provided by the science of *thermodynamics*. As will be seen later (section 7.4), this shows that the property we can use for defining equilibrium in many practical situations is *free energy*; in equilibrium this is a minimum. The free energy F is defined as

$$F = E - TS \quad \ldots \ldots \ldots \ldots \quad (33)$$

where E and S are the *internal energy* and the *entropy* of the system, respectively, and T is its *absolute temperature*. We shall now seek to understand the physical meaning of these terms.

7.2 Internal Energy

In thermodynamics it is usual to call the collection of atoms, molecules, etc., which forms the object of study, the *system*. A system can possess energy of various kinds. *Potential* energy, due to its position in some field of force which acts on it. *Kinetic* energy, due to its motion. In mechanics kinetic energy is usually associated purely with the *external* modes of motion, i.e. translation and rotation, of a system. But in real systems, as opposed to idealised *rigid* bodies, *internal* modes of motion are also possible because the forces coupling together the particles of the system allow these some flexibility of position. One particle can thus possess a motion different from another.

The internal modes of a system can be excited in various ways, the most familiar of which is to place the system in thermal contact with another system more intensively excited, i.e. with a *hotter* one. Thus if a hot piece of metal is placed against a cold one, the actively moving particles at the surface of the former jostle the particles of the latter and excite them into more active motion. Energy which is transferred from the one piece to the other in this intimate manner, by the individual movements of the various particles of the bodies, is called *heat*. When the internal modes of the two bodies are both excited by an amount such that each particle on the surface of contact gives, on average, to the neighbouring body as much energy as it receives, the bodies are said to be in *thermal equilibrium*. It is an observed fact that all bodies which are in thermal equilibrium with a given reference body are also in thermal equilibrium with one another. This feature they possess in common we recognise by saying that they all have the same *temperature*. A scale of temperature (e.g. the *gas scale*) is then chosen by calibrating some property of the reference body which varies in a simple manner with heating and cooling, e.g. the pressure of a fixed volume of a gas, or the length of a mercury thread in a glass tube, or the resistivity of a platinum wire. A more fundamental definition of temperature is also possible, based purely upon thermodynamical ideas, which leads to a temperature scale the same as the gas scale.

It is clear that we could in principle describe the thermal and mechanical condition of a system, i.e. what is called the *state* of the system, by giving the position and velocity of every particle as closely as is possible. However, this is not only impracticable; it is also unnecessary. When in practice we enquire about the state of a system we want information only about its macroscopic properties, about such variables as its temperature, pressure and volume. In chemically active systems the concentration of the reactants would also be important, and in elastic solids the stress and strain might be needed. But in all cases our needs would be served by the knowledge of a few macroscopic properties of the system; by giving the values of these we specify the *thermodynamical state* of the system.

The laws of thermodynamics are expressed in terms of quantities that depend only upon the thermodynamic state of a system and not upon the processes by which that state is reached.* The *internal energy*, E, of the system is one such property. For example, whatever means

---

* The difficulties which arise when dealing with properties which depend upon the manner in which a state is reached, i.e. upon the *history* of the system, are well illustrated by the small success achieved in setting up relations connecting quantities underlying the plastic behaviour of solids. The rate of *transient creep* in a metal, for example, depends not only upon the values of the stress, strain, and temperature, at the moment the creep rate is measured, but also on all the past values of these quantities, i.e. upon the entire history of the deformation. Because of this, the plastic properties of solids have not been successfully integrated into a scheme of simple relations analogous to those that exist between thermodynamical properties.

are used to raise the temperature of, say, a cup of water from 20° C. to 50° C., whether by direct heating or by mechanical friction, or by other more complicated methods, the internal energy of the water at 50° C. will exceed that at 20° C. by the same amount.

The internal energy of a system is the sum of all the kinetic energies and energies of interaction (potential energies) of the particles in the system. When the system is totally isolated from its surroundings its internal energy stays constant, but when it is in contact with them it can alter its internal energy by giving or receiving energy. Suppose we put energy into the system by supplying small amounts, dQ and dW respectively, in the forms of heat and mechanical work. Then the *First Law* of thermodynamics (principle of conservation of energy) states that

$$dE = dQ + dW \qquad \ldots \ldots \ldots \ldots \quad (34)$$

7.3 The Physical Nature of Entropy

Internal energy alone cannot decide the equilibrium state of a system. This can be seen from the fact that in some changes to equilibrium the internal energy *decreases* (e.g. as when a supercooled liquid freezes and gives out its latent heat of freezing), whereas in others the internal energy *increases* (e.g. as when a solid melts). The other property of the system which determines the equilibrium is its *entropy*. Like mass, volume, and internal energy, entropy is a *capacity* property, i.e. the amount of such a property in a homogeneous system is proportional to the amount of material in the system. Thus we can speak of the 'entropy per gram molecule', or the 'entropy per atom' or even of the 'entropy density' in a system. Entropy is also like internal energy in that it is a function only of the state of the system, so that the change in entropy accompanying a given change in a system depends only on the initial and final states and not on the path taken.

In pure thermodynamics the entropy, S, of a system is defined quite abstractly as follows. Suppose that a system at a temperature (absolute) T absorbs an infinitesimal amount of heat dQ and no other change occurs in it. Then its entropy increases by the amount dS, where

$$dS = dQ/T \qquad \ldots \ldots \ldots \ldots \quad (35)$$

An alternative treatment, derived from *statistical mechanics*, provides a physical picture of entropy. The aim here is to deduce the macroscopic properties of a system as statistical resultants of the properties of its particles.

To illustrate this second approach we shall discuss a simple example, one which will also prove useful when we study the theory of solid solutions. Suppose that a man is blindfolded and has to pack sixteen equal balls in a flat, square box; eight of the balls are white and eight are black. He will be able to arrange the balls in a square pattern in the box but will have no control over the distribution of the colours.

The kind of arrangement that might result is as shown in Fig. 45 (*a*), where the distribution is quite random, or *disordered*. A regular distribution such as that of diagram (*b*) might turn up, but this is unlikely. A simple calculation of the number of different ways of distributing the colours in the box shows that the chance of the particular one shown in diagram (*b*) turning up is only about 1 in 13,000.

It is important to notice that the improbability of this particular distribution is due not to the regular arrangement of the colours but to the fact that this is only one amongst thousands of other distributions, all with the same chance. The *particular* arrangement shown in diagram (*a*) is equally improbable. Its essential difference from that of diagram (*b*) lies in the fact that it is a member of a large class of distributions, all of which have the common feature of being disordered. Almost all of the 13,000 distributions belong to this class so that the chance of *some* disordered distribution turning up is practically unity. The distribution of diagram (*b*), on the other hand, is perfectly regular,

(a)   (b)   (c)

FIG. 45.

or *ordered*. It is unique in this respect, there are no others (apart from its mirror image). Thus the chance of *some* ordered distribution turning up is very small.

The diagrams of Fig. 45 can be thought of as representing an extremely small 'crystal', only sixteen 'atoms' in all, in which the interatomic forces are such that each atom is quite indifferent to whether its neighbours are of like or unlike species. The arguments can be carried over to much larger crystals, containing 10^{20} atoms or more, and the only difference is to increase enormously the number of distributions of the disordered kind, but not the others, so that the chance of finding such a crystal in a disordered state becomes almost certain.

In such large assemblies of atoms as these we could not hope to distinguish one distribution of the disordered state from another by experiment. On the other hand, we could tell, e.g. by X-rays, whether the crystal was in a disordered or an ordered state. The results of such observations would show repeatedly that the crystal was disordered. Again, if by some means we forced the crystal into the ordered state and then held it at temperatures where the atoms were mobile and could rearrange themselves on the lattice, we should observe the ordered state give way to the disordered one; moreover, once it became disordered the crystal would not, of its own accord, return to the ordered state again. The direction of these changes is fixed by the fact that, once the atoms become mobile, they begin randomly selecting various distributions from the entire set and the chance is then negligible that they should choose the ordered one from the myriads that present themselves for choice. We should thus observe a *spontaneous* and *irreversible* change from a transient state to a permanent state, i.e. from an unstable to a stable state, and should have to conclude that the system had moved towards thermodynamic equilibrium.

It follows that a purely statistical factor, i.e. the number of distributions associated with a thermodynamical state, plays a part in determining equilibrium, and inclines the system towards disordered states. We have based the argument on a particular kind of disorder, but the principle is general and applies to all kinds. Thus the same factor favours the disorder associated with atomic vibrations in a crystal and the disorder in atomic positions which appears when a crystal melts or a liquid vaporises. As a measure of the disorder of a state we might simply quote w, the number of distributions that belong to it. However, the numerical values of w for systems of macroscopic size are usually so large that it is easier to work with $\log_e w$ rather than w itself. In practice, disorder is measured by the quantity S, where

$$S = k \log_e w \qquad \qquad (36)$$

called the *entropy* of the system. Here k is Boltzmann's constant $(=1.38 \times 10^{-16}$ ergs per degree), and is equal to the gas constant R divided by Avogadro's number, N_0.

In the development of statistical thermodynamics it was realised at an early stage that the quantity $\log_e w$ always behaved like entropy, as defined by formal thermodynamics, and that these two quantities were in fact both measures of the same property of the system. The constant of proportionality, k, makes the statistical entropy identical with the formal entropy. In terms of entropy we can restate our statistical principle as follows: *Any change which takes place in a system isolated from its surroundings increases the entropy of that system towards a maximum associated with the stable state of the system.* This is the *Second Law* of thermodynamics.

It will be noticed from equation 36 that our statistical factor enters into thermodynamics as a quantity which has the dimensions of energy/temperature. Why is this? Why should an effect which depends purely on *numbers* of distributions have any connection with energy? The answer lies in two further effects: (1) in principle, and almost always in practice, different distributions of a system have different internal energies; (2) distributions with different internal energies have different chances of turning up, i.e. different *thermodynamic probabilities*.

The first effect can be appreciated by returning to Fig. 45. If the black and white 'atoms' are physically different species they will almost certainly show some preference for either like or unlike neighbours, i.e. their interaction energies will depend upon the kinds of neighbours with which they make bonds. If unlike atoms attract one another the bond energy, and hence the internal energy, is lowest when there is a maximum number of nearest-neighbour bonds between unlike atoms, as in diagram (b). Conversely, if like atoms attract more than unlike ones, the internal energy is lowest for distributions of the kind shown in diagram (c). In either case, the internal energy of a random distribution, e.g. diagram (a), is higher than that of one or other of these special distributions.

The fact that distributions with different internal energies have different thermodynamic probabilities is proved by the existence of many forms of matter with highly ordered distributions. If every distribution had the same probability then the statistical factor would operate alone and universal disorder would prevail. But in fact distributions of low internal energy have a greater probability of occurrence, especially at low temperatures. Let us denote the probability of a distribution of energy E turning up at a temperature T by $p(E, T)$. Then the probability of a thermodynamic state which contains w distributions of energy E turning up is simply $wp(E, T)$. This is a pure number, of course; denote it by Z. The equilibrium state at the temperature concerned is that for which Z is greatest. The historical development of thermodynamics is such, however, that the quantity usually used to define the equilibrium state is not Z directly, but the free energy,

$$F = -kT \log_e Z \quad \ldots \ldots \ldots \ldots (37)$$

which reaches a minimum for the state with the largest value of Z. Statistical mechanics shows that

$$p(E, T) = e^{-E/kT} \quad \ldots \ldots \ldots \ldots (38)$$

and if this is substituted in relation 37 we obtain

$$F = E - kT \log_e w = E - TS,$$

which is our relation 33.

This formula shows that a system becomes more stable the lower is its internal energy and the higher is its entropy. These two factors generally act in opposition, and a system with a low E generally also has a low S. This can be seen by considering Fig. 45 again. If unlike atoms attract, the state of lowest internal energy is that of diagram (b), but this state has lower entropy than that of diagram (a). Similarly, if like atoms attract, the state in diagram (c) has lowest energy, and this again has lower entropy than that of diagram (a). The controlling factor is the temperature. At sufficiently low temperatures TS is small for all values of S and the predominant term in the free energy formula is E; thus ordered states of low internal energy are preferred. At high temperatures TS is very large for disordered states and dominates the free energy; disordered states thus become stable as the temperature is raised.

7.4   Thermodynamical Definitions of Entropy and Free Energy

The idea of entropy originated, not from the statistical notions described above, but from the theory of the efficiency of heat engines; this theory provides us with a means of measuring the entropy of a system experimentally from the heat it has absorbed. A basic idea here is that of the *reversible* change. We imagine taking a system from an initial state, 1, to a final state 2, by a series of small changes applied so slowly that the system is very nearly in equilibrium at every stage of its transformation. In the limit where the difference from equilibrium vanishes such a sequence is described as being *reversible*. With changes of this kind one can use equation 35 to measure the change in entropy of the system purely in terms of heat it absorbs and its temperature. This change in entropy, from states 1 to 2, is given by

$$S_2 - S_1 = \int_1^2 (dQ/T),$$

where dQ is the heat absorbed and T is the instantaneous temperature at each infinitesimal step in the reversible sequence. In terms of state 1 as a standard we can thus determine the entropy of any other state from the heat absorbed. The equilibrium state at $0°$ K. is generally used as the standard and in terms of this as a zero the entropy of a system in equilibrium at $T°$ K. is given by

$$S = \int_0^T (dQ/T) \quad \ldots \ldots \ldots \quad (39)$$

where the integral is taken over the reversible change from $0°$ K. to $T°$ K.

Because the entropy is a function only of the state of the system, the system in this equilibrium state at $T°$ K. always has the entropy S given by equation 39, even though we may have brought the system to this state by violent and irreversible changes not involving the supply of energy in the form of heat. For example, we may have set the system in large-scale motion and allowed friction to bring it to the required temperature by converting the kinetic energy of large-scale motion into heat. In such cases, where we supply no energy in the form of heat, $\int(dQ/T)$ is zero. Nevertheless the entropy change is still the same as that obtained by a reversible heating to $T°$ K. Thus, in an irreversible change, the change of entropy is greater than $\int(dQ/T)$ if dQ now refers to the heat absorbed at each step in that irreversible change.

In an isolated system, which cannot exchange energy in any form with its surroundings, we must have $\int(dQ/T) = 0$. Thus the entropy of the system can only increase (in a spontaneous, irreversible, internal change), or remain constant (in equilibrium). The internal energy of an isolated system remains constant, of course. How is this reconciled with the fact that these spontaneous changes may take the system from distributions at one internal energy level to others at a different level?

The answer is that the internal energy of a complex system is partitioned out in various forms; some goes to heat vibrations, some to configurational energy in systems such as that shown in Fig. 45 (i.e. in the case where different neighbours have different bond energies), and so on. When a spontaneous change occurs in such a system, the thermal energy acts as a reservoir, either supplying or taking energy according as the case may be. Correspondingly the system either cools down or warms up. The attainment of very low temperatures by adiabatic demagnetisation is a practical application of this effect.

In most practical problems we have to deal with systems which are not isolated, i.e. which can exchange energy with their surroundings. Consider first the exchange of heat between two bodies, A and B, at temperatures T_A and T_B ($T_A > T_B$), respectively. We can regard these as jointly forming one isolated system. Suppose that an infinitesimal amount of heat dQ flows from A to B. Then the entropy of A decreases by dQ/T_A and that of B increases by dQ/T_B. The total entropy change is then

$$\frac{dQ}{T_B} - \frac{dQ}{T_A}, \text{ i.e. } \frac{dQ(T_A - T_B)}{T_A T_B},$$

and, since $T_A > T_B$, this is positive, being zero only at the equilibrium case where $T_A = T_B$.

In many problems of the kind we shall study it is inconvenient to include the surroundings of the system as part of a larger isolated system. We want a property belonging to the system itself which can be used without referring to surroundings, to define the equilibrium state of that system in the way that the entropy can be so used for an isolated system. We shall see that the free energy is such a property.

Consider a system which can be specified in terms of its internal energy E, volume V, pressure P, temperature T, and entropy S, and is able to exchange energy with its surroundings. Let an infinitesimal change occur in it. Then from the first law we have

$$dE = dQ - P dV \quad \ldots \ldots \ldots \ldots \quad (40)$$

where dQ is the heat the system takes from its surroundings and $P dV$ is the work it does on its surroundings. Let dS and dSx be the associated entropy changes in the system and its surroundings, respectively. Then we must have

$$dS + dSx \geqslant 0.$$

The system has taken heat dQ from its surroundings. Supposing then that the latter are also at the temperature T, we have $dSx = -dQ/T$, and hence

$$dS - (dQ/T) \geqslant 0.$$

Substituting from relation (40) for dQ gives

$$dS - (dE + P dV)/T \geqslant 0$$

i.e.
$$dE + P dV - T dS \leqslant 0 \quad \ldots \ldots \ldots \ldots \quad (41)$$

All quantities in this relation belong to the system itself. The system is in equilibrium when $dE + PdV - TdS = 0$, for then all changes are reversible.

Consider first those changes which may occur at constant volume and temperature. We then have $PdV = 0$, and the equilibrium condition reduces to $dE - TdS = 0$. This is equivalent to saying that $E - TS$ must be a minimum in the equilibrium state, since

$$\begin{aligned} d(E - TS) &= dE - TdS - SdT \\ &= dE - TdS \text{ (since } T \text{ is fixed)} \\ &= 0 \text{ (for equilibrium).} \end{aligned}$$

Thus the free energy, $F = E - TS$ (or more strictly the *Helmholtz Free Energy*) is a minimum for equilibrium with respect to changes at constant volume and temperature.

When the changes occur at constant pressure and temperature the equilibrium condition is $dE + PdV - TdS = 0$. This is expressed by saying that the *Gibbs Free Energy*, $G = E + PV - TS$, is a minimum in the equilibrium state with respect to changes at constant pressure and temperature.

In solid and liquid metals at atmospheric pressure PV is usually very small compared with the other thermodynamic quantities, E and TS. It is thus a reasonable approximation to ignore this term and to use the Helmholtz free energy to define equilibrium for all changes in these materials. For most changes of the kind we shall study, the criterion of minimum F is adequate; but it is always a good habit to review each one to see if the effect of pressure can justifiably be ignored.

7.5 Entropy of Mixing in Crystals

Although we shall not deal with the thermodynamics of alloys until Chapter X, it is convenient to work out here a quantity important in alloys, known as the *entropy of mixing*, because the calculation illustrates many of the main points involved in calculating entropies by the statistical method. The problem essentially is that of Fig. 45 (a). How many distributions belong to the disordered state, and what entropy is associated with them?

Consider a crystal of N atomic sites, n of which contain atoms of species A, and $N - n$ contain those of species B. Let the distribution of these two kinds of atoms on the sites be *completely random*. This state of arrangement is called a *random* or *disordered solid solution*, and is an idealisation of a type common in alloys. Over and above the total entropies of crystals of the pure components A and B (the crystal of A having n atoms and that of B having $N - n$ atoms) the solution crystal has an extra entropy due to the numerous ways in which the two kinds of atoms can be arranged amongst each other. This extra entropy is called the entropy of mixing.

To calculate it we have to find w, the number of distributions of atoms in the solution crystal, and then substitute in relation 36. But what defines a distribution? We appear to be faced with two different definitions, each of which seems plausible at first sight.

In the first type, which we shall call 'distributions of atoms' we imagine that we can separately distinguish every atom of a single species from all its neighbours, and that we can describe a particular distribution by saying which particular atom is in each site of the crystal. That is, we imagine that we can 'label' every atom and 'number' every site, and then describe the distribution by means of a statement such as 'of the A atoms, atom a is in site 11, b is in site 20, . . . , and of the B atoms, atom m is in site 4, n is in site 30, . . .' Alternatively, we suppose that we cannot tell one A atom from another, or one B atom from another; the only thing we can know is whether a given site is filled with an A atom or a B atom. A distribution in this case is described by a statement such as 'sites 11, 20, . . . , are filled with A atoms and the rest with B atoms'.

This second definition, as well as being more modest, also proves to be correct; there is physically no way of separately distinguishing two identical atoms. However, the correctness or otherwise of the definition is of no consequence in this problem, for both definitions lead to the same answer. This is because the entropy of mixing is a *relative* quantity, which measures the *extra* disorder of the solution crystal relative to those of the unmixed components, and any additional sources of disorder which appear equally in both the solution crystal and those of its components cancel out and leave the additional disorder of the solution crystal outstanding. Mathematically, this happens as follows. Let w, w_A, and w_B be the numbers of atomic distributions in the solution crystal and the pure crystals of A and B, respectively. Then the entropy of mixing of the solution crystal is given by

$$k \log_e w - k \log_e w_A - k \log_e w_B = k \log_e (w/w_A w_B).$$

Any source of disorder which contributes equally to w and to $w_A w_B$ disappears in the quotient $w/w_A w_B$. The spurious disorder introduced by a wrong definition, e.g. disorder associated with the various ways we could arrange differently labelled atoms of a single species in a crystal, is of this kind. Another kind is disorder associated with different *isotopes* of one of the species. This is a genuine disorder, since we can distinguish one isotope from another (e.g. we can separate them in a mass spectrograph), and gives rise to a real *entropy of isotope mixing*. But this entropy appears in just the same amount in the unmixed crystals as in the solution crystal, and so cancels out in the final answer for the entropy of mixing.

We shall make the calculation using distributions of sites. To calculate w, imagine that we have the empty lattice of the solution crystal, containing N sites, and begin putting into it the atoms of A and B. The first A atom can be inserted in N distinct ways, since there are

N sites available for it. The second one has $N-1$ places available to it for each of the places occupied by the first one. But the number of *distinct* ways of putting in the first two A atoms is only $N(N-1)/2$, not $N(N-1)$, since for every arrangement where atom a is in site p and b in q, there is also the one where a is in q and b in p; because the atoms are indistinguishable, the 'labels' a and b must be removed and these two arrangements must count as one only. Continuing, the number of distinct distributions when the third A atom is added is $N(N-1)(N-2)/3!$, where $3!=3\times2\times1$, since $N(N-1)(N-2)$ is the total number of arrangements for labelled atoms and there are 3! ways of arranging the three atoms on any particular set of three sites. Thus the total number of distinct ways of putting all the A atoms in is given by

$$\frac{N(N-1)\; .\; .\; .\; (N-n+2)(N-n+1)}{n!}=\frac{N!}{n!(N-n)!}\quad .\; .\; .\; (42)$$

For each way that we put the A atoms in, there is only one way of putting the $N-n$ B atoms into the remaining $N-n$ sites, so that the expression 42 is actually w for the solution crystal. We now need w_A and w_B. Each of these is unity, since all the atoms in a pure crystal are indistinguishable and interchanging them leads to no new distribution. Hence $w_A w_B = 1$, so that the expression 42 is a true measure of the extra disorder of the solution crystal. The entropy of mixing is thus given by

$$S=k\,\log_e\frac{N!}{n!(N-n)!}=k[\log_e N!-\log_e n!-\log_e (N-n)!]$$

This result is difficult to use because it contains factorials. We can, however, use *Stirling's approximation*

$$\log_e x\,!\simeq x\log_e x-x\quad .\; .\; .\; .\; .\; .\; .\; .\; (43)$$

which is very accurate provided x is a large number, i.e. $x>>10$. Substituting, this leads to

$$S=k[N\log_e N-n\log_e n-(N-n)\log_e (N-n)].$$

It is convenient to work in terms of the *concentration* of A and B. Let c be the atomic concentration of A in the solution, i.e. $c=n/N$. Then the concentration of B is $(1-c)$, where $(1-c)=(N-n)/N$. After substituting these quantities in the above expression, a short reduction then leads to the formula

$$S=-Nk[c\,\log_e c+(1-c)\log_e (1-c)]\quad .\; .\; .\; .\; (44)$$

for the entropy of mixing.

We notice that S is positive since c and $(1-c)$ are fractional quantities and give negative logarithms. In a crystal containing a *mole* of atomic sites, i.e. $N=N_0=$Avogadro's number, we can write $Nk=R=1\cdot987$ calories per degree. The entropy of mixing for this case is given by the curve of Fig. 46. The curve is symmetrical about the point $c=0\cdot5$, at which composition the entropy of mixing is greatest. Its value here is given by

$$S = -R[0.5 \log_e 0.5 + 0.5 \log_e 0.5] = 1.38 \text{ cal./degree.}$$

The slope of the curve is extremely steep near $c=0$ and $c=1$, showing that the entropy of a pure substance increases sharply as a small amount of a second one is added. This explains why it is so difficult to produce materials of high purity, for the free energy change, $dF(=dE-TdS)$, caused by contamination is almost certainly negative, since even if dE

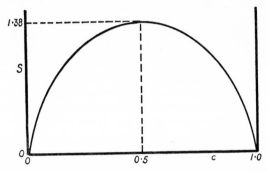

Fig. 46.—The Entropy of Mixing (cal./deg.) as a Function of Concentration.

is large and positive it is likely to be outweighed by the large value of TdS due to the large change of S with c in the region $c=0$.

7.6 Rate of Reaction

It is well known that systems often exist for long periods of time in states which are not the equilibrium ones as defined by lowest free energy. For example, the stable form of a mixture of oxygen and hydrogen at room temperature is water, but if we mix these gases at this temperature they can stay uncombined. Again, the structure of a quench-hardened steel is unstable, yet steels hardened in ancient times retain their structures to this day. Such systems are said to be *metastable*. Metallurgy itself depends on this property of metastability for the equilibrium form of most metals under atmospheric conditions is as an oxide or carbonate.

Metastability has many causes. With a metal exposed to a corrosive environment the slowness of reaction is due to the difficulty of bringing together the atoms and molecules of the participants. They can meet only at the surface of the metal and hence only a small fraction of the atoms of the metal is exposed to the reaction at any time; if this surface is clogged up with the products of reaction, or is protected by a film of some chemically inert substance, they cannot meet and react except by migrating through the protective layer.

In this section we shall discuss a particular cause of metastability which is of great importance in reactions in solids. It frequently happens that, in order to transform a system to a more stable state, the atoms of that system, or that part of it where the reaction begins, have to pass through positions where their energy is *raised*. As a simple illustration,

let the diagram of Fig. 47 represent the potential energy of an atom
as a function of its position. For the atom to move from the metastable
position (*a*) to the stable one (*c*) it has to pass through unstable ones
represented by (*b*). Unless it can obtain temporarily the necessary extra
energy to carry it over this potential energy barrier, it must remain in
the metastable position (*a*). The smallest energy, Q, which will allow
it to go over is called the *activation energy* of the reaction. The net energy
release (or absorption, in endothermic reactions) is H, the *heat of reaction*.

The speed of this reaction thus depends on (1) the number n of atoms
in the metastable position; (2) the frequency ν with which an atom in

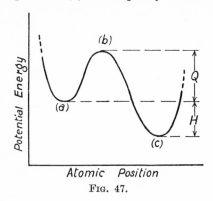

FIG. 47.

this position vibrates against the barrier and attempts to scale it; (3) the
probability $p(Q, T)$ that during such an attempt the atom has the
necessary activation energy, Q; this probability is given by equation 38,
with Q replacing E in that formula. In most problems in solids $p(Q, T)$
is very small, and under such conditions the *flux f* of reacting atoms, i.e.
the number which jump the barrier in unit time, is given by the formula

$$f = n\nu e^{-Q/kT} \quad \ldots \ldots \ldots \ldots \quad (45)$$

where kT has its usual meaning. In this expression Q refers to the
activation energy per atom. It is usual to express Q either in units of
electron volts per atom or as calories per mole. In the latter case Q is
the energy to carry a mole of atoms to the top of the barrier; accordingly, when Q has this meaning, k must be replaced by $R(=N_0 k)$ in the
above expression. It is thus customary to write equation 45 in the form

$$\text{Rate of reaction} = A e^{-Q/RT} \quad \ldots \ldots \ldots \quad (46)$$

where A is a constant which contains $n\nu$, and Q is the activation energy
per mole. This is a formula of great importance, obeyed in many physical
and chemical changes. To apply it in practice we write it as

$$\log_e (\text{rate}) = \log_e A - (Q/R)/T$$

which shows that the logarithm of the reaction velocity should vary
linearly with the reciprocal of the absolute temperature. The slope of
this line gives Q/R, and the intercept at $T^{-1} = 0$ gives A.

The profound effect of temperature upon reaction velocity is a result of the exponential function in equation 46. Suppose, for example, that $Q=40,000$ cal. per mole, a value not untypical of many changes in metals and alloys. Taking $R=2$ cal. per mole per degree, we find that at $300°$ K.,

$$e^{-Q/RT}=e^{-40,000/600} \simeq 10^{-29},$$

and that at $1000°$ K.,

$$e^{-Q/RT}=e^{-40,000/2000} \simeq 10^{-9}.$$

The reaction at $1000°$ K. has 10^{20} times the speed it has at $300°$ K. For example, if it takes 1 second at $1000°$ K. it would take 10^{22} seconds $\simeq 3 \times 10^{12}$ years at room temperature !. The reaction may be said to have ceased, for all practical purposes, at room temperature. Such behaviour is the basis of *quenching*. When a metal or alloy exists at a high temperature in a form different from that which is stable at room temperature, and the activation energy has a sufficiently high value, then by cooling very rapidly the structure characteristic of the high temperature can be obtained and preserved at room temperature, even though it is not stable. Quenching is thus a method for producing non-equilibrium structures in metals and alloys.

The use of equation 38 in setting up equation 45 means that we are really supposing the states of the system where the reacting atom is at (a) and (b) in Fig. 47 to be two different distributions. To be consistent we must admit that the positions (a) and (b) may be associated with different *numbers* of distributions, so that the probability of activation should also include a statistical factor. This effect is known to happen. For example, where the atom has to squeeze between its neighbours during the reaction it will alter the vibrational frequencies of these and so alter their entropy. Let the number of distributions associated with positions (a) and (b) be denoted by w_a and w_b respectively. Then equation 45 becomes

$$f=n\nu \left(\frac{w_b}{w_a}\right)e^{-Q/RT}$$

But from equation 36, (w_b/w_a) can be interpreted in terms of an *entropy of activation*, ΔS; thus $\Delta S=R \log_e (w_b/w_a)$. Writing the *energy of activation* as ΔE, and defining a quantity $\Delta F=\Delta E -T\Delta S$ as the *free energy of activation*, we can then write equation 45 in the forms

$$f=n\nu e^{\frac{\Delta S}{R}} e^{-\frac{\Delta E}{RT}}=n\nu e^{-\frac{(\Delta E-T\Delta S)}{RT}}=n\nu e^{-\frac{\Delta F}{RT}} \quad \ldots \ldots \quad (47)$$

References

'Introduction to Chemical Physics.' J. C. Slater, McGraw-Hill, 1939.
'Kinetics of Chemical Change.' C. N. Hinshelwood, Oxford, 1940.
'Introduction to Statistical Mechanics.' R. W. Gurney, McGraw-Hill, 1949.
'The Role of Statistical Mechanics in Physical Metallurgy.' C. Zener, in 'Thermodynamics in Physical Metallurgy', Amer. Soc. Metals, 1950.

CHAPTER VIII

THE THERMAL BEHAVIOUR OF METALS

We shall now apply the ideas developed in the last chapter to the study of various property changes which accompany changes of temperature in metals.

8.1 The Specific Heat of Crystals

As a metal is heated, disorder of various kinds sets in. Each involves the absorption of thermal energy and so contributes to the *specific heat* of the material. The most characteristic thermal disorder in solids involves the vibrations of atoms about their equilibrium positions; this thermal vibration accounts for almost all the specific heat in many cases.

The atoms in a crystal never rest. At all temperatures, even 0° K., they vibrate rapidly and continually. As the temperature is raised the *amplitude* of the vibrations increases, but the *frequency* does not change, except to a minor degree. Increasing the amplitude of vibration involves increasing the kinetic and potential energies of the atoms concerned, and the amount of this vibrational energy absorbed in raising the temperature by one degree is the *vibrational heat capacity*, or for unit mass of material, the *vibrational specific heat*. If the heating is done at constant pressure, *thermal expansion* also occurs. It will be remembered (see, e.g. Fig. 43) that the potential energy of atoms rises more rapidly, for *large* strains, when they move together to less than the equilibrium spacing than when they move further apart. Thus, when they vibrate against one another, their inward swing is smaller than the outward one and their mean distance of separation is greater than the equilibrium one. This thermal expansion increases as the temperature, and hence the amplitude of vibration, increases. This increase in the mean spacing of the atoms reduces their cohesion a little and thereby has the effect of slightly reducing the frequency of vibration.

To build up the theory we need some numerical measure of the thermal disorder associated with the vibrations. Visualising the complex movements of the atoms, it would seem impossible to obtain a quantitative measure. However, when the quantum theory is applied and the true nature of the disorder appreciated, a numerical value can easily be obtained. Quantum theory shows that a single particle vibrating in simple harmonic motion along a line, i.e. a *linear oscillator*, can have a vibrational energy chosen only from a set of values given by the formula $(x+\frac{1}{2})h\nu$, where $x=0, 1, 2, 3, \ldots$, etc., $h=$Planck's constant, and $\nu=$frequency of vibration. Even in its lowest energy level, $x=0$, the oscillator still vibrates and has the energy $\frac{1}{2}h\nu$. Since this energy persists even at 0° K., it is called the *zero-point energy*; its existence is a typical quantum-mechanical effect, analogous to the zero-point translational energy (Fermi energy) possessed by a free electron gas.

The analysis of the modes of vibration of a crystal lattice is a difficult problem, and many treatments are available which differ according to the extent and nature of the simplifying approximations made. As a first rough approximation we can regard the N atoms of the crystal (monatomic, with a simple lattice) as $3N$ independent linear oscillators, each of frequency ν. The factor 3 allows for the three degrees of freedom provided by the three-dimensional space in which each atom vibrates. We thus have $3N$ oscillators, each of which selects its energies from the set $(x+\tfrac{1}{2})h\nu$.

How do the selected values of x depend on temperature? At $0°$ K. the system of oscillators is in its lowest energy state, $x=0$. Raising the temperature involves putting in vibrational energy quanta, each of magnitude $h\nu$. Suppose the system warms up from $0°$ K. to $T°$ K. by taking up n of these quanta. Then the disorder and entropy are increased because of the numerous ways in which these quanta can be distributed amongst the oscillators. We count the number of these distributions in the following way. We have to distribute n indistinguishable 'objects' (the quanta) amongst $3N$ 'boxes', there being no limit on the number per box except that the total be n. Suppose for the moment that we can label the objects $a_1, a_2, \ldots, a_n$, and the boxes $z_1, z_2, \ldots, z_{3N}$. To represent any individual arrangement we write down the whole set of z's and a's in purely arbitrary order along a line, starting off with a z. For example:—

$$z_6\, a_2\, a_4\, z_2\, a_1\, a_7\, a_5\, z_8\, z_3\, a_9\, z_1 \ldots$$

Suppose that the objects between two z's belong to the box whose z stands to their left in the row. In the above example, a_2 and a_4 belong to z_6; a_1, a_7 and a_5 to z_2, none to z_8, a_9 to z_3, and so on. Clearly we can represent every possible arrangement in this way by writing down all the variants of the sequence. The number of ways of choosing a z to begin the sequence is $3N$, and the number of ways of writing down the remaining $n+3N-1$ symbols is $(n+3N-1)!$ so that in all the total number of arrangements is $(n+3N-1)!3N$. However, many of these are indistinguishable from each other. All which differ by a mere permutation of the boxes amongst each other, or of the objects amongst themselves, really constitute only one distinct distribution. Using the same arguments as those in section 7.5 we see that the number of such permutations is $n!3N!$. Hence the number of distinct distributions w is given by

$$w=\frac{(n+3N-1)!3N}{n!3N!}=\frac{(n+3N-1)!}{n!(3N-1)!}$$

The entropy is given by $S=k\log_e w$. Using Stirling's approximation, neglecting the 1 in comparison with the numbers $3N$ and $n+3N$, and differentiating with respect to n, we find that

$$dS/dn=k\log_e[(n+3N)/n].$$

HSM

The internal energy is given by $E = E_0 + nh\nu$, where E_0 is the energy at $0°$ K. Hence

$$dE/dn = h\nu.$$

The equilibrium heat content of the system at the temperature T is determined by the condition $dF/dn = 0$. Using the relation $dF/dn = (dE/dn) - T(dS/dn)$ and substituting, we obtain

$$n = \frac{3N}{e^{h\nu/kT} - 1} \quad \cdots \cdots \cdots \quad (48)$$

The specific heat at constant volume, C_v, is defined as dE/dT. When the crystal is heated at constant volume it exchanges no energy with its surroundings in the form of work, so that $dE/dT = dQ/dT$. If $N = N_0 =$ Avogadro's number, C_v is the *atomic heat* at constant volume. We thus obtain

$$C_v = \frac{d}{dT}(E_0 + nh\nu) = \frac{d}{dT}\left(\frac{3Nh\nu}{e^{h\nu/kT} - 1}\right)$$

$$= 3R\left(\frac{h\nu}{kT}\right)^2 \frac{e^{h\nu/kT}}{(e^{h\nu/kT} - 1)^2} \quad \cdots \quad (49)$$

for the atomic heat, where $R\,(= N_0 k)$ is the gas constant. This is Einstein's formula for the specific heat, first given in 1907.* It can be written as

$$C_v = 3R\left(\frac{\theta}{T}\right)^2 \frac{e^{\theta/T}}{(e^{\theta/T} - 1)^2} \quad \cdots \cdots \cdots \quad (50)$$

where $\theta\,(= h\nu/k)$ is called the *Einstein characteristic temperature* of the crystal. Fig. 48 shows the form of C_v as a function of T/θ. The specific

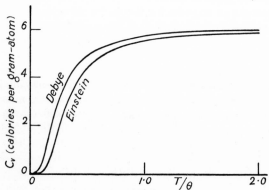

Fig. 48.—The Atomic Heat at Constant Volume as a Function of Temperature, according to Einstein's and Debye's Theories.

heat goes to zero at $0°$ K. and rises to a limiting value, $3R\,(= 6$ calories per mole per degree) at high temperatures. Many simple solids behave in this manner, and there can be no doubt that the theory provides

* A. Einstein, *Ann. Physik*, 1907, **22**, 180.

a sound first approximation to the actual thermal behaviour of crystals.

On the other hand, the specific heat as given by equation 50 falls off more rapidly on cooling to low temperatures than is observed in practice. The source of this discrepancy can be traced to the assumption that the atoms vibrate independently of each other. In practice, an atom does not vibrate about a fixed centre but about a moving centre defined purely by the positions of the nearby atoms, which are also vibrating. Because of the elastic coupling between the atoms, one cannot move without disturbing the others.

The nature of such coupled vibrations can be realised by analogy with standing vibrations in a stretched rubber string along which is mounted a set of equal weights at equal intervals. Various natural *modes of vibration* can be set up in the string, some of long wavelengths in which many weights move in unison, some of short wavelengths in which neighbouring weights move in opposition, and so on. The same ideas applied to the vibrating crystal of N atoms show that it possesses $3N$ different modes of vibration, each with its own characteristic frequency. The upper limiting frequency, v_m, corresponds to the separate vibrations of individual atoms. By applying the analysis leading to equation 48 separately to each mode, we find that the specific heat is given by

$$C_v = \frac{d}{dT} \left(\sum_{r=1}^{3N} \frac{h v_r}{e^{h v_r/kT} - 1} \right) \quad \ldots \quad \ldots \quad (51)$$

and the whole problem then becomes one of finding the *vibrational spectrum* of the lattice, i.e. of finding the number of modes with frequencies in any given range.

This is purely a problem in the mechanics of lattice vibrations; the thermodynamics has already been settled in equation 51. Mathematical difficulties make it difficult. In 1912 two independent attacks were attempted. The first, by Born and Kármán,* was a rigorous treatment based on an atomic model of the lattice, but limited to a one-dimensional crystal. The second treatment, by Debye, was three-dimensional but ignored the discrete atomic structure, apart from fixing the number of modes at $3N$ and the upper frequency at v_m. Debye regarded the vibrating crystal as an elastic *continuum* vibrating in $3N$ different modes. This led him to the formula

$$C_v = 3R \left[\frac{12T^3}{\theta^3} \int_0^{\frac{\theta}{T}} \frac{x^3 dx}{e^x - 1} - \frac{3\theta/T}{e^{\theta} T - 1} \right] \quad \ldots \quad \ldots \quad (52)$$

for the specific heat, where $\theta = h v_m/k$ (called the *Debye characteristic temperature*) and $x = h v/kT$. This gives a temperature dependence broadly similar to that of Einstein's theory (see Fig. 48); but at low temperatures, where θ/T becomes very large, it gives a specific heat proportional to

* *Physikalische Zeitschrift*, 1912, **13**, 297.

T^3, and this agrees much better with experiment than does Einstein's formula.

To test the accuracy of these specific heat formulae it is usual to determine a characteristic temperature θ by equating the theoretical and experimental specific heats at some selected temperature and then to use this θ to determine the theoretical specific heats at various temperatures. When a Debye θ is chosen in this way the theoretical specific heat often agrees extremely well with experiment over a wide temperature range. As an example we give a comparison in Table 4 for aluminium, taking $\theta=385°$ K.

TABLE 4.—SPECIFIC HEAT OF ALUMINIUM*

Temperature, ° K.	C_v (observed)	C_v (Debye)
54·8	1·127	1·11
70·0	1·851	1·88
84·0	2·446	2·51
112·4	3·502	3·54
141·0	4·183	4·23
186·2	4·833	4·87
257·5	5·382	5·35
278·9	5·499	5·42
296·3	5·526	5·48

TABLE 5.—DEBYE CHARACTERISTIC TEMPERATURES (° K.)

Na	Al	Cu	Ag	Fe	Pb	Be	C (diamond)
150	385	315	215	420	88	1000	2000

Table 5 gives some Debye temperatures. Since $\theta=h\nu/k$ in both Einstein's and Debye's theories, where ν is essentially the frequency of vibration of single atoms in the crystal, the characteristic temperature is connected with the elastic properties of the material through its dependence on ν. The factors determining ν can be realised by regarding a vibrating atom as a simple harmonic oscillator of mass m. If a displacement x of the oscillator produces a restoring force, f, on it equal to ax, the frequency of vibration is $(1/2\pi)\sqrt{a/m}$. If the atomic spacing is a, the restoring force f per atom is equivalent to a stress f/a^2 on unit area of the material, and a displacement x per atom is equivalent to a strain x/a in the material. If y is the appropriate elastic constant of the material, connecting this stress and strain, then $y=a/a$. Thus the frequency of vibration is given in order of magnitude by

$$\nu=(1/2\pi)\sqrt{ya/m} \qquad \ldots \ldots \ldots \ldots (53)$$

Since elastic constants are typically of order 10^{11} dyne/cm.², and $a \backsimeq 10^{-8}$ cm. and $m \backsimeq 10^{-23}$ gm., this gives frequencies in the range 10^{12} to 10^{13} per second. Substituting these in the relation $\theta=h\nu/k$ gives characteristic temperatures in the range 50 to 500° K., in agreement

* Data on specific heats are collected in Eucken, 'Handbuch der Experimentalphysik', Vol. 8/1, 1929.

with the observed range. Formula 53 shows that ν increases with increasing strength of binding (i.e. increasing y) and also with decreasing mass. Thus strongly bound crystals of light atoms, e.g. diamond, have high characteristic temperatures, and weakly bound crystals of heavy atoms, e.g. lead, have low temperatures.

While the Debye theory appears at first examination to be very satisfactory, a more detailed comparison with experiment reveals small discrepancies of a systematic nature. According to Blackman,* the main error lies in the form of distribution function used for the vibrational spectrum. Debye, analysing the natural vibrations of the elastic continuum, deduces that $N(\nu)d\nu$, the number of modes with frequencies from ν to $\nu+d\nu$, is proportional to ν^2 (Fig. 49). By extending the Born and Kármán method to three-dimensional lattices Blackman arrives at $N(\nu)$ distributions of the kind shown in Fig. 49. We notice that a strong

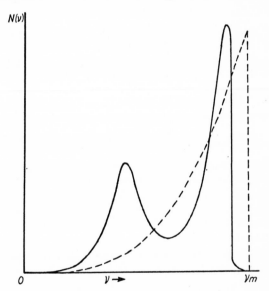

FIG. 49.—The Frequency Spectrum of a Crystal according to Debye (dotted line) and Blackman (full line).

maximum occurs at a frequency well below ν_m, in addition to the main maximum just below ν_m.

The quantity usually measured experimentally is C_p, the specific heat at constant *pressure*, not C_v, which is at constant *volume*; C_p is slightly greater than C_v (a few per cent. at room temperature) because some work is done against interatomic forces when a crystal is allowed to expand freely on heating. Thermodynamics shows that

$$C_p - C_v = a^2 VT/\chi \quad \ldots \ldots \ldots \quad (54)$$

* Reports on Progress in Physics (London, Physical Society), 1941, **8**, 11.

where a is the volumetric coefficient of thermal expansion, V is the volume per mole, and χ is the compressibility.

8.2   Change of Free Energy with Temperature: Polymorphism

Let us consider a pure metal for which there are two distinct crystalline forms, or *polymorphic phases*, A and B, with free energies that vary with temperature in the manner shown in Fig. 50. Then we expect phase A to be stable at temperatures below T_c, since it has the lower free energy there, and phase B to be stable above T_c. On heating or cooling the system should undergo a *phase change* as its temperature passes through the value T_c, provided equilibrium is attained. To

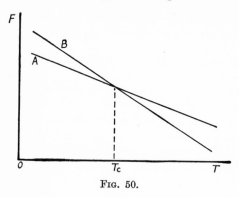

FIG. 50.

investigate such changes, we must first study the way in which the free energy of a crystal varies with temperature.

Suppose that the crystal, with specific heat C_p, is heated at constant pressure and its temperature is raised by an increment dT. The heat absorbed is given by $dQ=C_p dT$, and hence from the first law, $dE=C_p dT$.* The entropy increase dS accompanying the temperature change is given by $dS=dQ/T=C_p dT/T$. The change dF in free energy of the crystal as its temperature is raised from T to $T+dT$ is thus given by

$$dF=dE-TdS-SdT$$
$$=C_p dT-T(C_p dT/T)-SdT=-SdT \quad . \quad . \quad . \quad (55)$$

where S is the entropy of the crystal at the temperature T. The free energy at this temperature is thus

$$F=F_0-\int_0^T SdT,$$

---

* We are neglecting here the work PdV done by the system on its surroundings due to its thermal expansion; strictly we should write $dE=C_p dT-PdV$. However, the work done is very small, for solids, compared with $C_p dT$. The approximation is essentially the same as that by which we use F instead of G for the criterion of equilibrium (section 7.4).

where $F_0(=E_0)$ is the free energy (=internal energy) at 0° K. The entropy can be written as

$$S = \int_0^T \frac{C_p}{T} dT$$

so that the free energy at temperature T is given by

$$F = E_0 - \int_0^T \left(\int_0^T \frac{C_p}{T} dT \right) dT \quad \ldots \ldots \ldots (56)$$

Equations 55 and 56 show that the free energy decreases as the temperature increases, and that it decreases more rapidly the larger is the specific heat. Thus, if we have two phases A and B for a substance, and A has the lower E_0 and the lower specific heat, the system will be stable at low temperatures in the form A, but at sufficiently high temperatures B becomes more stable.

Only factors which contribute strongly to the specific heat are important in determining the slopes of free energy/temperature curves, and hence important to polymorphism. The lattice vibrations make the outstanding contribution. A large lattice specific heat is associated with a low characteristic temperature and hence with a low vibrational frequency. Since the vibrational frequency decreases as the strength of binding of the lattice decreases, the more weakly bound of the two phases A and B at 0° K. (i.e. the phase with the higher E_0) has the larger entropy of lattice vibrations. Thus the very factor—a weak binding—which renders a phase unstable at low temperatures gives it a relatively high stability at higher temperatures. This is no guarantee, of course, that it will actually become the most stable phase as the temperature is raised, since some other phase, of still higher entropy, e.g. liquid, may become stable before the temperature of the $A \rightarrow B$ transition is reached.

An interesting application of these ideas has been made by Zener.* He considers metals which at 0° K. are stable in the F.C.C. structure, and in which the B.C.C. structure is almost, but not quite, mechanically unstable (see section 6.3). The elastic resistance of such a B.C.C. structure to a shear in a $[\bar{1}10]$ direction on a (110) plane is unusually small, and so the lattice vibrations which involve this shear have low frequencies. These low frequencies give a large vibrational entropy and a steep fall of free energy with rise of temperature. It thus becomes possible that the B.C.C. structure will replace the F.C.C. at high temperatures. In a search for examples of this predicted transition, Barrett† discovered that lithium, which is B.C.C. at ordinary temperatures, can become F.C.C. at liquid-air temperature.

The vibrational specific heat *alone* cannot explain the polymorphism of

* C. Zener, *Phys. Rev.*, 1947, **71**, 846.   † C. S. Barrett, *Phys. Rev.*, 1947, **72**, 245.

iron, where the B.C.C. structure (α-iron) is replaced by the F.C.C. structure (γ-iron) at temperatures above 910° C. but reappears at temperatures above 1400° C. The specific heat of iron as a function of temperature is shown in Fig. 51, taken from the measurements of Austin.[*] Seitz[†] has used these results, together with the fact that the electronic specific heat is large in transition metals (see section 5.7), to explain the polymorphic behaviour. He deduces that the Debye characteristic temperature of γ iron is lower than that of α, and that this is mainly responsible for the $\alpha \rightarrow \gamma$ change at 910° C. However, the electronic specific heat of α becomes greater than that of γ above about 300° C., and at higher temperatures is sufficient to cause the return to α at

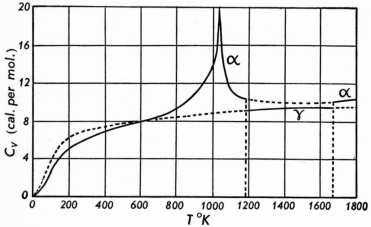

FIG. 51.—The Atomic Heat of Iron (after Austin).

1400° C.; the sharp peak in the curve is due to demagnetisation at the Curie temperature (see section 8.5).

Zener[‡] has used these and other data to calculate the increase in Gibbs free energy, ΔG_{Fe}, associated with the transformation of one mole of α iron into γ iron. His results are shown in Fig. 52, where the free energy is given in units of RT.

In passing through a sharp transition such as those described here the internal energy and entropy change sharply at the transition temperature from the values belonging to the old phase to those of the new one. When the transition occurs on heating the new phase has higher internal energy and entropy, and this energy is absorbed at the change point. On cooling, it is given out again. Practically all the energy is absorbed or liberated in the form of heat, and in such cases the change in internal energy, ΔE, accompanying the phase change is sensibly equal to the *latent heat*, ΔQ, which can be measured calorimetrically. Since

* J. B. Austin, *Journal Ind. and Eng. Chem.*, 1932, **24**, 1225.
† F. Seitz, 'Modern Theory of Solids', p. 487, McGraw-Hill, 1940.
‡ C. Zener, *Trans. Amer. Inst. Min. Met. Eng.*, 1946, **167**, 513.

the free energies of the old and new phases are equal at the change point, $\Delta F = 0$, so that $0 = \Delta E - T\Delta S$, i.e.

$$\Delta S = \Delta E/T = \Delta Q/T \quad \ldots \ldots \ldots \quad (57)$$

The entropy change is thus the latent heat divided by the transition temperature.

Polymorphic changes usually occur by *nucleation and growth*. Small groups of atoms take up the structure of the new phase and these *nuclei* then grow at the expense of the old phase, whose atoms they acquire in the process of growth, until the whole system has transformed.

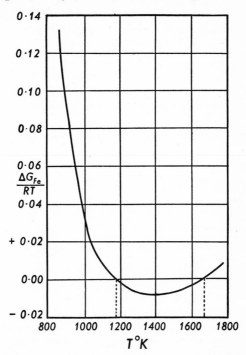

FIG. 52.—The Increase in Gibbs Free Energy, ΔG_{Fe}, associated with the Transformation of One Mole of α Iron into γ Iron, measured in Units of RT (after Zener).

In practice one usually has to go a little way past the ideal transformation temperature, into the range where the old phase is unstable, before the transformation occurs at an appreciable rate. This effect, known as *hysteresis*, is due to the difficulties of making nuclei; it will be discussed in Chapter XIV.

8.3 Lattice Defects in Equilibrium

In Chapter III we mentioned the possibility of certain lattice defects existing in equilibrium in crystals. Normally, a lattice defect raises the internal energy of its crystal.* It also raises the entropy of the crystal, however, since there are numerous ways in which it can be distributed through the lattice. Thus if defects are introduced into an otherwise perfect crystal at a temperature T, the free energy is lowered if the ensuing entropy increase, ΔS, is sufficient to make $T\Delta S$ greater than ΔE, the increase in internal energy, in the relation $\Delta F = \Delta E - T\Delta S$. Some of these defects will then appear as natural features of the crystal in equilibrium at this temperature.

Fig. 53 shows two of the main types of defect that have been discussed. The Frenkel defect is formed by the displacement of an atom from its normal position to an interstitial position. A crystal containing such defects thus has equal numbers of *vacancies* and *interstitial atoms*. Schottky defects, on the other hand, consist simply of vacancies (diagram (*b*)). The name *interstitialcy*† is now preferred to that of *interstitial atom* for the defect converse to the vacancy. This name emphasises that when the defect migrates through the crystal it probably does so by

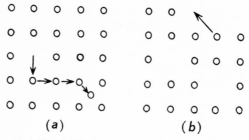

(*a*)   (*b*)

FIG. 53.—(*a*) A Frenkel Defect, and (*b*) Schottky Defects in a Crystal.

a sequence of jumps of the kind shown in diagram (*a*) rather than by the migration of a single unchanging atom from one interstitial position to another. The *configuration of atoms* is the feature that constitutes the interstitialcy, not the *particular* atom in the interstitial position at any instant. Another name sometimes used is the *crowdion*, introduced to describe a special form of interstitialcy in B.C.C. metals.‡

To illustrate the general method of calculating equilibrium concentrations of atomic defects we shall deal specifically with *vacancies*. Suppose we have a monatomic crystal of N atoms at a temperature T. Let u be the internal energy associated with one vacancy, i.e. the work required to remove an atom from a normal site inside the crystal and to place it in a normal site on its surface. To simplify the problem we assume (1) that u is independent of n, the number of vacancies present, and of the specific volume of the crystal; (2) that no other changes, e.g. in vibrational frequencies, accompany the introduction of vacancies. The total increase of internal energy due to the vacancies is then nu.

* See section 9.6 for an exceptional case.
† F. Seitz, *Acta Cryst.*, 1950, **3**, 355.
‡ H. Paneth, *Phys. Rev.*, 1950, **80**, 708.

The entropy of mixing of the N atoms and n vacancies in a crystal of $N+n$ sites is given by

$$S = k \log_e [(N+n)!/n!N!].$$

Using Stirling's approximation the free energy F of the crystal with n defects, relative to the free energy of the perfect crystal, is given by

$$F = nu - kT[(N+n) \log_e (N+n) - n \log_e n - N \log_e N].$$

The equilibrium value of n is that for which $dF/dn = 0$. Applying this condition we obtain

$$0 = u - kT[\log_e (N+n) + 1 - \log_e n - 1].$$

Rearranging, we have

$$n/(N+n) = e^{-u/kT}.$$

In general N is very large compared with n, so that we can approximate this to

$$n = Ne^{-U/RT} \quad . \quad . \quad . \quad . \quad . \quad . \quad . \quad . \quad . \quad . \quad . \quad . \quad . \quad . \quad . \quad (58)$$

where $U = uR/k = N_0 u$ is the energy of formation of a mole of vacancies.

We notice that the equilibrium number of defects rises rapidly with increasing temperature, due to the exponential form of the expression. As a numerical example, suppose that $U = 23{,}000$ cal./mol. and that $T = 1000°$ K. Then

$$\frac{n}{N} = e^{-\frac{23000}{2000}} = 10^{-5},$$

i.e. one site in 100,000 should be vacant at $1000°$ K. To calculate n for an actual crystal involves a knowledge of U, a quantity which is difficult to estimate from the theory of cohesion. Computations for copper give values in the range 20,000–40,000 cal./mol.[*] Frenkel[†] has given a simple argument for very roughly estimating U, as follows. An atom at the surface of a crystal makes bonds with only half as many atoms as does one inside the crystal. Hence U can be interpreted as the energy needed to break half of the atomic bonds. When vaporisation occurs, the atom leaves the surface and breaks the remaining half of the bonds. Thus U should be roughly equal to the heat of vaporisation. For copper the heat of vaporisation, 81,700 cal./mol., is considerably higher than the estimated value of U, so that Frenkel's method can be regarded as giving only the general order of magnitude of U.

Refinements to formula 58 have been suggested by Mott and Gurney.[‡] They take account of two effects, (1) a temperature dependence of U, associated with the thermal expansion of the crystal, (2) a contribution to the vibrational entropy from the slowly vibrating atoms round a vacancy, and they show that in rock salt these effects could increase

  [*] H. B. Huntington and F. Seitz, *Phys. Rev.*, 1942, **61**, 315, 325.

  [†] J. Frenkel, 'Kinetic Theory of Liquids', Oxford, 1946.

  [‡] N. F. Mott and R. W. Gurney, *Electronic Processes in Ionic Crystals*, Oxford, 1940.

the concentration of vacancies by 10^3 to 10^4 times that estimated from the simple theory.

Experimental methods for studying the concentration and properties of atomic defects in non-metallic crystals have been available for some years, based upon the special electrical properties associated with such defects. Methods for studying the defects in metals have also been developed recently.* The first step is to produce concentrations of such defects in excess of their equilibrium values at, e.g., room temperature. This can be done (1) by quenching from a high temperature, to retain in the metal the numerous defects created thermally at such temperatures, or (2) by cold working, taking advantage of the creation of atomic defects during the movements of dislocations, or (3) by irradiation with fast atomic particles which collide with atoms in the lattice and knock them out of their normal positions. The migrations of these defects through the crystal, and a gradual relapse to the equilibrium concentration as these defects disappear at free surfaces, grain boundaries, or dislocations, or annihilate one another (in the case of vacancies and interstitialcies), can then be followed experimentally by measurements of electrical resistance or of the damping of mechanical vibrations (*internal friction*). A detailed study of a silver-zinc (30 per cent. Zn) alloy† by the internal friction method has given a value of $U=12,000$ cal./mol. It is anticipated that these newly-developed methods will soon provide precise values for the energies to form and move various kinds of atomic defects in metal crystals.

8.4   Melting and the Structure of Liquid Metals

Like all true solids, metals melt sharply at single temperatures. The change from the solid to the liquid state produces sharp changes in most of the properties of a metal. The structure-sensitive mechanical properties are profoundly affected; for example, on melting, the plastic properties of the solid change into the *viscosity* of the liquid, in which the material can support a shear stress only if it flows at a rate proportional to stress. Other properties change equally sharply, but less drastically. Most metals increase their volume some 2 to 4 per cent. on melting, although a few with crystal structures of lower co-ordination, e.g. bismuth and gallium, contract on melting. As regards simple metals we can interpret the latent heat of melting as the energy involved in pulling the atoms apart to the more open structure of the liquid. Due to differences in cohesion, the latent heats of melting are spread widely over the range 500 to 5000 cal./mol. Since the melting point also increases with increasing cohesive strength, the entropy of melting (i.e. latent

---

* For a comprehensive review of this work, see T. Broom, 'Advances in Physics' (*Philosophical Magazine Supplement*), 1954, **3**, 26. Evidence for vacancies in aluminium alloys has been obtained by correlating densities with X-ray lattice parameters; see E. C. Ellwood, *J. Inst. Metals*, 1951-52, **80**, 217, 605; E. C. Ellwood and K. Q. Bagley, *J. Inst. Metals*, 1951-52, **80**, 617.

† A. E. Roswell and A. S. Nowick, *J. Metals*, 1953, **5**, 1259.

heat divided by melting temperature) is insensitive to differences in cohesion. In fact, the entropies of melting of most metals fall in the range of 2 to 5 cal./degree/mol.

The small increase in volume associated with the melting of a typical metal means that the atoms of the latter must be quite closely packed in the liquid state, at least at temperatures near the melting-point. This conclusion is supported by X-ray analyses of the structure of liquid metals. These show, at temperatures near the melting point, that each atom is surrounded by nearest neighbours much the same as it is in the crystal.* On melting, the *long-range* correlations in the positions of distant atoms are destroyed, but the *short-range* correlations in the positions of neighbouring atoms are largely preserved.

The existence of the liquid state presents statistical thermodynamics with one of its most challenging problems. The gaseous state is understandable; at high temperatures the thermal energy is too strong for the interatomic or intermolecular bonds and the substance disintegrates into separate atoms or molecules. At low temperatures the interatomic bonds prevail and pull the atoms together into a condensed aggregate. Since the forces acting on any atom in the aggregate from its immediate neighbours are essentially the same for all atoms it is natural to expect the same kind of grouping to develop round every atom, i.e. to expect the atoms to condense into a crystal. But why should there be *two* condensed states of matter? What is it that causes atoms sometimes to prefer condensation *without* crystallisation?

Another important question concerns the sharp change of state at the melting point. When ice floats in water at 0° C., one of them is

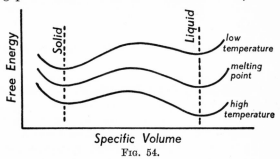

Fig. 54.

unmistakably a crystalline solid and the other equally definitely a liquid. No intermediate states exist. Why is this? Why are the states intermediate in structure between the solid and liquid thermodynamically unstable? Interpreted in terms of free energies, the absence of intermediate states must mean that condensed systems behave as in Fig. 54. Here we show the free energy of a system as a function of its specific volume at various temperatures. The lowest point on a curve

* A good account of the study of liquids by X-rays is given in 'The Structure of Metals', C. S. Barrett, 2nd Edition (1952), p. 261.

represents the stable state at the temperature concerned. The curves have two minima, associated respectively with the solid and liquid states. At the melting point the two minima have the same level. At low temperatures that of the solid is lower, and vice versa at high temperatures. But at no temperature is any state represented by the central parts of the curves thermodynamically stable.

Many theories of melting have been proposed. The basic difficulty, which none of them fully overcomes, is to postulate a structure for the liquid which is realistic, yet precise enough to permit the calculation of its main properties. In what appears to be the most promising line of approach the liquid is regarded either as a polycrystalline solid, the crystals of which are only a few atoms across,* or as a solid densely packed with dislocations. Since a grain boundary can be regarded as a sheet of dislocations (see section 15.4), these are equivalent descriptions. Points in favour of this picture of the structure of liquids are as follows:—

(1) It agrees with the X-ray observations in that it maintains short-range correlations in atomic positions while destroying long-range ones.

(2) It gives a formula for the viscosity of the liquid of a type known to satisfy many experimental observations on liquid metals.†

(3) It provides an explanation for a proportionality observed between latent heat of melting and shear strain energy.‡ This explanation rests on the fact that the energy of a dislocation consists predominantly of shear strain energy; the latent heat of melting on this view is thus the sum of the strain energies of the dislocations introduced on melting.

The main difficulty with this view is that the proposed structure of the liquid is too complex to be amenable to mathematical analysis. Thus it has not yet been proved that such a structure is, at certain temperatures, more stable thermodynamically than either the single crystal or the gas. Nor has it been shown that with increasing density of dislocations, giving rise to an associated increase in specific volume, the free energy changes as in Fig. 54. If these features could be proved to be inherent in it, the theory would be strongly established. Another difficulty in the theory is that it does not obviously explain why liquids can be drastically supercooled without freezing, under certain conditions (see section 14.3). One might think that since embryonic crystals are present in the liquid, these ought to grow as soon as the freezing point is reached. As a tentative explanation Frank§ has suggested that the shell of atoms in contact with a central atom, in the liquid, may

* R. W. Gurney and N. F. Mott, *Reports Prog. Phys.*, 1938, **5**, 46.
† W. Shockley, Report of 9th Solvay Conference, p. 431, Brussels (1952).
‡ N. F. Mott, *Proc. Roy. Soc.*, 1952, **A215**, 1.
§ F. C. Frank, *Proc. Roy. Soc.*, 1952, **A215**, 43.

not be arranged in a structure suitable for nucleating an extensive crystal. They may be the same, approximately, in number and spacing as in the solid state, but differently arranged. Frank argues that, in some cases, such local groups may have lower energies than similar small groups with the right structures for nucleating large crystals.

8.5 The Curie Point in Ferromagnetic Metals

In section 6.2 we considered the state of affairs inside a ferromagnetic domain at temperatures only where minimum internal energy could be used as a criterion for the stable structure. Experiment shows, however, that the saturation magnetisation varies with temperature as in Fig. 55. At low temperatures its value corresponds to a complete align-

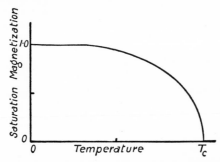

FIG. 55.—Variation of Saturation Magnetisation with Temperature.

ment of the available d spins, but as the temperature is raised it begins to fall, slightly at first and then ever more rapidly, until the *Curie point, Tc,* is reached. Beyond here the material is no longer ferromagnetic, only paramagnetic. The Curie points of iron, cobalt, and nickel are 780° C., 1075° C., and 365° C. respectively.

Evidently as the temperature is raised an increasing number of electrons set their spins in opposition to the local orientation in their domain. The reason for this is that the system can gain entropy in this way, and so lower its free energy. For example, if there are N electrons, n of which are oriented down, and $N-n$ up, the field direction, the system has an additional entropy given by

$$S = k \log_e [N!/n!(N-n)!],$$

relative to the fully magnetised state. At any temperature a balance is struck between this entropy factor and the corresponding increase in internal energy due to the exchange interaction energy.

The precise form of the curve of Fig. 55 depends on the fact that the disordering of the spins is an example of what is called a *co-operative phenomenon.* At low temperatures, when all spins are parallel, a large increment of internal energy is needed to reverse the spin of one electron against the combined forces from all its neighbours. But as more and more electrons reverse their spins, with increasing temperature, it becomes progressively *easier* for others to do the same since those already with reversed spins try to pull the others into their own orientation. When sufficient electrons point in both directions the change of internal energy with further disordering becomes negligible and general disorder sets in; this is the Curie point. This co-operative action of the electron spins causes the demagnetisation curve of Fig. 55 to become increasingly precipitous as the temperature is raised.

In the temperature range where the disordering takes place the specific heat is unusually large. As shown in Fig. 51, it climbs to a high peak at the Curie point. This extra specific heat is associated with the disordering of the spins. All structural changes such as this, in which the transition develops continuously over a range of temperature (cf. the order-disorder transformation in Chapter XIII), give rise to specific heat peaks of the same general type. Such continuous changes are called *second order changes*, as opposed to those such as melting and polymorphic changes, where the entire transition occurs at a single temperature, which are called *first order changes*. The specific heat peak bears the same relation to a second order change as does a latent heat to a first order one. The narrower the temperature range over which a second order change occurs the higher and narrower is its specific heat peak. In the limit where the entire change takes place at a single temperature the specific heat peak becomes of infinite height and zero width. This is of course precisely what happens in a first order change; since heat (latent heat) is absorbed without a rise in temperature the specific heat at the transition temperature is infinite.

REFERENCES

In addition to the references given in this chapter, the following may be consulted for general reading:

'Introduction to Chemical Physics.' J. C. Slater, McGraw-Hill, 1939.

'The Theory of the Properties of Metals and Alloys', Chapter I. N. F. Mott and H. Jones, Oxford, 1936.

'Introduction to Solid State Physics.' C. Kittel, Wiley, 1953.

CHAPTER IX

THE STRUCTURE OF ALLOYS

An alloy is a macroscopically homogeneous substance which possesses metallic properties and is composed of two or more chemical species. Any chemical species can serve as an alloying element, although the only ones added in substantial amounts are metals. For simplicity we shall deal only with alloys containing two elements, i.e. *binary* alloys. The study of more complex alloys is more involved but introduces little in the way of new principles.

When a second element is introduced into a metal a new thermo-dynamical variable—composition—immediately calls for attention; the material now contains more than one *component*. For most scientific work the *atomic concentration* is used to measure composition; e.g. if there are n atoms of a component A in an alloy of N atoms, the atomic concentration of A is n/N. In much practical work the *weight percentage* is specified. In certain cases *electron concentration* is used to measure composition. By electron concentration is usually meant the ratio of the number of free electrons to atoms in the alloy; this varies with atomic concentration in alloys containing metals of different valencies. In simple cases, where each atom contributes all its valency electrons to the free electron cloud, the electron concencentration is easily found from the valencies; e.g. a brass consisting of 60 copper atoms (uni-valent) to every 40 zinc atoms (divalent) has 140 valency electrons to every 100 atoms and so has an electron concentration of 1·4.

9.1 Effects of a Second Element on the Structure of a Metal

Suppose that we have a solid pure metal and by some means intro-duce into it atoms of another substance. The atoms of both types are then allowed to adjust their positions and crystal structure until thermo-dynamical equilibrium is achieved, i.e. until the free energy reaches its lowest value. What structures will exist in the alloy? We can think of the two types of atoms as (*a*) being indifferent to one another, or (*b*) attracting one another, or (*c*) repelling one another. By this we mean that the internal energy (*a*) stays unchanged, or (*b*) becomes lower, or (*c*) becomes higher, respectively, when the atoms are redistributed amongst the atomic sites so as to increase the number of unlike nearest neighbours. As a beginning we can draw up the following generalisations:

(1) If each atom is indifferent to the type of its neighbours, the two types behave as if they were not different and become dispersed amongst each other so thoroughly that the mixture is homogeneous right down to the atomic scale of magnitude. This state of affairs, already anti-cipated in Fig. 45 (*a*), is called a *random solid solution*. In many alloys

the structure approximates to this idealised form and the atoms are distributed amongst each other in *nearly* random arrangements.

(2) If dissimilar atoms are attracted more than similar ones the tendency is for atoms of one type to have nearest neighbours of the other type (Fig. 45 (*b*)). The nature of the resulting structure varies widely according to the factors determining the attraction. When formed from true metals the structure is usually an *ordered solid solution* or *superlattice*. When the components differ electrochemically from one another the bonds between their atoms become partly of *ionic* type (see section 1.7) and in many such cases the structure is termed an *intermetallic compound*. In the extreme case where the added component is a strongly electronegative non-metal, e.g. sulphur, oxygen, chlorine, a true chemical compound is formed and the material no longer possesses the metallic qualities of an alloy.

(3) If dissimilar atoms attract less than similar ones the two types tend to separate into distinct and different crystals which are joined only at common grain boundaries. Some grains are rich in atoms of one type and others rich in atoms of the other type. These heterogeneous equilibrium structures are called *phase mixtures*. The existence of phase mixtures in an alloy system does not, however, invariably mean that dissimilar atoms attract less than similar ones; the principles governing their formation will be discussed in the next chapter.

We shall now make a closer study of these alloy structures.

9.2 The Structure of Solid Solutions

A solid solution can exist over a *range of composition*; at any composition within this range the material is fully homogeneous and its physical properties and lattice constants differ infinitesimally from those possessed by neighbouring compositions. A few solid solutions exist over the entire range of composition from the one pure metal to the other (see section 11.1), and in such cases the components are said to be completely *miscible*. Mostly, however, the range of homogeneous solid solution is limited. When this range includes the composition of one of the pure components, the solution is described as a *primary* one based on that component; in such cases it is convenient, for nearby compositions, to describe that component as the *solvent* and to regard the added element (the *solute*) as being *dissolved* in it. Solid solutions are frequently also formed at higher concentrations of the added element, with ranges of homogeneity which do not extend to a pure component. These are called *secondary solid solutions*. Usually, but not always, secondary solutions have crystal structures different from those of the components. Secondary solutions and intermetallic compounds are alike in that neither possesses a range of homogeneity extending to a pure component. As a recognition of this feature they are both described as *intermediate phases*.

The abundance of solid solutions in alloys is due to the fact that bonding in most of these approximates closely to the ideal metallic type in which atoms are not linked directly to one another by chemical bonds, but are kept together by their mutual attraction to the free electrons passing between them. This type of bond is largely indifferent both to the precise proportions of the participating atoms and to their precise distribution in the array of atomic sites, and it thus favours the formation of random solutions over wide ranges of composition. In non-metallic crystals such as sodium chloride on the other hand, the ionic nature of the bond demands fixed proportions of atoms in fixed distributions.

Solid solutions can be either *substitutional* or *interstitial*. Those of the type shown in Fig. 45 (*a*), in which all atoms lie on a common array of sites, are substitutional solutions. Interstitial solutions are those where the atoms of one component are relatively so small that they occupy the spaces, or *interstices*, between the atoms of the other one, the latter forming a complete array in themselves (Fig. 56).

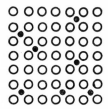

FIG. 56.—An Interstitial Solid Solution.

The distribution of atoms in a substitutional solution generally depends on temperature. Many solutions that are ordered at low temperatures become disordered (nearly random) at high temperatures. This *order-disorder* change, thermodynamically similar to the magnetic change of section 8.5, will be analysed in Chapter XIII. When the atoms are perfectly ordered, as in Fig. 45 (*b*), they actually form a *new* lattice, called a *superlattice*, which is larger than the lattice of the disordered solution. In the perfectly ordered solution the true lattice vectors (see section 3.3) must join similar *atoms* and not merely similar points in the skeleton frame of atomic sites, whereas in the disordered alloy there is no distinction in the sites (i.e. they are randomly filled) and vectors joining neighbouring sites can be used to define a lattice. A perfect superlattice is of course only possible at a critical and simple proportion of atoms. In practice the atomic proportions at which superlattices have been observed are 1 : 1 and 3 : 1. Systems which show superlattices at such ratios also show partial or imperfect order at neighbouring compositions. Superlattices are not of course formed in all solid solutions which are homogeneous at the critical compositions, for their formation depends on the type of atomic forces present. Examples of superlattices can be found in both primary and secondary solutions. Some typical ones are shown in Fig. 57.

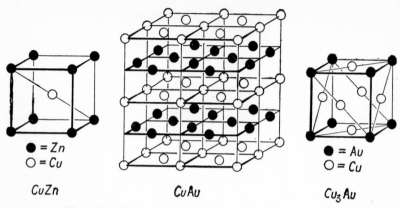

FIG. 57.—The Structures of Some Typical Superlattices.

9.3   Primary Substitutional Solid Solutions

We shall now discuss those features of atomic structure which determine the extent to which one metal can dissolve in another, forming a primary, substitutional solid solution. The pioneering work of Hume-Rothery and his school has led to the following general rules:—*

(1) *The Atomic Size Factor*. Increasing difference in the diameters of the solute and solvent atoms decreases the range of primary solution. If the diameters differ by more than 15 per cent. of that of the solvent the solubility is small; the size factor is then said to be *unfavourable*.

(2) *The Electrochemical Factor*. The more electropositive the one component, and the more electronegative the other one, the greater is the tendency to form intermetallic compounds rather than wide solid solutions. This leads to a small primary solubility (see section 10.6).

(3) *The Relative Valency Effect*. Other things being equal, a metal of lower valency is more likely to dissolve one of higher valency than vice versa. This rule is valid mainly in alloys of copper, silver and gold, with those of higher valency.

The size factor rule was deduced from a comparison of the solubilities of various elements in copper, silver, and gold, but more recent surveys of solubilities in magnesium, aluminium and iron suggest that it might also apply to divalent, trivalent, and transition metal solvents. It should be noticed that the rule does not promise a large solubility when the size factor is favourable; to obtain such a solubility it is necessary also that the atoms be similar electrochemically, otherwise they will form compounds. The rule enables one to rationalise many otherwise perplexing differences in solubility. For example, Table 6 shows that of the divalent metals beryllium, cadmium and zinc, the first dissolves substantially in copper but not in silver, the second behaves in just the opposite manner, while the third dissolves substantially in both.

* General references are given at the end of this chapter.

TABLE 6.—SOLUBILITIES AND ATOMIC SIZE FACTORS OF
BERYLLIUM, CADMIUM AND ZINC, IN COPPER AND SILVER

(*Size factors calculated from interatomic distances in crystals of pure components*)

| Solute | Maximum Solubility, Atomic per cent. | | Atomic Size Factor, per cent. | |
	In Copper	In Silver	In Copper	In Silver
Be	16·6	3·5	—12·9	—22·9
Cd	1·7	42·5	+16·5	+ 3·1
Zn	38·4	40·2	+ 4·2	— 8·0

The size factor effect originates in the lattice distortion due to the differences in sizes of the atoms situated on a common lattice (see section 10.7). An average value for the lattice distortion can be obtained by measuring the change in lattice parameter, by means of X-rays, consequent upon dissolving a second element in the parent metal. In very dilute solutions the distortion varies from place to place, being greatest near a solute atom and smallest in regions remote from such atoms; a description of the strain field round a solute atom in a dilute solution can be given with the aid of the theory of elasticity.* In concentrated solutions the position is by no means clear, for then most of the solute atoms are nearest neighbours to one another and a description of the distortion in terms of elastic strain fields is no longer possible. Zener† has recently pointed out an interesting connection between elastic constants and maximum solubility in primary solutions. Misfitting solute atoms lower the elastic constants because the atoms next to a solute atom are strained out of their normal lattice positions to places where the radius of curvature of the energy versus displacement curve is less sharp; since the elastic constants are proportional to this curvature (see section 6.3) they also are reduced. Solutes which produce the greatest reduction in elastic constants, per unit amount dissolved, are also those that enter least into solution.

To apply the size factor rule one must first choose some measure of the atomic diameter. Experience has shown that the most practical and useful measure is the closest distance of approach of atoms in the crystal of the pure element. This has the advantage that one does not need to know the structure of the alloy before applying the rule; the rule is then capable of predicting instead of merely interpreting. It raises several difficulties, however, especially when the solute atom changes its electronic state on alloying, as for example when changes occur in the degree of ionisation, electron concentration, or crystal structure. It also leads to some anomalies. For example, an atom of antimony distorts (expands) the lattice of copper more than an atom of cadmium does, if the distortion is measured in terms of atomic diameters, and

* See, for example, N. F. Mott and F. R. N. Nabarro, *Proc. Phys. Soc.*, 1940, **52**, 86, and J. D. Eshelby, *J. Appl. Phys.*, 1954, **25**, 255; also see section 10.7.

† C. Zener, Chapter 2 in 'Thermodynamics in Physical Metallurgy', *Amer. Soc. Met.*, 1950.

yet the solubility in copper of antimony (5·9 atomic per cent.) is greater than that of cadmium (1·7 atomic per cent.). The explanation of such effects appears to lie in the influence of the *ionic diameter*. The atom of antimony is larger than that of cadmium, but the core of the atom, inside the valency electron cloud, is smaller. In a full metal like copper the exchange repulsion of the filled shells of the ions determines the minimum atomic spacing (see section 6.3), and this favours the sub-stitutional solution of atoms of small ionic diameter.

A particularly interesting observation by Hume-Rothery and his school concerns the effect of *electron concentration* on solubility. If we take copper or silver as solvents and add to them elements of higher valency, choosing only those with favourable size and electrochemical factors, we find that a definite relation exists between the limit of pri-mary solubility and the valency of the solute. When the composition is measured in terms of electron concentration the solubility limit is about 1·4 (valency electrons per atom) in numerous cases. Thus zinc dissolves in copper up to about 40 atomic per cent., the trivalent elements aluminium and gallium dissolve up to about 20 per cent., and the tetravalent silicon and germanium up to about 12-13 per cent. These figures agree with the above rule of the limiting electron concentration, which predicts that the solubilities of di-, tri-, and tetra-valent solutes in a monovalent metal should be respectively 40, 20, and 13·3 per cent. when other factors are favourable.

9.4   The Structure of Intermediate Phases

Intermediate phases in alloys may be grouped broadly into three main classes, (a) electrochemical compounds, (b) size factor compounds, and (c) electron compounds. There is no sharp distinction between these classes, however, and numerous examples can be found of alloy struc-tures that belong partly to one and partly to another. The word 'com-pound' has taken firm root in the terminology of the subject, in spite of the facts that only in class (a) is there any obedience to the ordinary valency laws of chemistry, and that many of the structures in class (c) consist of secondary solid solutions of variable composition and good metallic properties.

The electrochemical compounds are formed when one element is strongly electropositive and the other is strongly electronegative. Some examples are Mg_2Si, Mg_3Sb_2, and ZnS. Their compositions satisfy the valency laws and in general the range of solubility in them is small. They usually have high melting points. With the exception of this group it is preferable to regard intermediate phases in alloys not as chemical compounds, but as structures rather similar to primary solid solutions (ordered or disordered) in which the atoms are held together by an essentially metallic bond. In some intermediate phases the dis-tribution of atoms is disordered and an appreciable range of solubility exists; these are secondary solid solutions. In others the distribution is ordered and these may be regarded as either ordered solid solutions or intermetallic compounds. When the electrochemical factor is inappreciable the formation of these phases depends on the atomic size factor and valency electron concentration, such that if a crystal structure is possible in which atoms pack together well (size factor compounds) or which has low electronic energy (electron compounds), it has low free energy and a good chance of being more stable than any other structure at the composition concerned.

Size factor compounds are of two main types; those to be discussed in the next section, where one atom is much smaller than the other, and those where the difference in atomic diameters is about 20 to 30 per cent. An important group of the latter type are the *Laves phases* with compositions according to the formula AB_2. Examples are $MgCu_2$, $AgBe_2$, $MgZn_2$, $TiFe_2$, $MgNi_2$, and $CaMg_2$. The chief reason for the existence of these phases is the fact that when the participating atoms differ in size by about 22·5 per cent. they can pack together in crystal structures of higher co-ordination than the maximum (12) that can be achieved in structures of equally sized spheres. In a Laves phase of formula AB_2 each A atom has 12 B neighbours and 4 A neighbours, giving a co-ordination number of 16. The co-ordination number for each B atom is 12, so that the average co-ordination number in the structure is 13·33. These high co-ordination numbers are of course entirely consistent with the metallic bond (see section 3.1) but not with ionic or homopolar bonds.

Hume-Rothery and Westgren first observed that over a wide range of alloy systems phases of similar crystal structures are formed at the same ratios of valency electrons to atoms. These phases are termed *electron compounds*. The electron concentrations at which they are observed are 3/2 (i.e. 3 electrons to 2 atoms), 21/13, and 7/4. Some examples are:—

I$_A$. *Body-centred Cubic (β brass) Structure, Electron: Atom Ratio*=3/2.
     (Cu, Ag, or Au) Zn, CuBe, AgMg, Cu_3Al, Cu_5Sn, (Co, Ni, or Fe) Al.
I$_B$. *Complex Cubic (β manganese) Structure, Electron: Atom Ratio*=3/2.
     (Ag or Au)$_3$ Al, Cu_5Si, $CoZn_3$.
I$_C$. *Hexagonal Close Packed Structure, Electron: Atom Ratio*=3/2.
     AgCd, Cu_5Ge, Ag_7Sb.
II. *Complex Cubic (γ brass) Structure, Electron: Atom Ratio*=21/13.
     (Cu, Ag, or Au)$_5$ (Zn, or Cd)$_8$, Cu_9Al_4, Cu_{31}, Sn_8, (Fe, Co, Ni, Pd, or Pt)$_5$ Zn_{21}.
III. *Hexagonal Close Packed (ε brass) Structure, Electron: Atom Ratio*=7/4.
     (Cu, Ag, or Au) (Zn, or Cd)$_3$, Cu_3Sn, $CuBe_3$, Ag_5Al_3.

In determining these electron concentrations the elements are taken to contribute the following number of valency electrons per atom: Cu, Ag, Au, 1; Mg, Zn, Cd, Be, 2; Al, 3; Sn, Si, Ge, 4; Sb, 5; Fe, Co, Ni, Pt, Pd, 0. It will be noticed that the transition metals are given zero valency. This is partly explainable on the basis of their electronic structures; in their alloys the incomplete outermost d band has to be filled when the electron concentration is increased, as well as the outermost s band, and this reduces the contribution of these metals to the free electron cloud. Raynor[*] has shown that intermediate phases formed when transition metals are dissolved in aluminium are understandable on the basis that the transition metal atoms *absorb* electrons. Consider, for example, the phases $CrAl_7$, $MnAl_6$, $FeAl_3$, Co_2Al_9, $NiAl_3$. If the electron concentrations of these are calculated on the basis that each aluminium atom contributes 3 electrons, and that each transition metal atom absorbs electrons to fill the vacancies in its d shell (i.e. 0·61 for nickel, 1·71 for cobalt, etc.), the electron concentrations are approximately constant, except for $FeAl_3$. Thus:—

Phase	$CrAl_7$	$MnAl_6$	$FeAl_3$	Co_2Al_9	$NiAl_3$
Electron concentration	2·05	2·05	1·58	2·12	2·09

These phases may therefore be classified as electron compounds.

Electron compounds are also found in certain ternary alloy systems at the appropriate concentrations, and in general they can exist over a small range of composition about the exact ratio. Both ordered and disordered distributions of atoms are found.

The existence of these phases is a direct consequence of the nature of the metallic bond; it is evident that the stability of such a phase depends essentially upon the electron concentration and the pattern of atomic sites, while the actual distribution of atoms amongst these sites is of minor importance. As we shall see, this is in entire agreement with the conclusions to be arrived at from the zone theory of alloys.

9.5 Interstitial Phases

An important group of interstitial phases consists of the hydrides, nitrides, carbides, and borides, of the transition metals, in which the small non-metallic atoms take up interstitial positions between the metallic atoms, the latter usually forming by themselves a complete close-packed structure, or a slightly distorted form of the structure. Hydrogen, nitrogen, carbon, and boron are not strongly electronegative and with transition metals they form true alloys with metallic properties; but with more electropositive metals they form compounds of non-metallic type, e.g. calcium carbide.

With transition metals they form intermediate phases of simple crystal structure when the radius of the interstitial atom is less than 0·59 of that of the metal atom. Usually these structures are centred about compositions of the type M_4X, M_2X, MX, and MX_2, where M and X represent metal and non-metal atoms, respectively. They are commonly of F.C.C. or C.P.Hex. type, and occasionally B.C.C., with the metal atoms occupying the normal atomic sites of the structure,

* G. V. Raynor, Chapter I, in 'Progress in Metal Physics, I' (Ed. B. Chalmers), Butterworth, 1949.

and the non-metal atoms occupying the interstices. When the ratio of the radii exceeds 0·59 the interstices are no longer large enough to hold the non-metal atoms without distortion and more complicated crystal structures are then formed. In carbon steel, for example, the ratio of the radii is 0·63, so that the carbon atom is too big to fit easily into the B.C.C. lattice. The intermediate phase formed in this case is *cementite*, Fe_3C; this has metallic properties but a complicated crystal structure. Jack[*] has succeeded in preparing a series of *carbo-nitrides* of iron in which carbon and nitrogen atoms are freely interchangeable and which have compositions in the range Fe_2X to Fe_3X, where X stands for the non-metal atoms.

In addition to forming intermediate phases, hydrogen, nitrogen, carbon, and boron dissolve to an appreciable extent in transition metals, forming primary interstitial solid solutions. It seems that here also the atomic size factor is important in determining the solubility. Thus in steel the carbon atoms fit more easily into the interstices of the F.C.C. lattice than those of the B.C.C. one, and the solubility is higher in the former (maximum of 1·7 wt. per cent. in F.C.C. and 0·02 wt. per cent. in B.C.C.). This solubility difference in the two polymorphic forms of iron is of great technical importance, as much of the heat-treatment of steels is based upon it.

The solution of carbon (and nitrogen) in *ferrite*, the B.C.C. form of iron, although very limited, is interesting because the interstitial atoms distort the structure into a *body centred tetragonal* form. This can best be seen in *martensite*, which is a supersaturated solution of carbon in ferrite prepared by quenching from temperatures in the F.C.C. range. X-ray studies show that, in martensite, one of the cubic axes of the body centred cell becomes longer and the other two (equal) axes become shorter. The length c of the long axis (the *tetragonal* axis) and the length a of a short axis are given in Fig. 58.

The tetragonal distortion round an atom of carbon or nitrogen in ferrite can also be detected in extremely dilute solutions by the *internal friction* method of Snoek.[†] The principle here is that if, say, a tensile stress is applied along one of the cube axes of a ferrite crystal, carbon or nitrogen atoms will gradually reassemble in those particular interstitial positions that cause this axis to become the tetragonal axis. This allows the crystal to become slightly longer in the direction of the applied force and so enables the latter to do more work. If the applied force is oscillated, so that first one axis and then another is stressed in tension, and at such a speed that the interstitial atoms have time to jump into the newly favoured sites during each oscillation, work will be done repeatedly. This work can be measured, e.g. from the damping of the oscillations, thus providing a basis for studying both the tetragonal distortion and the movements of the interstitial atoms.

---

[*] K. H. Jack, *Proc. Roy. Soc.*, 1948, **A195**, 34, 40, 56.
[†] J. L. Snoek, *Physica*, 1941, **8**, 711.

The tetragonal distortion occurs because the carbon and nitrogen atoms occupy positions of the kind marked x in Fig. 59. Not all of these positions are filled, of course, since the amount in solution is always small. It should be noticed that the positions in the middle of the top

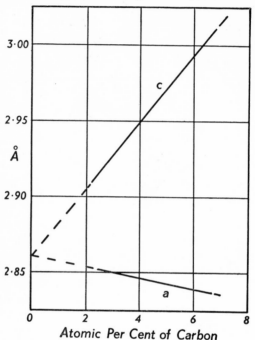

Fig. 58.—Variation of c and a axes with carbon content in martensite (after Kurdjumov).

and bottom faces are structurally identical with those at the middle of the vertical edges of the cell. In either position an interstitial atom pushes apart the two very close iron atoms situated directly above and

Fig. 59.—Interstitial Positions for Carbon and Nitrogen Atoms in B.C.C. Iron.

below it, and so elongates the lattice along its vertical axis. The positions shown in the figure represent only one of the three sets of sites available in the B.C.C. cell. The two other sets, which correspond to the two other possible tetragonal axes, involve the positions in the middle of the horizontal cell edges and the side faces of the cell.

A study of the B.C.C. cell shows rather surprisingly that these are not the positions of the largest interstitial holes in the cell. Why then do the carbon and nitrogen atoms prefer them? Zener* explains this as a consequence of the elastic properties of the B.C.C. lattice (see section 6.3). The work required to push away the two nearest iron atoms, producing the tetragonal distortion, is small. Thus, although the holes at the points x in Fig. 59 are rather small for the interstitial atoms, the two iron atoms, above and below each such hole, which are mainly responsible for the smallness can in fact be pushed apart rather easily.

9.6 The Zone Theory of Alloy Phases

The importance of the electron concentration as a factor controlling the formation of alloy phases is now generally recognised, even though its influence is often masked by the effects of the atomic size and electrochemical factors. In many alloys of copper, silver, or gold, with added elements of higher valency, similar phases occur at equal electron concentrations; the primary, a phase, solid solution (F.C.C.) reaches the limit of its range of existence at an electron concentration of 1·4, and a β phase (often B.C.C.) appears at a concentration of 1·5, and so on. These effects attracted the attention of Jones,† who realised that they originated from the Brillouin zone structure of the phases. His theory will now be outlined.

In Chapter V it was shown that for free electrons the $N(E)$ curve, representing the density of electronic states as a function of the energy of those states, is a parabola (Fig. 34), and that when the zone structure is taken into account the $N(E)$ curve deviates widely from this parabola. The deviation begins when the electron concentration first becomes sufficient to cause the expanding Fermi surface, i.e. the envelope of the highest occupied quantum states, to approach the zone boundary at its nearest points. The density of states climbs to a peak as the expanding surface touches the boundary and then drops sharply as the remaining corner regions of the zone become filled up.

Suppose that we have an alloy system with two possible phases, 1 and 2, whose $N(E)$ curves are as shown in Fig. 60. Suppose also that the solvent metal is monovalent, and that its own crystal structure is that of phase 1; its electron concentration is too low for E_{max}, the energy of the highest occupied level, to reach to the point A in Fig. 60. We now add to it a second metal of higher valency which enters into primary solution. As more and more of this solute is added the electron concentration steadily rises, and E_{max} correspondingly rises with it. At first, where E_{max} is below the point A, only the parabolic parts of the $N(E)$ curve are filled and the phases 1 and 2 are equally favoured so far as the relation between Fermi energy and crystal pattern is concerned; the value of E_{max} is the same in both phases.

* C. Zener, Chapter XI, in 'Imperfections in Nearly Perfect Crystals', Wiley, 1952.
† H. Jones, *Proc. Roy. Soc.*, 1934, **144**, 225; *Proc. Phys. Soc.*, 1937, **49**, 250.

Beyond the point A, however, the $N(E)$ curve for phase 1 rises to its peak at B, due to the fact that the zone boundary is now being reached in this crystal structure. The rise to the point C in the second structure does not occur until a higher electron concentration is reached. In the range A to B, then, the $N(E)$ curve of phase 1 is higher than that of phase 2. Now, when the $N(E)$ curve is higher, more electrons can be accommodated within all states up to a given E_{max}, so that for the same electron concentration E_{max} will be lower for the structure with the higher $N(E)$ curve. Hence phase 1 will be more stable than phase 2, so far as Fermi energy is concerned, for alloy compositions such that E_{max} lies between A and B.

Beyond the point B the Fermi energy of phase 1 begins rising sharply, due to the steep fall of $N(E)$ as the corners of the Brillouin zone fill up.

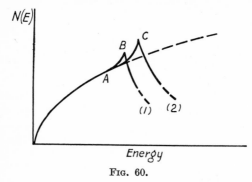

Fig. 60.

At the same time, the range B to C is a favourable one for phase 2, so far as its Fermi energy is concerned. Thus, once the electron concentration causes E_{max} to rise beyond the point B, phase 1 begins to become less stable in comparison with phase 2. The composition for which E_{max} reaches the point B is therefore a critical one for the alloy system. At this composition the Fermi energy favours phase 1 strongly, but at slightly higher concentrations of solute this phase should become unstable and we may expect a phase mixture to form, consisting of phases 1 and 2 with compositions corresponding to the points B and C, respectively. This is the qualitative basis of the theory.

We shall now give a simplified form of the quantitative theory, which enables one to calculate the critical electron concentrations at which the phases coexist. If we identify phase 1 with the α phase (F.C.C.), i.e. the primary solutions of copper, silver, or gold, and phase 2 with the corresponding β phase, then point B should occur at an electron concentration a little less than 1·4 and point C should occur at 1·5.

To check this we shall calculate the actual electron concentration corresponding to B, i.e. the concentration at which the Fermi surface first touches the zone boundary. The calculation will be made for the case where the electrons are nearly free, so that the Fermi surface is practically spherical when it first touches the zone boundary. The method is to equate two formulae for λ_{min}, the wavelength associated with the electrons of highest energy, which in this case is just short enough to make Bragg reflection possible at the places where the Fermi surface touches the zone boundary. The first formula relates λ_{min} to the number of electrons per unit volume. Equation 15 gives this relation as

$$\lambda_{min} = 2(\pi V/3N)^{1/3},$$

where N is the number of free electrons in volume V of the metal. The second expression relates λ_{min} to the number of atoms (more strictly to the number of unit cells; see below). In the F.C.C. lattice the most widely spaced planes which give Bragg reflections are the {111}. Reflection occurs first from these planes when $\lambda = 2d$, where d is their spacing; this λ is the λ_{min} corresponding to the peak B in Fig. 60. If a is the lattice parameter then $d = a/\sqrt{3}$ and $\lambda_{min} = 2a/\sqrt{3}$. The volume of the structure cell (see section 3.1) is a^3, and in the F.C.C. lattice this cell contains 4 atoms. Hence, if N_0 is the number of atoms in volume V of the metal, $a^3/4 = V/N_0$. This gives $a = (4V/N_0)^{1/3}$, and hence

$$\lambda_{min} = (2/\sqrt{3})(4V/N_0)^{1/3}.$$

Eliminating λ_{min} from these two expressions finally gives the electron concentration, N/N_0, beyond which the F.C.C. phase becomes unstable as

$$N/N_0 = (\pi\sqrt{3})/4 = 1 \cdot 36,$$

which, as we expected, is a little smaller than 1·4.

A similar analysis can be made for the B.C.C. phase. Reflection here first occurs from the {110} planes, which gives $\lambda_{min} = a/\sqrt{2}$. There are 2 atoms in the B.C.C. structure cell. Following the same line of argument we obtain for the critical electron concentration

$$N/N_0 = (\pi\sqrt{2})/3 = 1 \cdot 48,$$

in agreement with the value, 1·5, at which the phase is found. The other electron compounds can be explained in a similar manner.

We conclude that, when other factors determining the crystal structure are either favourable or insignificant, the alloy will adopt the crystal structure which gives it the lowest possible Fermi energy; this is obtained when the crystal possesses a set of reflecting planes of a spacing such that Bragg reflection can just occur for electrons of smallest wavelength moving perpendicularly to them.

An interesting consequence of this Fermi energy factor is the *defect lattice*, which occurs in certain alloys, notably the B.C.C. NiAl phase. Here it is found that when the nickel content is reduced to below 50 atomic per cent. some of the sites vacated by the nickel atoms *remain vacant*, in such numbers that the number of electrons *per unit cell* remains constant at the value associated with the stability of the β phase. This is in agreement with the zone theory, for the basic factor determining E_{max} is the number of electrons per unit cell. In most cases this factor is essentially the same as the number of electrons per atom, and it is only in defect lattices that the distinction between them is significant. It should be noticed that the vacancies in defect lattices have a different thermodynamic origin from those discussed in section 8.3; the latter depend entirely on the entropy of mixing for their existence.

The Hume-Rothery rule of electron compounds appears to involve the assumption that a solute atom in a crystal gives all its valency electrons to the common pool of free electrons. Actually this cannot be true if the atom has a valency different from that of the solvent. For if, say, more electrons are stripped off it than off each solvent atom it will be left with an excess positive charge, which is inconsistent with the macroscopic notion of an electronic conductor as a material in which electrons flow freely towards positive charges and neutralise them by concentrating there. An analysis by Mott* of the electrical resistivities of alloys has shown that the excess charges remaining on solute atoms in metals must be small, so that most of their valency electrons remain localised on them. More recently, Friedel† has studied the distribution of electrons in dilute solutions of metals such as nickel, zinc, gallium, tin, and arsenic, in copper, silver, and gold. He shows that *one* electron is certainly given by each solute atom (as is also given by each solvent atom) to the free electron cloud, but that most, if not all, of the additional valency electrons are not given; instead, they remain bound to their parent atoms in localised electronic states whose energies lie below the Fermi distribution. However, this does not invalidate the Hume-Rothery rule, for each localised electronic state is created from one belonging originally to the Fermi distribution and so must be subtracted from the distribution. The effect is that, when high valency solute atoms are dissolved in, say, copper, the Fermi surface expands towards the zone boundary, not because more electrons are put into the zone, but because a corresponding number of electronic states are taken from it.

REFERENCES FOR GENERAL READING

'The Structure of Metals and Alloys.' W. Hume-Rothery and G. V. Raynor, Institute of Metals, 1954.

'The Theory of the Properties of Metals and Alloys.' N. F. Mott and H. Jones, Oxford, 1936.

'Modern Theory of Solids.' F. Seitz, McGraw-Hill, 1940.

'Structure of Metals.' C. S. Barrett, McGraw-Hill, 1952.

'Atomic Theory for Students of Metallurgy.' W. Hume-Rothery, Institute of Metals, 1946.

Recent Reviews

G. V. Raynor, Chapter I in 'Progress in Metal Physics, I' (Ed. B. Chalmers), Butterworth, 1949.

G. V. Raynor, 'The Band Theory of Metals' in 'Reports on Progress in Physics.' The Physical Society, 1951.

N. F. Mott, Chapter III in 'Progress in Metal Physics, III'. Pergamon Press, 1952.

* N. F. Mott, *Proc. Camb. Phil. Soc.*, 1936, **32**, 281.

† J. Friedel, *Phil. Mag.*, 1952, **43**, 153.

CHAPTER X

THE FREE ENERGY OF ALLOY PHASES

One of the ultimate objectives of work of the kind described in the previous chapter is the calculation of the free energies of alloy phases from the characteristics of their component atoms. This would enable one to predict the phase structure of an alloy at any composition and temperature. The programme is immensely difficult, however, and so far it has only been possible to make a few predictions, of a modest nature, from general principles. The biggest difficulty is the calculation of the internal energy of an alloy; as we saw in section 6.3, even in pure metals this is possible only in a few simple cases. In alloys additional complications are provided by the effects of size and electrochemical differences between the alloying elements, and by the dependence of Fermi energy on electron concentration and Brillouin zone structure. In certain simple cases we can predict compositions at which the internal energy should change rather sharply; for example, as described in section 9.6, the energy rises sharply when the electron concentration is such that quantum states in the corners of a Brillouin zone begin to be occupied, and the alloy structure concerned may then give way to some other which has lower energy in this range of composition.

Experimentally, the structures of alloys have been much studied, the results being assembled in *equilibrium diagrams* which give the ranges of composition and temperature in which various structures are stable. Examination of such diagrams shows that there are certain features common to most alloy systems. Thus many systems have equilibrium diagrams of the same qualitative form. Others have more individualistic diagrams in which several standard features, common to many diagrams, are arranged in various ways. These standard features are largely independent of the individual properties of the atoms concerned and are due instead to the nature of the thermodynamical laws governing the equilibrium of multi-component systems. They can be explained by making very simple assumptions about the properties of the atoms. As our main task in this chapter and the next is to explain these general features, we shall make numerous assumptions which certainly do not retain their validity when applied to every alloy system, but which nevertheless provide a very reasonable framework for discussing alloy systems in general and a useful starting point for exploring the peculiarities of particular ones.

We shall in general neglect the effect of external pressure as a variable, because of the small effect of atmospheric pressure on the free energies of condensed phases.*

* A discussion of the effect of pressure on equilibrium in alloys is given by J. S. Marsh in 'Principles of Phase Diagrams', McGraw-Hill, 1935.

10.1   The Free Energy of Solid Solutions

Consider a substitutional solid solution at a temperature $T°$ K., made up from component metals A and B in atomic concentrations c and $1-c$, respectively. We shall assume that the distribution of these atoms on the lattice is entirely random, and defer until later the consideration of the complications which appear when, as in practice, the distribution deviates from randomness. If the solution has an internal energy E_0 at $0°$ K. and a specific heat C_p its internal energy at $T°$ K. is $E_0 + \int_0^T C_p dT$.

The entropy is the sum of that associated with the heating, i.e. $\int^T \frac{C_p}{T} dT$, and the entropy of mixing, $-Nk[c \log_e c + (1-c) \log_e (1-c)]$, where N is the total number of atoms. The free energy at the temperature T is thus

$$F = E_0 + K\,(c, T) + NkT[c \log_e c + (1-c) \log_e (1-c)] \quad . \quad . \quad . \quad (59)$$

where the function

$$K\,(c, T) = \int_0^T C_p dT - T \int_0^T \frac{C_p}{T} dT$$

depends on composition and temperature.

The next problem is to find an expression for E_0. Many features of alloys can be co-ordinated by the simple assumption that in a solid solution there are three possibilities, (1) that similar atoms attract each other, (2) that dissimilar atoms attract each other, and (3) that atoms of both types are attracted equally to one another. To express these tendencies in a simple mathematical form it is customary to assume (1) that the energy E_0 is the sum of all the energies of interaction of nearest neighbours in the alloy, and (2) that the energy of interaction of a pair of neighbours depends only on their species and not upon the type and distribution of other atoms in their neighbourhood. The validity of these assumptions will be discussed at the end of this section. Denote the co-ordination number of the crystal structure by z. Then on average in the random solution there will be zc atoms of type A next to any given atom and $z(1-c)$ of type B. Since there are N atoms in all, there are Nc of type A and $N(1-c)$ of type B. Thus the numbers, N_{AA}, N_{BB}, and N_{AB}, of pairs of neighbours of types AA, BB, and AB, respectively, are given by

$$N_{AA} = 1/2 \,.\, Nc \,.\, zc = Nzc^2/2$$
$$N_{BB} = 1/2 \,.\, N(1-c) \,.\, z(1-c) = Nz(1-c)^2/2$$
$$N_{AB} = Nc \,.\, z(1-c) = Nzc(1-c).$$

In the formula for N_{AA} the factor $1/2$ allows for the fact that we have counted, for each individual A atom, the number of its nearest neighbours which are also A atoms; thus each AA bond has been counted twice and we have therefore to divide Nzc^2 by 2 to obtain the number of AA pairs. Similarly for the BB pairs.

Denote the bond energies of AA, BB, and AB bonds, respectively, as V_{AA}, V_{BB}, and V_{AB}. Then we can write

$$E_0 = N_{AA}V_{AA} + N_{BB}V_{BB} + N_{AB}V_{AB}$$
$$= \tfrac{1}{2}Nz[c^2V_{AA} + (1-c)^2V_{BB} + 2c(1-c)V_{AB}]$$
$$= \tfrac{1}{2}Nz[cV_{AA} + (1-c)V_{BB} + c(1-c)(2V_{AB} - V_{AA} - V_{BB})] \quad . \quad (60)$$

The first two terms in this expression give the energies $\tfrac{1}{2}NzcV_{AA}$ and $\tfrac{1}{2}Nz(1-c)V_{BB}$ of crystals of the pure components before they are made up into the solid solution. The sign of the third term $\tfrac{1}{2}Nzc(1-c)$ $(2V_{AB} - V_{AA} - V_{BB})$ thus decides whether the energy of the solution is higher or lower than that of the unmixed crystals. If $2V_{AB}$ is higher than $V_{AA} + V_{BB}$, replacing AA and BB bonds by AB bonds raises the internal energy, so that at low temperatures (i.e. where $F \simeq E_0$) the solution has a higher free energy than a *phase mixture* (see section 10.2) characterised by segregation of dissimilar atoms and congregation of similar ones. The case where dissimilar atoms attract is represented when $2V_{AB}$ is lower than $V_{AA} + V_{BB}$, and indicates a tendency to form an ordered solution (see section 9.1) or a compound. The ideal solution is that where $2V_{AB} = V_{AA} + V_{BB}$, for then the internal energy is independent of the distribution of atoms.

The free energy of the solid solution is given by substituting formula 60 for E_0 into formula 59. At this stage all we need to consider is the

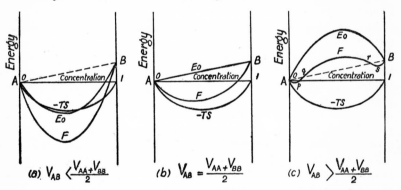

(a) $V_{AB} < \dfrac{V_{AA} + V_{BB}}{2}$ (b) $V_{AB} = \dfrac{V_{AA} + V_{BB}}{2}$ (c) $V_{AB} > \dfrac{V_{AA} + V_{BB}}{2}$

FIG. 61.—The Free Energy of a Solid Solution as a Function of Composition.

qualitative shape of the curve of free energy as a function of composition. By selecting various values for V_{AA}, V_{BB} and V_{AB}, we can examine some of the different types obtained. Examples are shown in Fig. 61 for cases where $V_{AA} < V_{BB}$. In these we have not entirely ignored the variation of $K(c, T)$—the specific heat term—with composition. To a first approximation this function varies linearly with c and the effect of this can be taken up by appropriately adjusting the slopes from A to B in Fig. 61; this does not affect those features of the curves that are important in the following discussion.

KSM

Before we can decide on the stable state, i.e. on the *constitution*, of any alloy in the three systems of Fig. 61, it is first necessary to examine the conditions for a homogeneous phase to be stable; this will be done in section 10.3. We shall find that the curvature of F as a function of c is very important. In both cases (*a*) and (*b*) this curvature, d^2F/dc^2, is positive over the whole range of c so that both curves have a simple U shape with a single minimum. Curve (*c*), however, which represents the case where similar atoms tend to cluster together, has two minima, p and s, and a region of negative curvature (i.e. d^2F/dc^2 is negative) lying between two points of inflexion ($d^2F/dc^2=0$), q and r.

We shall now examine the validity of the approximations made in the above analysis.

The assumption of randomness was made for mathematical simplicity. However, it can only be rigorously true if (*a*) the internal energy is independent of the distribution of atoms (ideal solutions), so that all distributions are equally likely to occur (see section 7.3), or if (*b*) the solution is extremely dilute, in which case the solute atoms are too far apart to interact and are thus unable to influence each other's positions. In many cases that will interest us the solutions are neither ideal nor dilute, so that non-random distributions occur. In these the deviation from randomness is always in that direction which leads to a lower internal energy. We shall discuss some effects of these deviations in Chapters XIII and XIV. The error made in our free energy expression from the assumption of randomness, when applied to homogeneous and disordered, but non-random, solutions, is not large; for although we overestimated the internal energy by assuming randomness, we also over-estimated the entropy of mixing, and these two errors make contributions of opposite signs to the free energy. Moreover, *strong* deviations from randomness usually cause the solution to become ordered, or to break down into a phase mixture, and in either case the solution can no longer be classified as homogeneous and disordered, the only type to which equation 59 is meant to apply.*

The assumption of nearest neighbour bond energies is clearly appropriate in cases where the electrochemical factor predominates, and inappropriate in those where Brillouin zone effects, which depend on the long-range crystal pattern, make important contributions to the internal energy. It may also be inappropriate in cases where the atomic size factor is important, for it seems that the strain energy due to the difference in size of the dissolved atoms can be partly relieved if the latter either separate into two distinct phases (which implies $2V_{AB}>V_{AA}+V_{BB}$) or assemble into an ordered distribution (which implies $2V_{AB}<V_{AA}+V_{BB}$). In copper-silver alloys separation into a phase mixture occurs, whereas in copper-gold alloys ordering occurs. It has even been shown, in

---

* Further considerations of the effect of non-randomness may be found in 'Introduction to Chemical Physics', J. C. Slater, pp. 301-304, and in a paper by A. W. Lawson, *J. Chem. Phys.*, 1947, **15**, 831.

gold-nickel alloys, that separation into two phases occurs at low temperatures, whereas above the homogeneity temperature there is a preference for dissimilar atoms to become nearest neighbours.* In view of such effects it is doubtful, even in systems where formula 60 appears to be valid, if V_{AA}, V_{BB}, and V_{AB} can be given their literal meanings. On the other hand, practically any formula for E_0 would begin with terms of the type $V_1c + V_2(1-c) + V_3c(1-c)$, where V_1, V_2, and V_3 are constants, and the concept of nearest neighbour bond energies is useful in that it provides these terms with the aid of a very simple physical picture.†

As regards the influence of the specific heat term, $K(c, T)$, on the shape of the curve of free energy as a function of composition, experience has proved that in many alloy phases it is a fair approximation to take for the specific heat of the alloy the weighted average of those of its components (the *Neumann-Kopp* rule). However, as we shall see in section 10.7, the strain energy round a solute atom can affect the specific heat by altering the vibration frequency of neighbouring atoms, and thereby cause a deviation from the rule.

10.2 Phase Mixtures

In its equilibrium state an alloy (or any other multi-component system) often exists in *heterogeneous equilibrium*, i.e. the material of the system is not homogeneous throughout; some parts of it have different compositions, structures, and properties from others. These different parts are joined along their boundary surfaces and, in principle at least (and often in practice) can be parted from one another by splitting along these boundaries. When a system is dissected in this way into a number of separate pieces, each of which is homogeneous, the pieces can be collected into groups such that all the material in each group is constant in composition, structure and properties, and is different from that in all other groups. The material in each such group is said to belong to a distinct *phase* of the system, and the system as a whole is described as a *phase mixture*. A simple example is that of pieces of ice floating in water; there are two phases in this case, ice and liquid water.

The reason for the existence of phase mixtures will be discussed in the next section; as a preliminary to this discussion we shall now explain the *lever rule*, which determines the proportions of the phases in a system. Suppose that we have a binary alloy of components A and B in concentrations c and $1-c$, respectively. Suppose that the alloy contains two phases, 1 and 2, in which the concentrations of A are c_1 and c_2, respectively; see Fig. 62. Let the proportion (i.e. fraction of atoms) of phase 1 in the alloy be x. That of phase 2 is then $1-x$. To find x in terms of c, c_1, and c_2, we observe that in N atoms of alloy the number of

* P. A. Flinn, B. L. Averbach, and M. Cohen, *Acta Met.*, 1953, **1**, 664.

† More general formulae for the internal energy have been given by G. Borelius, *Ann. Physik*, 1934, **20**, 57; 1935, **24**, 489; 1937, **28**, 507; 1938, **33**, 517; and H. K. Hardy, *Acta Met.*, 1953, **1**, 202.

A atoms is Nc. Similarly the numbers of A atoms in phases 1 and 2 are Nxc_1 and $N(1-x)c_2$, respectively. Hence

$$c = xc_1 + (1-x)c_2,$$

from which it follows that

$$\left. \begin{array}{l} x = (c-c_2)/(c_1-c_2) = m/l \\ (1-x) = (c_1-c)/(c_1-c_2) = n/l \\ x/(1-x) = (c-c_2)/(c_1-c) = m/n \end{array} \right\} \quad \ldots \ldots \ldots \quad (61)$$

where l, m, and n are the lengths defined in Fig. 62. These relations constitute the *lever rule*, and are necessary for determining the constitution of phase mixtures.

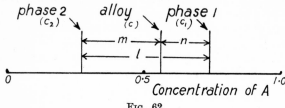

FIG. 62.

To find the average values of *capacity* properties (see section 7.3) in a phase mixture it is sufficient to take a weighted average of the values possessed by the phases. This procedure is valid provided the numbers of atoms in the boundaries between adjoining particles of different

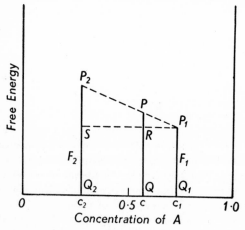

FIG. 63.

phases is negligible compared with those in the particles themselves. As an illustration we shall find the free energy, F, per unit amount of the phase mixture from those, F_1 and F_2, respectively, of the phases 1 and 2. In Fig. 63 let $P_1Q_1 = F_1$ and $P_2Q_2 = F_2$. Then the free energy F of the alloy of concentration c is given by

$$F = F_1 + (F_2-F_1)(QQ_1/Q_1Q_2).$$

From the construction in Fig. 63 we have $(F_2-F_1)=P_2S$ and $QQ_1/Q_1Q_2 =PR/P_2S$, so that $F=QP$. Hence the free energy of the phase mixture is given in the diagram by the point where the straight line joining the free energies of the coexisting phases intersects the line representing the composition of the alloy.

10.3 The Stable State of an Alloy

We are now in a position to deduce the stable state of an alloy from the arrangement of its free energy curves. As a beginning, let us deal with systems having the free energy curves shown in Fig. 64. Taking Fig. 64 (a) first, the alloy of composition c might exist as a homogeneous solution or as a phase mixture, and we have to decide which of these has the lower free energy. When it exists as a phase mixture of the two pure components, A and B, its free energy is given from the rule in section 10.2 by the point F, where the straight line joining F_A and

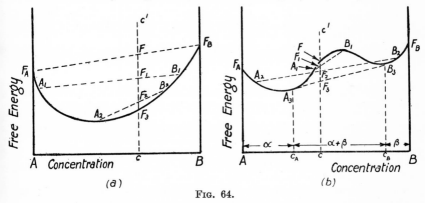

Fig. 64.

F_B intersects the composition line cc'. If some solution occurs, so that the phase mixture becomes that of two solid solutions, the free energy is lowered; for example, if the coexisting phases are those represented by the points A_1 and B_1, the free energy of the alloy is F_1, which is lower than F. Clearly, the more homogeneous the alloy becomes, i.e. the nearer A_1 and B_1 move towards the common point F_3 on the free energy curve, the lower does F_1 become. In the limit where A_1 and B_1 merge into F_3 the alloy becomes a homogeneous solution and its free energy attains its lowest value, F_3. This remains true even in the face of mixtures where one of the phases (e.g. A_2) has lower free energy than F_3; for in such cases the free energy of the other phase (e.g. B_2) is always so much higher that the free energy of the mixture (e.g. F_2) is greater than that of the homogeneous solution. The reason why the homogeneous solution is always the stable state for alloys in this system is because the free energy curve has a simple U shape, i.e. d^2F/dc^2 is positive everywhere, so that any straight line joining two points on the curve lies above that part of the curve between the points.

Consider now the diagram of Fig. 64 (*b*) which is typical of the case (see Fig. 61 (*c*)), where part of the free energy curve has negative curvature. If the alloy of composition *c* were to exist as homogeneous solution its free energy would be *F*. By separating into a phase mixture, however, it can lower its free energy; for example, the free energy F_1 of the mixture $A_1 + B_1$ is lower than *F*. As A_1 and B_1 separate more widely the free energy becomes progressively lower until a point is reached where further intensification of the composition difference between the phases causes the free energy to rise again. Thus the mixture $A_2 + B_2$ has a free energy, F_2, that is higher than that, F_3, of the mixture $A_3 + B_3$.

We see that the stable state for the alloy is the phase mixture for which the line connecting the two representative points on the free energy curve lies lowest: *this line is the common tangent touching the free energy curve at A_3 and B_3.* Between the compositions c_A and c_B, which

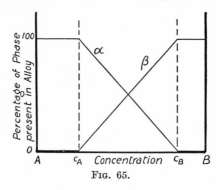

FIG. 65.

correspond to A_3 and B_3, the alloy thus consists of a mixture of two phases with compositions c_A and c_B. The proportions of these two solid solutions can be found from the lever rule. Denote the *A*-rich phase by *α* and the other by *β*. Then we have:—

Proportion of $\alpha = (c_B - c)/(c_B - c_A)$; *proportion of* $\beta = (c - c_A)/(c_B - c_A)$.

Since $c_B - c_A$ is constant, and $c_B - c$ and $c - c_A$ each varies linearly with *c*, the amounts of the two phases vary linearly with composition in the range $c_A < c < c_B$, as in Fig. 65. In the composition ranges from *A* to c_A and from c_B to *B* the homogeneous solution is the stable state of the alloy; any attempt to form a phase mixture, whatever the compositions of the coexisting phases, increases the free energy. Thus, as shown in Fig. 65, these are single phase regions.

To summarise, as we increase the concentration of *B* in *A*, starting with pure *A*, the following phases appear:—

(1) Up to the composition c_A the *B* atoms enter into homogeneous solution in *A*. When c_A is reached no more *B* can be dissolved in *A*, if stability is to be preserved; this is expressed by saying that, at c_A, the solvent *A* has become saturated with the solute *B*, that the limit of

solubility of B in A has been reached, or that the boundary of the α phase has been reached.

(2) Beyond c_A the surplus atoms of B take with themselves some A atoms and form particles of a second phase, β, a solution of A in B of composition c_B. Proceeding through the $\alpha + \beta$ region the proportion of β increases at the expense of that of the α until c_B, the boundary of the β phase, is reached. From here up to the pure component B the alloy consists of a homogeneous solution of A in B.

The common tangent construction is basic in the analysis of free energy curves. In Fig. 66 we show the free energy curves of a system in which intermediate phases, β and γ, appear in addition to the primary phases, α and δ. As before, we construct tangents, PQ, RS, and TU, to touch adjacent curves near their minima. The positions of these tangents are those defined by a piece of string, fixed at A' and stretched

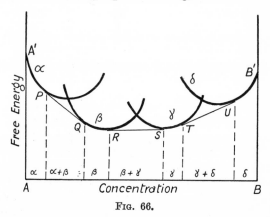

FIG. 66.

tightly round the curves to the point B'. In the region $A'P$ homogeneous α is the stable phase, whereas between P and Q a phase mixture $\alpha + \beta$ is formed, the compositions of these phases being given by the points P and Q, respectively. Then follows a region from Q to R where homogeneous β is stable. This is succeeded by a two-phase region, $\beta + \gamma$, and so on.

We conclude with the following rules:—

(1) For compositions where the lowest free energy is that given by a point on the free energy curve of a single phase, a homogeneous system is stable, consisting of this phase.

(2) For compositions where the lowest free energy is given by a point on a common tangent to the free energy curves of single phases, the system is stable in the form of a mixture of these phases.

(3) In a homogeneous system the overall composition is the same as that of the phase; in a phase mixture the compositions of the phases remain constant, but their proportions change, as the overall composition is changed.

10.4   The Equations of Phase Equilibrium; the Phase Rule

Since the common tangent construction is so important to the interpretation of free energy curves, it is useful to know the mathematical relations which it represents. Referring to the tangent A_3B_3 of Fig. 64 (b), we find that the mutual equilibrium of the two phases is expressed in two mathematical equations, both derived from the fact that A_3B_3 is a common tangent.

First, the slope of the free energy curve must be the same at c_A and c_B. Thus, denoting the free energies at these two compositions by F_A and F_B, respectively, the first condition is that

$$dF_A/dc_A = dF_B/dc_B \quad \ldots \ldots \ldots \ldots \ldots \quad (62)$$

Second, the tangent at A_3 must lie along the same line as that at B_3. This implies that
$$dF_A/dc_A = (F_B - F_A)/(c_B - c_A) \quad \ldots \ldots \ldots \quad (63)$$

In systems containing more than two components the number of equilibrium relations is correspondingly larger. It is important to know how many independent equations of this type there are. Suppose we have, in a system containing n components, an equilibrium between r coexisting phases. In each phase there are $n-1$ independent concentration variables, since the concentration of any one component can no longer be chosen freely once those of all the other $n-1$ components have been chosen. The free energy curve of a phase thus becomes a surface in which the free energy is a function of $n-1$ independent concentration variables. The slope of this surface at any point is thus defined by $n-1$ terms of the type $\partial F/\partial c_i$, where c_i is the concentration of the component i; applied to our binary system this reduces to one term, dF/dc, as used in equation 62. In equilibrium the slope on any one free energy surface has to equal that on each of the other $r-1$ surfaces (at the points of equilibrium); this condition of equality of slopes is thus expressed by means of $(n-1)(r-1)$ independent equations, each of the type of equation 62. The second condition, expressed in equation 63 for the binary system, involves $r-1$ equations in the general case, since the heights (i.e. the positions along the free energy axis) of $r-1$ free energy surfaces have to be fixed, relative to that of the remaining one, in order that they shall all touch the same tangent. Thus, altogether, $n(r-1)$ independent equations are needed to express the equilibrium of r coexisting phases in a system of n components.

This conclusion allows us to deduce the famous *phase rule* of Willard Gibbs. The rule is concerned with the number of variables (e.g. temperature, pressure, composition) whose values have to be specified in order to define the thermodynamic state of a system uniquely. This number can of course be large if we admit the influence on the system of electrical, magnetic, gravitational, and elastic, fields, and also include surface effects. But in most problems of phase equilibrium we are not normally concerned with these additional variables and in a general treatment they can be disregarded. We admit then temperature, pressure, and composition as the variables. How many concentration variables are there? We have seen that in each phase the concentration of $n-1$ components can be chosen freely. Hence, with r phases, there are $r(n-1)$ independent concentration variables. Including temperature and pressure, this gives $r(n-1)+2$ variables in all.

These are not all independent of each other because of the $n(r-1)$ thermodynamic relations between the phases. The number of independent variables, or *degrees of freedom*, v, as they are called, is given by

$$v = r(n-1)+2-n(r-1) = n-r+2 \quad \ldots \ldots \quad (64)$$

This is the phase rule. For condensed systems in which pressure is disregarded as a variable it reduces to

$$v = n-r+1 \quad \ldots \ldots \ldots \ldots \ldots \quad (65)$$

A few examples will show the use of equation 65. For a pure metal $n=1$, so that $v=2-r$. Thus if the metal is in a state in which it contains only one phase, either solid or liquid, then $r=1$ and $v=1$. There is one degree of freedom left to the system, its temperature. This means that it is possible for the system to persist in this state even though its temperature is allowed to change, i.e. the solid and liquid phases both exist over a range of temperature. If the metal is in a state where it contains two phases, solid and liquid, then $r=2$ and $v=0$. There are no degrees of freedom so that this state of affairs is only possible at a single temperature, the melting-point.

In binary alloys we have $n=2$ and $v=3-r$. In a single-phase state we have $v=2$, which means that the system can persist in this state even though the temperature and composition are varied *independently*. If two phases coexist we have $v=1$, i.e. the state can persist over a range of temperature, but only if the compositions of the phases change in a prescribed way in order to maintain the mutual equilibrium of the phases. We notice that, by taking homogeneous liquid and solid solutions as the coexisting phases, melting can occur over a range of temperature. If three phases coexist in the binary alloy, then $v=0$. This can only happen at a particular temperature and a particular composition of each of the phases. We shall meet examples of these types of phase equilibria (e.g. coexistence of one liquid and two solid phases at a eutectic point) in Chapter XI.

10.5 Interfaces between Phases

With few exceptions it is observed that the transition which occurs when passing through a particle of one phase into an adjoining particle of another one is extremely sharp and confined to a thin boundary layer. The clearly marked surface of a liquid in equilibrium with its vapour is a simple example of this. It is not difficult to see why the boundary layer should be thin. The condition for the coexistence of phases is that the free energy of the system as a function of some variable should possess more than one minimum. In the equilibrium of alloy phases discussed in section 10.3 the variable is composition (see Fig. 64 (b)). In the equilibrium of the solid and liquid phases of a pure substance, an appropriate variable is the specific volume, as used in Fig. 54. On grounds of continuity we expect the material in the interface between two such phases to form boundary layers intermediate in structure and composition between those of the adjoining phases. But this means that its free energy (per unit amount) must be high, since the free energy climbs to high values in the regions between the minima associated with the phases. To reduce the amount of such intermediate material the system reduces the boundary layers until they are as thin as possible, generally down to atomic dimensions in the case of interfaces between alloy phases.* Further reductions can be achieved by altering the shapes of the particles of the phases so as to minimise the area of high energy surfaces of contact.

The boundary between two phases in an alloy may either be of the *coherent* type, across which one can trace a continuity of lattice structure from the one phase to the other, and which has a small surface energy, or of the *incoherent* type, across which there is no continuity of lattice and which has a large surface energy. We shall discuss the conditions governing the choice of these two types of boundary in Chapter XIV. The incoherent boundary resembles in many respects the large-angle grain boundary discussed in sections 3.8 and 3.9. The magnitude of the surface energy is about the same in both cases, and, as Smith† has shown, the surface tension ideas described in section 3.9 are applicable to both.

Smith has emphasised that the surface energies of incoherent boundaries play an important part in determining the distributions of the phases in phase mixtures. Small amounts of a second phase in an otherwise homogeneous, polycrystalline alloy have a tendency to form at the grain boundaries of the latter, since an economy in the total boundary area can be achieved in this way, part of the large-angle boundary between the grains becoming the incoherent boundary of the second phase. Fig. 67 shows the type of structure which is often formed in such cases, where a piece of second phase, β, is lodged in the junction between three grains of the main phase, α. After prolonged annealing at high temperatures the shapes of such included phases become adjusted to minimise the surface energy of the system. Using the idea of surface tension, Smith deduces the *dihedral angle* or the *contact angle* (e.g. the angle θ in Fig. 67) from the balance of surface tension forces at the junction of the grain boundary (OC in Fig. 67) and the two phase boundaries (OA and OB). If these surface tensions are denoted by $T_{\alpha\alpha}$ and $T_{\alpha\beta}$, respectively, then θ is given by the relation

$$T_{\alpha\alpha} = 2T_{\alpha\beta} \cos (\theta/2) \quad \ldots \ldots \ldots \quad (66)$$

* A two-dimensional example of this effect appears in slip-planes (see section 15.2).
† C. S. Smith, *Trans. Amer. Inst. Min. Met. Eng.*, 1948, **175**, 15.

The equilibrium shapes of the included phase for various dihedral angles are shown in Fig. 68. The dihedral angle can have any value from 0° to 180°, depending on the value of $T_{\alpha\alpha}/2T_{\alpha\beta}$. If $2T_{\alpha\beta} < T_{\alpha\alpha}$ the dihedral angle is zero and the second phase can spread as a continuous film between the grain boundaries of the main phase. If

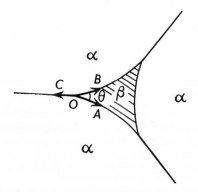

FIG. 67.—A Second Phase (β) at the Junction between three Grains of a Phase (α).

$2T_{\alpha\beta} > T_{\alpha\alpha}$ the dihedral angle is not zero and complete spreading is not possible.

These conclusions are of great practical importance in the case where the second phase has a low melting point. If the contact angle is zero,

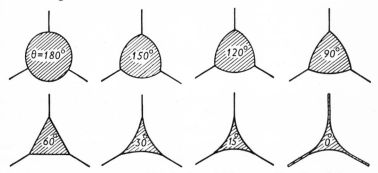

FIG. 68.—Shape of a Particle of a Second Phase as a Function of the Dihedral Angle (after C. S. Smith).

annealing above the melting point of the second phase will cause the alloy to disintegrate along its grain boundaries, since these will be covered with continuous films of the liquid second phase. The *hot-shortness* of many steels and non-ferrous alloys containing certain impurities is due to the presence of such liquid phases that 'wet' the grain boundaries. An interesting example of these effects has been discussed by Smith, concerning the distribution of bismuth and lead in copper.

Neither bismuth nor lead dissolves appreciably in copper at temperatures below 900° C., and they form a second phase which is liquid at such temperatures. Very small additions of bismuth to pure copper render the latter extremely brittle and fragile, because they spread as continuous thin films between the grains of the copper; the dihedral angle of the copper-bismuth interface is zero. The addition of lead to the alloy, however, increases the surface tension of the interface between the solid copper and the liquid lead-and-bismuth phase, so that the second phase no longer spreads completely over the grains of copper. When the amount of lead is about equal to that of bismuth the material is no longer brittle.

10.6   The Free Energy of Intermediate Phases

In Fig. 66 the free energy curves of the intermediate phases β and γ were shown as having simple U forms. This shape is reasonable for discussing general principles since it gives a low energy over a certain

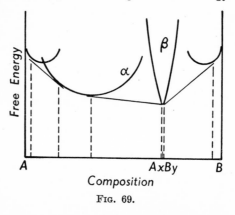

FIG. 69.

range of composition, where the phase is likely to be stable, and a sharply rising energy outside this range, where the phase is unlikely to exist. If the intermediate phase is a solid solution, in which case the interaction term $(2V_{AB}-V_{AA}-V_{BB})$ is likely to be small, the free energy curve should form a broad, shallow U, and the phase should exist over a range of composition; e.g. the phase a in Fig. 69. When a chemical compound is formed, however, with an exact ratio between the numbers of participating atoms, the free energy must rise very sharply as the composition deviates away from the ideal stoichiometric value. Intermetallic compounds should thus have free energy curves of the type β in Fig. 69, with a sharp minimum at the composition representing the compound A_xB_y. Clearly, in this case the phase cannot appear over a wide range of composition.

On the other hand, if a phase appears over a narrow range of composition one cannot conclude, without further investigation, that it is a compound; for, as shown in Fig. 70 (a), a solid solution phase (β) may be confined to a narrow range of composition (c_1, c_2) because the common tangents (pq and rs) to the neighbouring phases are almost parallel. Usually in such cases a small change in temperature alters the relative slopes of the tangents sufficiently to produce a large change in c_1 and c_2, provided the free energy curve of the β phase is broad and shallow.

It is sometimes found that an intermediate phase, based on a simple structural formula, A_xB_y, is formed in a composition range which does not in fact include the ideal stoichiometric composition. An example of this is found in the copper-aluminium system, where the phase $CuAl_2$ exists only on the aluminium-rich side of the exact $CuAl_2$ composition.

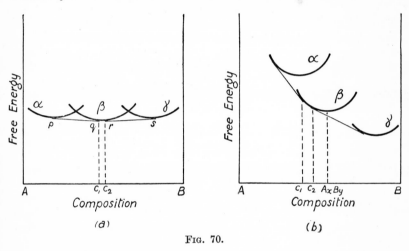

FIG. 70.

Such cases may be explained by the free energy diagrams of the type shown in Fig. 70 (b). Here the positions of the phases a and γ are such that the composition range (c_1, c_2) over which the β phase is stable does not include the minimum point of its free energy curve. Rushbrooke* has applied this explanation to the case of the $CuAl_2$ phase.

The Hume-Rothery rule of the electrochemical factor (see section 9.3) can also be explained from free energy curves. For example, in Fig. 69, the greater the chemical affinity between the A and B atoms in the compound A_xB_y, the lower is the minimum in the free energy curve of this phase. The result of this is to increase the steepness of the common tangent joining this phase to the B-rich primary solution, so that the boundary of this phase appears at a lower concentration of A in B. In other words, the greater the tendency to form an intermetallic compound, the smaller is the extent of primary solubility.

* *Proc. Phys. Soc.*, 1941, **52**, 701.

10.7   The Variation of Solubility with Temperature

In many alloy systems the limit of the range of primary solution increases with rising temperature. The general reason for this is as follows. If an alloy exists as a phase mixture at low temperatures it does so because the internal energy of the mixture happens to be lower than that of a homogeneous phase at that particular composition. As the temperature is raised the entropy plays an increasingly important part in determining the free energy, since the term TS in the relation $F = E - TS$ increases with T. A disordered solution has a greater entropy, other things being equal, than a phase mixture, due to its entropy of mixing. Thus homogeneous and disordered solutions become preferred to phase mixtures at high temperatures.

In certain cases the limit of primary solubility decreases with rising temperature. Referring to Fig. 66 we see that the limit of the α phase must behave like this if it has a lower entropy than the adjoining β phase. For then, since $dF/dT = -S$ (see section 8.2), the free energy curve of the β phase will move downwards to lower free energy values, relative to the free energy curve of the α phase, as the temperature is raised. Thus the common tangent PQ will become steeper and the point P, which marks the boundary of the α phase, will move towards A'. This state of affairs is most likely to exist when the β phase is a disordered solution, since then it will have a greater entropy of mixing than the α phase at the composition at which it coexists with the α phase. A very common example, as we shall see in the next chapter, is that where the α and β phases are the disordered solutions of B in solid and liquid A, respectively. But the effect can also appear when the β phase is a disordered secondary solution. In brass, for example, the primary solution of zinc in copper decreases on heating at temperatures above $450°$ C.; above this temperature the next phase which appears in the system, i.e. β-brass, is a disordered solution (see Fig. 86).

We shall now examine quantitatively the variation of solubility with temperature for the case of the simple system of Fig. 61 (c). For mathematical simplicity we shall deal only with the symmetrical case where $V_{AA} = V_{BB} = V_0$, say. Also we shall write $2V_{AB} - V_{AA} - V_{BB} = 2(V_{AB} - V_0) = 2V$. Then equation 60 becomes

$$E_0 = \tfrac{1}{2}NzV_0 + Nzc(1-c)V.$$

Substituting this into equation 59 gives, for the free energy,

$$F = \tfrac{1}{2}NzV_0 + K\,(c, T) + Nzc(1-c)V$$
$$+ NkT[c \log_e c + (1-c) \log_e (1-c)] \quad . \quad . \quad (67)$$

For simplicity we shall assume that the specific heat term, K, does not vary appreciably with c. Then, since only the shape of the free energy curve is needed to find the solubility limit, not its absolute position along the free energy axis, we need no longer retain K in the formula; similarly, the term $\tfrac{1}{2}NzV_0$ can also be omitted. It is convenient to work with the free energy per atom, $f(=F/N)$, rather than the total free energy, F. We thus have

$$f = zVc(1-c) + kT[c \log_e c + (1-c) \log_e (1-c)].$$

Of the terms in this expression c and z are pure numbers, V is energy and k is energy divided by temperature. It follows that zV/k has the dimensions of temperature, and it is convenient to measure the temperature of the system by means of the dimensionless parameter,

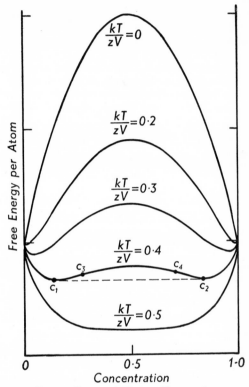

FIG. 71.—Free Energy Curves at Various Temperatures, according to Equation 67.

kT/zV. Accordingly, we show in Fig. 71 the variation of f with c at various temperatures defined by $kT/zV = 0$, 0·2, 0·3, 0·4, and 0·5. At low temperatures the free energy rises in the middle of the diagram because the number of high-energy AB bonds is a maximum there. But as the temperature rises this effect is counterbalanced by the entropy of mixing term and the free energy does not climb so high. Each curve shows two minima (e.g. c_1 and c_2 at $kT/zV = 0.4$) which gradually converge as the temperature is raised. When the temperature reaches the critical value $kT/zV = 0.5$, the free energy no longer rises in the middle of the diagram and there is no longer any region of negative curvature (i.e. $d^2F/dc^2 \geqslant 0$

for all c at this temperature). Thus, in spite of the reluctance of unlike atoms to bond with one another, alloys for which $2V_{AB} > V_{AA} + V_{BB}$ can exist as homogeneous, disordered solid solutions over the whole range of composition at sufficiently high temperatures; in practice, however, melting often occurs before the temperature range of complete miscibility in the solid state is reached.

The simplifying feature of the symmetrical system shown in Fig. 71 is that the equations of equilibrium (equations 62 and 63) reduce in this *particular* case to the condition $df/dc = 0$; i.e. the solubility limits coincide with the minima in the free energy curve. By finding the positions of these minima at various temperatures we can thus determine the variation of solubility with temperature. This is shown by the full line in Fig. 72.

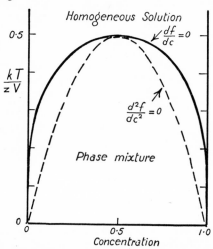

Fig. 72.—The Variation with Temperature of the Compositions at which $df/dc = 0$ and $d^2f/dc^2 = 0$ for the Alloy System Represented by Equation 67. The Full Curve ($df/dc = 0$) marks the Solubility Limit.

An analytical expression for the solubility limit can be found by applying the condition $df/dc = 0$ to equation 67. This gives the concentrations c_1 and c_2 at the minima as a function of temperature. We have

$$df/dc = 0 = zV(1-2c) + kT[\log_e c - \log_e (1-c)] \quad \ldots \quad (68)$$

for the equation of the solubility curve. A few alloy systems, e.g. gold-platinum, show solubility curves which are somewhat distorted versions of that defined by this equation, but in most cases the temperature where $kT/zV = 0.5$ is above the melting point. When the solubility is very small the equation may be simplified to a more useful form. By rearrangement it becomes

$$\frac{c}{1-c} = e^{\frac{-zV(1-2c)}{kT}}$$

Assuming that $(1-c)$ and $(1-2c)$ can be approximated to unity, this gives

$$c = exp(-zV/kT) \quad \ldots \ldots \ldots \ldots \ldots \ldots \quad (69)$$

Thus in systems of very limited solubility we expect the solubility limit to rise with temperature according to an exponential law. Although this result has been derived for a particularly simple system it has a wide range of application, and the solubility limits of many dilute solutions are proportional to a temperature factor of the type $exp(-\Delta H/RT)$ where ΔH is the *heat of solution*, i.e. the heat absorbed by the system when one gram mole of solute atoms enters into solution. Fig. 73 shows the data of Fink and Freche,* plotted by Zener,† for the solid solutions of various metals in aluminium. It will be observed that, at temperatures in the range 400 to 600° C., the logarithm of the solubility varies

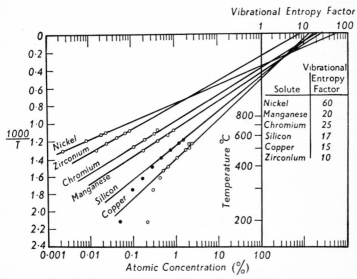

FIG. 73.—The Data of Fink and Freche on the Solubility of Various Metals in Aluminium (after Zener).

linearly with the reciprocal of the temperature, in agreement with equation 69. The deviations at lower temperatures, in the direction of a greater solubility than that predicted by extrapolation of the high-temperature results, are undoubtedly due to the difficulty of establishing equilibrium at temperatures where diffusion is slow.

Zener has pointed out an interesting effect which appears when the results in Fig. 73 are extrapolated to the line $1/T=0$. According to equation 69, they should converge here to the point where $c=100$ per cent. But actually they extend beyond this point. Zener interprets

* W. L. Fink and H. R. Freche, *Trans. Amer. Inst. Min. Met. Eng.*, 1934, **111**, 304.
† C. Zener, Chapter II in 'Thermodynamics in Physical Metallurgy', Amer. Soc. Metals Seminar, 1950.

this as being due to a *vibrational entropy factor* ΔS, and writes the formula for solubility as

$$c = e^{\frac{\Delta S}{R}} e^{\frac{-\Delta H}{RT}} \quad \ldots \ldots \ldots \ldots \quad (70)$$

This vibrational entropy factor originates in the finite strains which exist round solute atoms (see section 9.3) and reduce the vibrational frequencies of the surrounding atoms, so lowering their characteristic temperature. Zener emphasises that one of the main factors responsible for a positive heat of solution is the strain energy caused by the difference in size of the solute and solvent atoms, and points out that a solute atom with a high heat of solution should have a high vibrational entropy factor. This correlation is confirmed in Fig. 73. The slopes of the lines show that nickel has the largest heat of solution and the largest entropy factor. Similarly, copper has the smallest heat of solution and one of the smallest entropy factors.

Darken and Gurry* have noted that primary solubility is severely limited (e.g. 1 atom per cent. or less) if the free energy of solution (i.e. $\Delta H - T\Delta S$) is greater than about $4RT$ at the temperature considered. For example, the average heat of mixing in Fig. 73 is about 10,000 cal./mol. and the average solubility at $1000°$ K. is about 1 per cent. Darken and Gurry apply their result to an interpretation of Hume-Rothery's size factor rule. The strain energy of an isotropic elastic continuum, strained by the insertion into a spherical hole of radius r_0 of a rigid sphere of radius r_1, is $8\pi\mu r_0^3\epsilon^2$, where $\epsilon = (r_1 - r_0)/r_0$ and μ is the shear modulus.† Taking $\mu = 4 \times 10^{11}$ dyne/cm.² and $r_0 = 1\cdot5 \times 10^{-8}$ cm., the degree of misfit ϵ needed to provide a strain energy of 8000 cal./mol. is 14 to 15 per cent., i.e. the same as the critical size factor in the Hume-Rothery rule. As Darken and Gurry point out, although elasticity theory cannot be applied rigorously to the strains near a solute atom, nevertheless the theory does provide a good basis for understanding why the solubility is small when the size factor is greater than 15 per cent.

Returning to Fig. 71 again, we notice that those free energy curves which rise in the middle of the diagram have two points of inflexion (e.g. c_3 and c_4 at $kT/zV = 0\cdot4$) where $d^2f/dc^2 = 0$. The positions of these points may be found by differentiating equation 68, i.e.

$$\frac{d^2f}{dc^2} = 0 = -2zV + kT\left(\frac{1}{c} + \frac{1}{1-c}\right),$$

giving

$$c(1-c) = kT/2zV \quad \ldots \ldots \ldots \ldots \quad (71)$$

This function is plotted as a broken curve in Fig. 72. Such curves for which $d^2f/dc^2 = 0$ are often called *spinodal lines*.

* L. S. Darken and R. W. Gurry, 'Physical Chemistry of Metals', McGraw-Hill, New York, 1953.

† For the derivation of this formula from the theory of elasticity see, for example, J. Frenkel, 'Kinetic Theory of Liquids', Clarendon Press, Oxford, 1946 (p. 10).

CHAPTER XI

THE EQUILIBRIUM DIAGRAM

From the relative positions of the free energy curves at various temperatures it is possible to determine the composition limits of the phases stable at these temperatures and to assemble the results into an *equilibrium diagram* (or *constitutional diagram*, or *phase diagram*) which gives the positions of the phase boundaries over a range of temperature. Our main task in this chapter will be to deduce some of the standard types of equilibrium diagrams from various arrangements of free energy curves. We shall mainly be concerned with equilibrium between solid and liquid phases, but the method is quite general and equally applicable to the study of other types of equilibria, such as those in the solid state. For convenience we shall confine our discussion

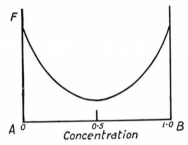

FIG. 74.—A Free Energy Curve for a Completely Miscible Liquid Phase.

to systems in which there is complete miscibility in the liquid state, and to ensure this, we shall use throughout a free energy curve for the liquid phase which has the simple U shape shown in Fig. 74.

The general problem of how one phase changes into another, when the temperature of the system is changed, cannot be solved with the aid of the theory of equilibrium alone, but requires the additional ideas belonging to the theory of nucleation, which will be discussed in Chapter XIV. However, certain effects involving the redistribution of alloying elements during phase changes can be interpreted from the equilibrium diagram, and we shall discuss these at the end of this chapter.

11.1 Complete Miscibility in the Solid State

The simplest systems are those in which the components are so similar that in the solid state they form a homogeneous disordered solution over the whole range of composition. For this to be possible these components must have atoms of similar sizes and electronic structures, and must crystallise in the same crystal structure. The heat of solution term in the expression for the free energy of mixing is then very small, and the free energy curve as a whole is similar to the curve of $-TS$ against composition, where S is the entropy of mixing. Thus the free energy curve of the solid solution in this case is also of the type of Fig. 74. To derive the equilibrium diagram we have then to investigate the relative positions of two such curves, for the solid and liquid respectively, at various temperatures.

Consider then the diagrams of Fig. 75, where we show these curves

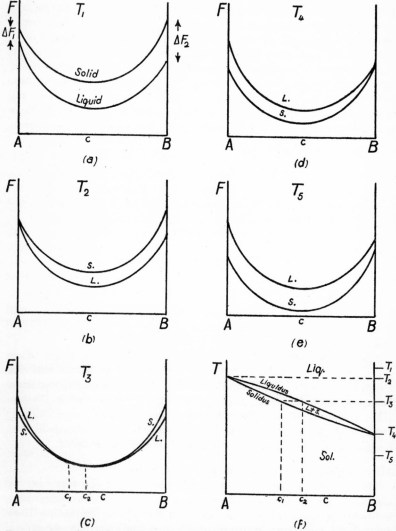

FIG. 75.—(a) to (e) Free Energy Curves for the Solid and Liquid Curves of an Alloy System at Temperatures T_1, T_2, T_3, T_4 and T_5, where $T_1 > \ldots > T_5$; (f) the Corresponding Equilibrium Diagram.

at a series of temperatures. At high temperatures all alloys in the system are liquid and the free energy curve of the liquid phase lies wholly below that of the solid (e.g. temperature T_1, diagram a). Similarly, at low temperatures (e.g. T_5) the curve of the solid lies wholly below that of the liquid. On cooling through the temperature range of solidification, then, the free energy curve of the liquid moves upward, across that of the solid. In the example taken in Fig. 75 it is supposed that the freezing point (T_2) of the pure component A is higher than that (T_4) of component B, and this is indicated by a slight tilting of the curves, relative to one another, so that ΔF_1, in diagram (a), is smaller than ΔF_2. On cooling from T_1 the free energy curves first meet when the temperature reaches T_2, and they meet at the composition representing pure A. This is the freezing point of this pure component (diagram b). Due to the tilt of the curves, however, all other compositions are still liquid at this temperature. As the temperature falls further, to T_3, the curves intersect and give a range of composition, from A to c_1, in which the homogeneous solid is stable, and a second range, from c_2 to B, in which the homogeneous liquid is stable. The common tangent construction shows, however, that alloys with compositions between c_1 and c_2 are stable in the form of phase mixtures of solid (c_1) and liquid (c_2). As the temperature falls progressively the point of intersection of the two free energy curves moves from the A-rich end to the B-rich end of the diagram, and the composition range of the phase mixture, c_1 to c_2, also moves in this direction. Eventually T_4 is reached, at which all compositions except pure B are solid, and below this temperature every alloy in the system is stable in the form of a homogeneous solid solution.

Assembling these results into an equilibrium diagram, we obtain that shown in diagram f, which is typical of this type of system. The diagram is divided into three separate areas, the fields in which liquid, liquid and solid, and solid, are stable, by the phase boundary lines known as the *liquidus* and *solidus*, respectively. It should be noted that the alloys in such a system must freeze over a range of temperature, and that in the two-phase region the compositions of the coexisting phases must be different. Examples of alloy systems with such diagrams are silver-gold (see Fig. 76), copper-nickel and gold-platinum.

11.2   Partial Miscibility in the Solid State

We shall now consider systems in which the components are only partially soluble in each other, in the solid state, at the temperature of solidification, and in which no intermediate phases are formed. In systems in which the component metals freeze in the same crystal structure but are sparingly soluble in each other, the free energy curve for this structure has the form shown in Fig. 77 (a) (see section 10.1). In systems in which the component metals freeze in different crystal structures, two solid solutions, α and β, occur, each of which has the crystal structure of its primary component. The two-phase field between them, $\alpha + \beta$, covers the composition range where the lowest free energy is given by the common tangent to the free energy curves of the two solutions, as shown in Fig. 77 (b). The general form of the equilibrium diagram is the same for both types of system. We shall derive it by using the free energy curve of the first type, although it will become apparent that the same argument also applies to the second type.

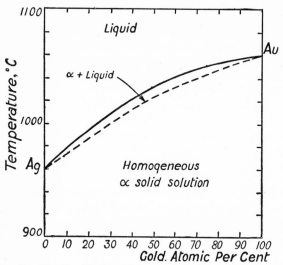

FIG. 76.—The Equilibrium Diagram of the Silver-Gold System.

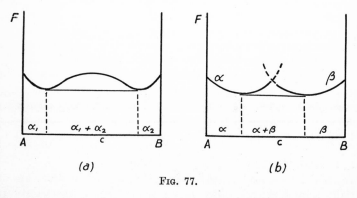

FIG. 77.

Fig. 78 shows the free energy curves of the solid and liquid at temperatures $T_1, \ldots, T_5$, where $T_1 > \ldots > T_5$. Cooling from T_1 raises the curve of the liquid, and an intersection with that of the solid first occurs at the A-rich end. Thus at T_2, just below the melting point of pure A, alloys rich in A consist of α_1 solid solution (see diagram b), whereas with increasing concentrations of B a two-phase ($\alpha + liquid$) region occurs and is followed by a region where all alloys are still wholly liquid. At lower temperatures the liquid free energy curve also crosses that of the solid at the B-rich end of the diagram, and a range of composition then exists at this end in which the B-rich solid solution, a_2, is stable (diagram c). At such temperatures two common tangents exist, giving two

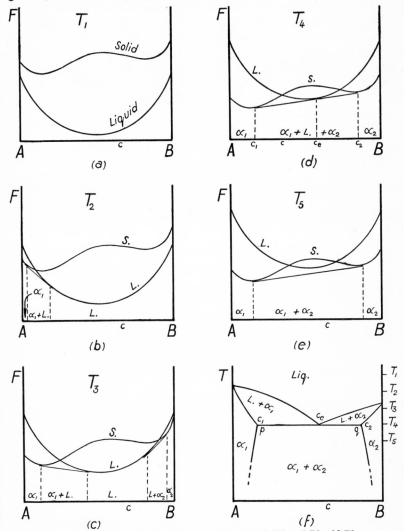

FIG. 78.—(a) to (e) Free Energy Curves for the Solid and Liquid Phases of a System with a Eutectic Type of Diagram, shown in (f).

separate two-phase regions, $a_1+liquid$ and $a_2+liquid$, respectively. Further cooling brings these two tangents together and narrows the composition range between them in which homogeneous liquid is still stable. Eventually a temperature T_4 is reached where the two tangents coalesce into one tangent which touches simultaneously three points on the free energy curves (diagram *d*). This is called the *eutectic temperature*, and is the lowest temperature at which an alloy in the system can be wholly or partially liquid. The composition c_e at which an alloy can still be wholly liquid at this temperature is called the *eutectic composition*.

The equilibrium diagram derived from these curves is shown in diagram *f*, and is typical of eutectiferous systems. The line *pq* is of special importance. It is an isothermal and marks the limiting temperature below which no alloy can be wholly or partially liquid, if in equilibrium. That it should be an isothermal follows from the arrangement of the

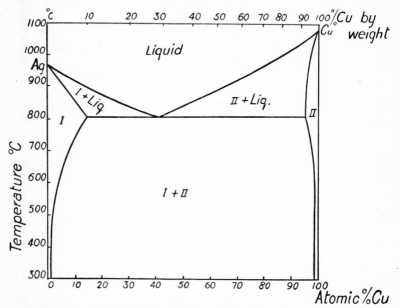

FIG. 79.—The Equilibrium Diagram of the Silver-Copper System.

free energy curves near the eutectic temperature, T_4; just above, all alloys from c_1 to c_2 contain some liquid, whereas at a fraction of a degree lower they are all solid. The solidus temperature from c_1 to c_2 is therefore independent of composition, and so must be an isothermal. Below the eutectic temperature the solubility limits of the two solid phases decrease with decreasing temperature, as described in section 10.7. The equilibrium diagrams of several alloy systems are of the simple eutectic type, e.g. silver-copper (Fig. 79), lead-tin, lead-antimony, aluminium-silicon, and chromium-nickel.

Some systems with free energy curves fairly similar to those of Fig. 78 have equilibrium diagrams of a different form. These occur mainly when the melting points of the components differ widely, and can be understood by reference to Fig. 80. Here, two separate solid solutions are formed. The important point is that the free energy curve of the β phase is so much higher than that of the α phase that, when the temperature falls sufficiently for the β phase to be formed, the latter makes its appearance first in the composition range which, at higher temperatures, consisted of the phase mixture $\alpha + liquid$ (see diagrams b and c). The behaviour in this case is the opposite of that shown in Fig. 78, for here a free energy curve (β) 'breaks through' the common tangent joining

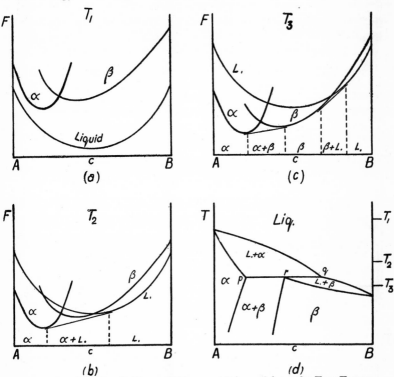

FIG. 80.—A Peritectic Type of Diagram (d) formed from the Free Energy Curves of Diagrams (a), (b) and (c).

two other free energy curves as the temperature is *lowered*. In the eutectic case, on the other hand, the liquid phase free energy curve breaks through the common tangent joining the free energy curves of the solid phases as the temperature is *raised*. It follows that in the range where the break-through occurs the arrangement of phase boundary lines for the system of Fig. 80 is essentially the inverse of that for a eutectic system. Thus if the equilibrium diagram of Fig. 80 is turned upside down it will be seen to resemble closely that of a eutectic system. Such diagrams are said to be of the *peritectic* type. The composition at the point r is the *peritectic composition* and the line pq, which of course is an isothermal, marks the *peritectic temperature* where the β

phase free energy curve touches the common tangent to the other two curves. Immediately below the peritectic temperature there is a wide composition range in which some β phase is present, whereas above this temperature no β is formed in any alloy. Silver-platinum is an example of a system with a peritectic type of diagram.

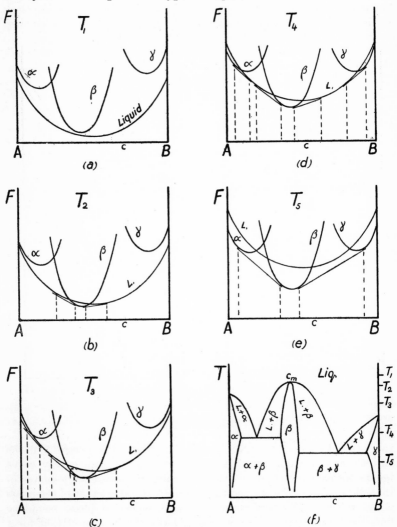

FIG. 81.—A Form of Equilibrium Diagram Obtained when an Intermediate Phase forms directly from the Liquid.

11.3 Systems Containing Intermediate Phases

The equilibrium diagrams of systems which contain intermediate phases are naturally more complex and varied than those we have considered so far, and for the sake of simplicity in this section we shall consider those with only one intermediate phase. This phase can be formed on freezing in two different ways, and these lead to two different types of equilibrium diagram.

In the first the intermediate phase forms directly from the liquid alone. The sequence of events on cooling in this case is as shown in Fig. 81. The free energy curves are arranged here so that, on cooling, the liquid phase curve crosses the curve of the intermediate phase (β) before those of the primary solutions (α and γ). Further cooling (T_3 and T_4) causes the α and γ phases to appear at the ends of the system. The arrangement of common tangents in this case happens to be such that the four tangents of diagram d merge on cooling into the two tangents of diagram e, and two eutectics are formed, between the intermediate phase and each of the primary phases. The equilibrium diagram is therefore as shown in diagram f. The eutectics shown in this

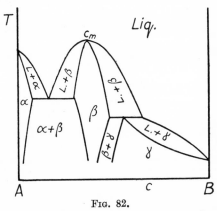

Fig. 82.

diagram are not inevitable in systems of this kind. It is possible to have peritectics instead. For example, if the free energy curve of the γ phase in Fig. 81 is suitably placed relative to the others it can be caused to break through the common tangent joining the liquid and β phases, so giving an equilibrium diagram of the type of Fig. 82.

The general feature of all systems in which an intermediate phase forms directly from the liquid is a maximum in the solidus and liquidus curves where the phase is formed. The composition c_m at the maximum, which is also the point where the solidus and liquidus curves touch each other, is close to the composition at which the minimum occurs in the free energy curve of the intermediate phase. In most cases it does not coincide exactly with this minimum, because the free energy curve of the liquid is usually not horizontal at the point where it first touches the curve of the intermediate phase. For this reason the composition rarely agrees precisely with the ideal stoichiometric formula for the phase.

Many alloy systems form intermediate phases in the manner described above, examples being bismuth-tellurium, magnesium-tin, magnesium-lead and magnesium-cadmium.

The second way in which an intermediate phase may be formed

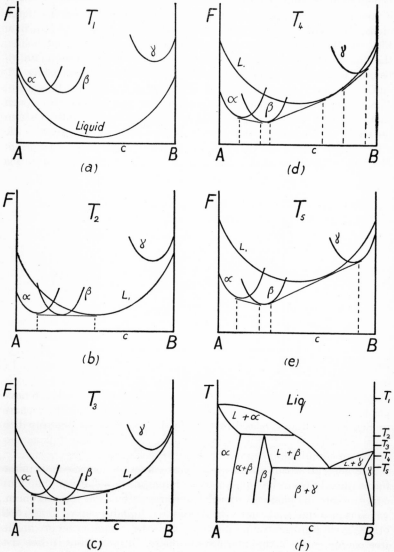

Fig. 83.—A Form of Equilibrium Diagram obtained when an Intermediate Phase is formed through a Peritectic Reaction.

during freezing is by a peritectic reaction between solid and liquid in a partly solidified alloy. This occurs when the free energy curve of the intermediate phase breaks through, during cooling, the common tangent joining the free energy curves of the liquid and some other solid phase. A peritectic type of diagram then ensues, as shown in Fig. 83. As in previous cases, variations in the form of this diagram are possible. For example, if the solid solution γ does not appear until the temperature is low, it may form in a composition range previously covered by a common tangent to the liquid and intermediate phases. In this case the γ also will form by a peritectic reaction, as in Fig. 84.

Intermediate phases form by peritectic reactions in many alloy systems, simple examples being found in lead-bismuth and sodium-potassium.

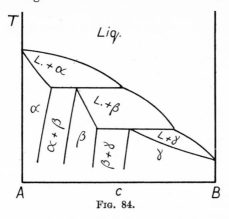

FIG. 84.

11.4 More Complicated Equilibrium Diagrams

Although we have dealt only with simple types the treatment has been taken far enough to show how the main features of binary equilibrium diagrams result from various arrangements of free energy curves. The equilibrium diagrams of many important alloy systems are complicated by the presence of several intermediate phases and by phase transformations in the solid state. These complicated cases can be analysed in the same way as the simple ones, however, and no new features are involved. Phase changes in the solid state lead to precisely the same arrangements of phase boundary lines as those obtained from the solid-liquid change. Thus *eutectoid* and *peritectoid* changes are commonly observed in the solid state which are exact analogues of the eutectic and peritectic forms of the solid-liquid change.

A well-known example of a eutectoid change is that which occurs in iron-carbon alloys, the equilibrium diagram of which is shown in Fig. 85. The change in this case stems from the polymorphic change which occurs in pure iron at 910° C. (see section 8.2). Above this temperature the face centred cubic form is stable, and below it, the body centred cubic form. Solutions of carbon in these two forms are known as γ-iron, or *austenite* (F.C.C.), and a-iron, or *ferrite* (F.C.C.), respectively, and the *iron carbide* compound is called *cementite* (Fe_3C). The form of the diagram in the ranges 700 to 1100° C. and 0 to 2 per cent. carbon is very similar to that of the eutectic diagram of Fig. 78. As the temperature falls the two common tangents, connecting the austenite-ferrite and austenite-cementite free energy curves, merge to give a eutectoid change at 723° C. Zener* has made a quantitative analysis of the equilibria between these phases in carbon and alloy steels.

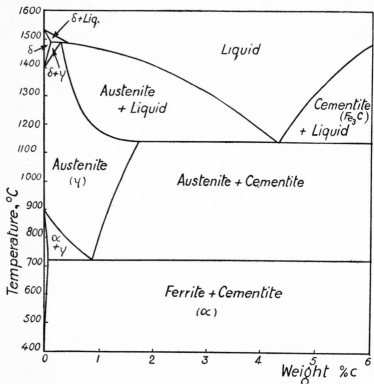

FIG. 85.—The Equilibrium Diagram of the Iron-Carbon System.

A familiar example of a diagram with several intermediate phases is that of the copper-zinc system shown in Fig. 86. A sequence of electron compounds is formed in this case and these phases appear in a cascade of peritectics, falling from the copper-rich end to the zinc-rich end. In addition, the δ-phase, which forms at about 70 per cent. zinc out of a mixture of γ and liquid, becomes unstable on further cooling and a eutectoid decomposition into γ+ε occurs. The change which occurs at about 50 per cent. zinc in the temperature range 450 to 470° C. is not a phase change but an order-disorder change in the β phase.

11.5 The Distribution of Alloying Elements During Phase Changes

We shall now consider how phase changes which occur on the heating or cooling of alloys are to be interpreted in terms of the equilibrium

* C. Zener, *Trans. Amer. Inst. Min. Met. Eng.*, 1946, **167**, 513.

diagram. The different possibilities which arise when the temperature of an alloy is changed are as follows:—

(1) It passes through a single-phase field of the equilibrium diagram, and no changes of phase take place.
(2) It passes through a two-phase field where the compositions of the coexisting phases vary with temperature.
(3) It crosses an isothermal phase boundary line, as in eutectic and peritectic changes.

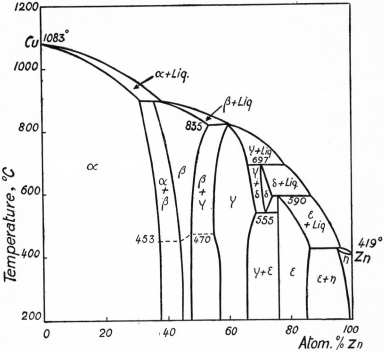

FIG. 86.—The Equilibrium Diagram of the Copper-Zinc System.

We shall discuss the second case by reference to Fig. 87. Consider the alloy of composition c initially at the temperature T_1. It consists entirely of homogeneous α phase. As its temperature changes from T_1 towards T_5 no change occurs in its constitution until the phase boundary line pq is reached at T_2. The alloy then enters the two-phase ($\alpha+\beta$) field. At any temperature in this field the equilibrium compositions of the coexisting phases lie along the two lines pq and rs. Thus at T_3 the compositions of α and β are c_α and c_β respectively. Applying the lever rule at this temperature we deduce that α/β, the relative amount of α to β, is given by

$$\alpha/\beta=(c-c_\beta)/(c_\alpha-c).$$

The combined use of the equilibrium diagram and the lever rule thus enables us to state the *equilibrium constitution* of the alloy, i.e. to identify the phases present, and to state their compositions and the relative amounts of them. This is the main application of the equilibrium diagram in metallurgy.

The behaviour on passing through the two-phase field from T_2 to T_4 may therefore be summarised as follows:—

(1) The relative amounts of the two phases change continuously as the temperature changes, such that the alloy begins at T_2 consisting entirely of α and arrives at T_4 consisting entirely of β.

(2) The composition of each of the two phases in the alloy varies with temperature in such a way that the composition of α moves along part of the line pq and that of β moves along part of the line rs.

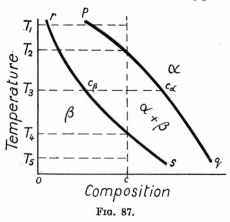

FIG. 87.

This description of the changes assumes that equilibrium is fully maintained at every stage during the change in temperature, and this is only possible if the temperature changes sufficiently slowly. The compositions at which the phases coexist in equilibrium change continuously through the two-phase field so that, if equilibrium is to be maintained, a substantial and continual redistribution of the alloying elements has to take place between the phases. This involves the *migration* or *diffusion* (see Chapter XII) of the atoms of these components through the phases. In practice only a partial redistribution usually occurs and the grains of β which are formed vary in composition about the mean value c. The composition in the centre of each grain is less than c, since this is the first part to form, and the composition near the rim of the grain is correspondingly greater than c. A solid solution in this condition is said to be *cored*, a condition commonly observed in cast alloys which have passed, during freezing, through a liquidus-solidus range of the type of Fig. 87.

An interesting practical application of this non-equilibrium effect has been made by Pfann in the process of *zone-melting*.* In a system with an equilibrium diagram of the type of Fig. 88 the *distribution coefficient* k, defined as the ratio of solute concentration in the solid and liquid (i.e. $k = c_0/c = c/c_1$), is less than unity, so that the liquid will always contain more solute than the solid, when they coexist in equilibrium. Suppose then that we have a long bar of alloy and, with a suitable travelling furnace, pass along it a short molten zone. Then the concentration of solute in the liquid will be higher than in the solid, so that as the zone moves along the bar some solute will be transported from the starting end to the other one. The solid which freezes at the starting end is purer, by a factor of about k, than average, while that which freezes last contains an excess of solute. By repeatedly passing such molten zones along the bar, all in the same direction, the starting

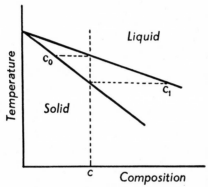

FIG. 88.—Part of an Equilibrium Diagram for a Solute which Lowers the Freezing Point of the Solvent.

end can be made increasingly pure. Zone-melting thus provides a means for purifying the one end of the bar. The technique has been applied to the purification of germanium crystals, which are used in transistors (see section 5.4). By passing six molten zones along a germanium ingot containing an impurity believed to be arsenic, Pfann and Olsen† were able to reduce the impurity content in the first six inches of the bar to one part in 10^{10}. Clearly, with repeated passes in the same direction a limiting distribution must eventually be reached which cannot be changed further. Pfann deduces that for this limiting case the concentration c at a distance x from the starting end is given by

$$c = A \exp(Bx) \quad \ldots \ldots \ldots \ldots \quad (72)$$

where $k = Bl/(e^{Bl} - 1)$ and $A = c_0 Bd/(e^{Bd} - 1)$,

k being the distribution coefficient, c_0 the average composition, and d and l the lengths of the bar and the molten zone, respectively. As an

* W. G. Pfann, *Trans. Amer. Inst. Min. Met. Eng.*, 1952, **194**, 747.
† W. G. Pfann and K. M. Olsen, *Phys. Rev.*, 1953, **89**, 322.

illustration, if $k=0{\cdot}1$, $d=10$, and $l=1$, the ultimate concentration at $x=0$ is about $10^{-14}c_0$. Since the concentration at the starting end decreases by a factor of about k in each pass, at least fourteen passes would be needed to approach the limiting distribution.

A further analysis of the redistribution of solute atoms during solidification has been made by Chalmers and his associates.* An important effect discussed by them is *constitutional supercooling*. During the solidification of a cooling melt in a system of the type of Fig. 88 the liquid next to the solid-liquid interface is continually enriched with solute atoms not accepted by the solidifying material. Unless convection and diffusion in the liquid are extremely effective in smoothing out the distribution of solute in it, a concentration gradient will develop, as in Fig. 89. It follows then, since the liquidus temperature varies with composition in this system (see Fig. 88), that it will also vary with distance

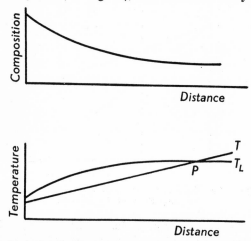

Fig. 89.—The Variation in Composition, Actual Temperature (T) and Liquidus Temperature (T_L) with Distance, into the Liquid, from the Solid-Liquid Interface (after Chalmers).

through the liquid from the interface, and in the manner shown in Fig. 89. If the actual temperature T in the liquid varies in the manner also shown in this diagram there will be a layer of liquid, up to the point P from the interface, in which the actual temperature is below the liquidus temperature, i.e. in which constitutional supercooling has occurred. There is an enhanced tendency to form dendrites (see section 3.8) under such conditions since, if a part of the interface happens to advance further into the liquid than the remainder, it will project into a region of more intense supercooling and freezing will take place more rapidly on it, thus forming a 'spike' of solid projecting into the liquid.

* J. W. Rutter and B. Chalmers, *Canadian J. Phys.*, 1953, **31**, 15; W. A. Tiller, K. A. Jackson, J. W. Rutter and B. Chalmers, *Acta Met.*, 1953, **1**, 428; B. Chalmers, *Trans. Amer. Inst. Min. Met. Eng.*, in press (1954).

Various effects of this instability in the velocity of the interface, some of which are important in the technology of casting alloys, have been discussed by Chalmers.

We turn now to discuss the behaviour of alloys when passing through an isothermal phase boundary line. The diagram of Fig. 90 serves to discuss both the eutectic (eutectoid) and peritectic (peritectoid) changes, since if $T_1 > T_3$ it is of the eutectic type, and if $T_1 < T_3$ it is of the peritectic type. Consider the alloy of composition c the temperature of which

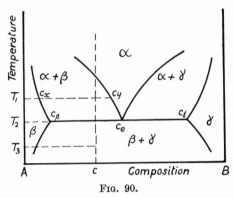

FIG. 90.

is changing from T_1 towards T_3. It begins as a phase mixture of α and β in the proportions

$$\alpha/\beta = (c - c_x)/(c_y - c).$$

As its temperature approaches T_2 the proportion of β phase increases and the concentration of component B in the α phase increases. At T_2 the alloy arrives at the isothermal boundary consisting of α and β of compositions c_e and c_β, respectively, and in the proportions

$$\alpha/\beta = (c - c_\beta)/(c_e - c).$$

As soon as the temperature passes beyond T_2 the α phase becomes unstable and, if equilibrium is preserved, must decompose into $\beta + \gamma$. Immediately beyond this temperature, then, the alloy consists of β and γ in the proportions

$$\beta/\gamma = (c_\gamma - c)/(c - c_\beta).$$

It should be noticed that the β phase separates in two distinct stages in the above process. First, there is a separation of *primary* β which occurs when passing through the $\alpha + \beta$ region, and second, more β is formed from the decomposition of the α phase at T_2. In the case where a eutectic (eutectoid) system is under examination these different forms of β can usually be distinguished by metallographic examination under the microscope. The β-phase formed from a eutectic decomposition usually occurs in the form of a fine dispersion with the γ phase, this type of multi-phase structure being known as a eutectic.* The amount of eutectic in the alloy is clearly the same as the amount of α phase from which it has been formed, i.e.

$$\text{eutectic/alloy} = (c - c_\beta)/(c_e - c_\beta).$$

The amount of β phase in the eutectic is given by

$$\beta/\text{eutectic} = (c_\gamma - c_e)/(c_\gamma - c_\beta),$$

and is thus independent of c.

The behaviour of the alloy on passing from T_3 to T_1 in Fig. 90 is the opposite of that described above. Thus the alloy will arrive at T_2 consisting of β and γ, with compositions c_β and c_γ respectively. On passing through T_2 towards T_1 the γ-phase will react with part of the β-phase, through a diffusion of solute and solvent from one to the other, to form the appropriate amount of α phase of composition c_e.

It must be emphasised that the alloy only behaves in the manner just described when the temperature is made to change so slowly that all the diffusion processes necessary to accomplish the required redistribution of solute and solvent atoms can take place fully. In practice the temperature usually changes too quickly for these processes to maintain constitutional equilibrium and various non-equilibrium distributions, analogous to coring, are formed. Thus on cooling through a peritectic change, i.e. on passing from T_3 to T_1 in Fig. 90, the new phase α which results from the reaction between the β and γ phases is formed as a layer sandwiched between these parts of the alloy, and so insulates them from each other and tends to stifle further reaction.

REFERENCES TO CHAPTERS X AND XI

For discussions of applications of the free energy principle to the equilibrium of alloy phases the following books and papers are recommended:

'Introduction to Chemical Physics.' J. C. Slater, McGraw-Hill, 1939.

'Introduction to Statistical Mechanics.' R. W. Gurney, McGraw-Hill, 1949.

'Physical Chemistry of Metals.' L. S. Darken and R. W. Gurry, McGraw-Hill, 1953.

'Thermodynamics of Alloys.' C. Wagner, Addison-Wesley Press, 1952.

'Thermodynamics of Alloys.' J. Lumsden, Institute of Metals, London, 1952.

'Thermodynamics in Physical Metallurgy.' Amer. Soc. Metals Seminar, 1950.

H. W. B. Roozeboom, *Zeit. Phys. Chem.*, 1894, **15**, 147.

A. J. C. Wilson, *J. Instit. Metals*, 1944, **70**, 543.

J. L. Meijering, *Philips Res. Rep.*, 1948, **3**, 281.

Experimental values of thermodynamic functions for metals and alloys are collected in:

'Metallurgical Thermochemistry.' O. Kubashewski and E. L. Evans, Butterworth-Springer, 1951.

'Metals Reference Book.' C. J. Smithells, Butterworth, 1949.

---

* A description of the structure of eutectics is given in 'Metallography', by C. H. Desch, Longmans, Green & Co.

The experimental techniques involved in the determination of equilibrium diagrams are discussed in:

'Metallography.' C. H. Desch, Longmans Green & Co., 6th Ed. 1944.

'Metallurgical Equilibrium Diagrams.' W. Hume-Rothery, J. W. Christian and W. B. Pearson, The Institute of Physics, London, 1951.

'Structure of Metals.' C. S. Barrett, McGraw-Hill, 1953.

'The Principles of Metallographic Laboratory Practice.' G. L. Kehl, McGraw-Hill, 1949.

'Procedures in Experimental Metallurgy.' A. U. Seybolt and J. E. Burke, Wiley, 1953.

General analyses of the forms of equilibrium diagrams may be found in:

'Principles of Phase Diagrams.' J. S. Marsh, McGraw-Hill, 1935.

'Ternary Systems.' G. Masing, Reinhold Publishing Co., 1944.

CHAPTER XII

DIFFUSION IN METALS AND ALLOYS

The phenomenon of diffusion is of great importance in metallurgy from both the theoretical and practical points of view. Apart from its own intrinsic interest, it demands attention because of the fact that many phase changes in alloys involve a redistribution of the various kinds of atoms present, and the rates of such changes are controlled by the speeds of migration of the participating atoms.

12.1 The Statistical Nature of Diffusion and Fick's Law

If a bar of alloy, which should exist in equilibrium as homogeneous solid solution, but which in fact has a concentration gradient along its length, is heated for some hours at a temperature near its melting point, the atoms migrate along the bar so as to even out the composition. There is a macroscopic flow of solute down the gradient and a counter-flow of solvent in the opposite direction. It is useful to distinguish between the macroscopic flow itself and the individual atomic movements which constitute it; we therefore apply the term *diffusion* to the macroscopic flow, not the individual atomic movements.

Diffusion is caused by innumerable haphazard wanderings of individual atoms. Thermal agitation supplies an atom at occasional intervals with sufficient activation energy to jump from one atomic site to a neighbouring one. These energy fluctuations are caused by collisions with neighbouring atoms and can throw the atom in any direction. The path of the atom is thus an unpredictable, haphazard zigzag. Nevertheless, if large numbers of atoms make such movements they produce a systematic flow down the concentration gradient. Thus consider a plane surface across the bar, normal to the gradient. Because there are more solute atoms on one side of the plane than the other then, even if each migrates quite randomly, more will wander across the plane from the high concentration side than from the other, and a statistical drift down the gradient will result.

To develop this argument quantitatively consider the following idealised case:—

(1) The volumetric concentration C (the number of atoms per c.c.) varies along the bar (i.e. along the x axis) only.*

(2) The concentration gradient, $\partial C/\partial x$, is small enough for the concentration difference between neighbouring atomic planes to be regarded as infinitesimal; this condition is almost always satisfied in practical cases of diffusion.

(3) Each atom migrates by a series of jumps, randomly from site to site.

* It is a little more convenient to use the volumetric concentration, rather than atomic concentration, when setting up the equations of diffusion.

(4) The average frequency, f, of jumps made by a single atom is constant at a constant composition.

(5) The length of a jump, b, is constant.

Consider in Fig. 91 a sequence of atomic planes normal to the concentration gradient, each of unit area, spaced at intervals b along the bar. If C_1 and C_2 ($C_1 < C_2$) are the concentrations of diffusing atoms in planes 1 and 2, respectively, the corresponding numbers of these atoms in the planes are given by $n_1 = C_1 b$ and $n_2 = C_2 b$. In a small increment of time δt (where $f\delta t \ll 1$) the number of atoms which jump off plane 1 is $n_1 f \delta t$. On average one-half of these jumps are in each direction, so

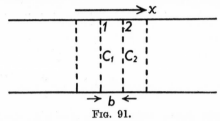

FIG. 91.

that the number of atoms which make the transition $1 \to 2$ is $\frac{1}{2}n_1 f \delta t$. Similarly the number of $2 \to 1$ transitions is $\frac{1}{2}n_2 f \delta t$. Hence the *flux*, J, of atoms, i.e. the number which pass through a plane of unit area in unit time, is given by

$$J = \tfrac{1}{2}(n_1 - n_2)f = \tfrac{1}{2}b(C_1 - C_2)f.$$

Writing $C_1 - C_2 = -(\partial C/\partial x)b$, this becomes

$$J = -D(\partial C/\partial x) \quad \dots \dots \dots \dots \dots \dots \quad (73)$$

where

$$D = \tfrac{1}{2}b^2 f \quad \dots \dots \dots \dots \dots \dots \dots \quad (74)$$

Equation 73 is Fick's *first law* and D is the *diffusion coefficient*, usually measured in units of cm.^{2} per sec. We notice that the rate of flow of atoms is proportional to the concentration gradient and is directed down the gradient, both of which follow directly from the statistical nature of diffusion.

We shall now set up a more general equation in order to be able to deal with *non-stationary* states of flow, i.e. those in which the concentration in a fixed region changes with time. Consider a volume element enclosed by two atomic planes in Fig. 91 which are not neighbours but are spaced a distance l apart. We assume that l is greater than b but nevertheless small enough for the difference in concentration along the element to be regarded as infinitesimal. Then if the concentration in the first plane is C, that in the second is $C + l(\partial C/\partial x)$. The flux across the first plane is given by $J = -D(\partial C/\partial x)$,

and that across the second one by

$$J + l(\partial J/\partial x) = -D(\partial C/\partial x) - l\partial[D(\partial C/\partial x)]/\partial x.$$

The rate of accumulation of diffusing atoms in the element is the difference of these two fluxes, i.e.

$$-l(\partial J/\partial x)=l\partial[D(\partial C/\partial x)]/\partial x.$$

This must be equal to $l(\partial C/\partial t)$ since no atoms are gained or lost during the process. We thus obtain Fick's *second law*:—

$$\frac{\partial C}{\partial t}=\frac{\partial}{\partial x}\left(D\frac{\partial C}{\partial x}\right) \quad\text{.............}\quad (75)$$

or in the special case in which D is constant along the bar,

$$\frac{\partial C}{\partial t}=D\frac{\partial^2 C}{\partial x^2} \quad\text{.................}\quad (76)$$

The generalisation of these formulae to two or three dimensions is quite straightforward. In three dimensions equation 75 becomes

$$\frac{\partial C}{\partial t}=\frac{\partial}{\partial x}\left(D_x\frac{\partial C}{\partial x}\right)+\frac{\partial}{\partial y}\left(D_y\frac{\partial C}{\partial y}\right)+\frac{\partial}{\partial z}\left(D_z\frac{\partial C}{\partial z}\right) \quad\text{...}\quad (77)$$

where D_x, D_y, and D_z are the coefficients of diffusion along the x, y, and z axes, respectively. In cubic crystals the diffusion coefficient is isotropic (see section 3.6), i.e. $D_x=D_y=D_z$, but in crystals of lower symmetry diffusion can be anisotropic. Zinc and tin, for example, are known to be anisotropic and it has been shown in bismuth (rhombohedral structure), near its melting point, that the rate of diffusion perpendicular to the rhombohedral axis is some 10^6 times that parallel to the axis.

In order to apply equations 75, 76 or 77 to any problem, it is necessary to solve them for the experimental conditions in question. Solutions have been derived for certain cases.* An important case is that of diffusion across a plane interface between adjoining columns of solution and solvent, as illustrated in Fig. 92. If the columns are sufficiently long for there to be no appreciable change in composition at their outer ends, during the period of diffusion, the columns can then be regarded as being of infinite length, and the solution of equation 76 for this particular case can be shown to be

$$C=\frac{C_0}{2}\left[1-\frac{2}{\sqrt{\pi}}\int_0^{\frac{x}{2\sqrt{Dt}}}e^{-y^2}dy\right],$$

where C is the concentration after a time t at a distance x from the interface, C_0 is the initial concentration in the solution, and D is the diffusion coefficient. The second term in the brackets is the *probability integral*, or *Gauss error function*, values of which may be found in mathematical tables (y is an integration variable with a purely mathematical significance; the important quantity in the probability integral is the value of

* R. M. Barrer, 'Diffusion in and through Solids', Cambridge University Press
H. S. Carslaw and J. C. Jaeger, 'Conduction of Heat in Solids', Oxford, 1947.

its upper limit, $x/2\sqrt{Dt}$). Examples of the type of concentration curve obtained from this formula are shown in Fig. 92. As a direct inspection of equation 76 will confirm, the concentration steadily rises in those parts of the bar where the curvature, $\partial^2 C/\partial x^2$, is positive, falls in those parts where the curvature is negative, and remains constant in those parts where the curvature is zero.

The quantity $\sqrt{Dt}$ is of great importance in diffusion. It measures the order of magnitude of distance that an average atom will wander from its starting point by random migration, and hence roughly gives the distance over which the concentration can change substantially

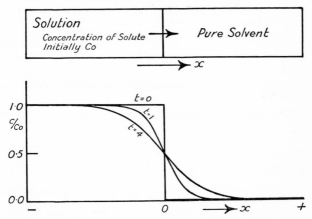

FIG. 92.—Diffusion across a Boundary from a Solution into a Solvent.

during a diffusion anneal. It can thus be used to estimate roughly the time of annealing to produce a given redistribution of solute atoms; e.g. if x is the distance over which the concentration varies in a cored solid solution, the time of annealing needed to remove the coring substantially, by diffusion, is of order x^2/D.

12.2 The Variation of D with Temperature

Experiment shows that the coefficient of diffusion increases with temperature according to the usual activation energy formula,

$$D = D_0 exp(-\Delta H/RT) \quad . \quad . \quad . \quad . \quad . \quad . \quad . \quad . \quad (78)$$

where D_0 is a constant and ΔH is the *heat of activation*. In this section we shall interpret D_0 and ΔH in terms of atomic movements. We have seen that $D = \frac{1}{6}b^2 f$, where f is the frequency of jumping along the x axis. Now f is equal to the product of the number of vibrations of the atom in unit time which have the correct direction of vibration, and of the probability that the atom has the requisite activation energy to surmount the barrier. This is approximately

$$(1/3) v exp(-\Delta H/RT),$$

where ν is the frequency of atomic vibrations, and where the factor 1/3 is introduced because the jumps contribute to atomic migrations along the y and z axes as well as to the x axis. The exponential factor provides for the fact that only for a certain proportion of attempted jumps is the necessary activation energy available. Hence we obtain for the diffusion coefficient

$$D = (1/6)b^2\nu exp(-\Delta H/RT) \quad \ldots \ldots \ldots \quad (79)$$

More precise calculations of the factor $b^2\nu/6$ have been made by Zener* and Le Claire.† If we take $b^2 = 10^{-15}$ cm.^{2} and $\nu = 10^{13}$ sec.$^{-1}$, then $b^2\nu/6 = 1 \cdot 5 \times 10^{-3}$ cm.^{2} sec.$^{-1}$. In practice D_0 is found to vary widely about this value, ranging from about 10^{-9} to 10^4 cm.^{2} sec.$^{-1}$ in alloys. In the most reliable measurements, however (e.g. those on *self-diffusion*; see below), D_0 usually ranges from 10^{-1} to 10 cm.^{2} sec.$^{-1}$. Zener has emphasised that a part of the discrepancy arises from the fact that the entropy of the system must increase while the atom is making the jump, since the surrounding atoms will temporarily suffer a severe elastic strain. Thus we write

$$D_0 = (1/6)b^2\nu exp(\Delta S/R) \quad \ldots \ldots \ldots \ldots \quad (80)$$

where ΔS is the *entropy of activation*. Zener gives a method for estimating ΔS from the temperature dependence of the elastic constants, and obtains the result

$$\Delta S \simeq \beta(\Delta H/T_m) \quad \ldots \ldots \ldots \ldots \quad (81)$$

where T_m is the absolute melting temperature, and β is a parameter that depends on elastic constants and has a value between 0·25 and 0·45 for most metals.

A good illustration of the application of equation 80 is in the diffusion of interstitially dissolved carbon atoms in ferrite (see section 9.5). The elementary process of diffusion here consists simply of the jumping of a carbon atom from one interstitial site into a neighbouring interstitial site. The activation energy for this jump is used mainly in straining apart the neighbouring iron atoms between which the carbon atom passes. This strain energy which is imparted to the surrounding lattice causes a lowering of the elastic constants and hence an increase in the vibrational entropy, as discussed in sections 9.3 and 10.7. Zener deduces for this system that $\beta = 0 \cdot 43$, that $exp(\Delta S/R) = 12$, and that $D_0 = 0 \cdot 026$. These results are in good agreement with the very accurate experimental values, $D_0 = 0 \cdot 020$ cm.^{2} sec.$^{-2}$ and $\Delta H = 20{,}100$ cal. per mol., obtained by Wert.‡

12.3 The Variation of D with Concentration

When actual concentration-depth curves are determined on alloys, they are rarely as symmetrical as that of Fig. 92. Even in a simple

* C. Zener, Chapter 11 in 'Imperfections in Nearly Perfect Crystals' (Ed. W. Shockley), Wiley, 1952.
† A. D. Le Claire, *Phil. Mag.*, 1951, **42**, 673.
‡ C. Wert, *Phys. Rev.*, 1950, **79**, 601.

system such as copper-nickel the curve deviates from the ideal type, as Fig. 93 shows. Diffusion occurs much more readily in the copper-rich end of the specimen than in the nickel-rich end. Such effects are common in concentrated solid solutions and lead to the conclusion that in such cases the diffusion coefficient is not constant, even at constant temperature, but varies with the composition of the alloy. Thus in such cases one must use the more general form of Fick's law, equation 75, rather than the simpler form given by equation 76. A technique for the determination of D as a function of composition by the application of equation

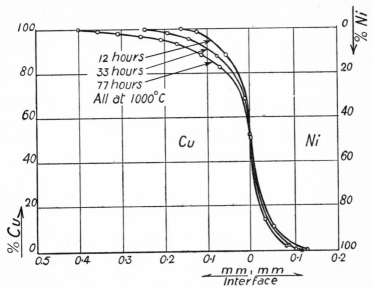

Fig. 93.—Concentration-Depth Curves for the Interdiffusion of Copper and Nickel (after Grube and Jedele).

75 to curves of the type of Fig. 93 was worked out by Matano,[*] and an outstanding general investigation of the effect was made by Rhines and Mehl,[†] who showed that, in the primary solid solutions of silicon, aluminium, tin, zinc, cadmium and beryllium in copper, D may increase by a factor of about 10 as the concentration is increased from zero to the solubility limit.

The explanation of this dependence on concentration rests on two effects. First, the cohesive forces of the material in general vary with composition. For example, the interatomic binding in nickel is greater than that in copper; without committing ourselves to any particular atomic mechanism of diffusion we expect the activation energy for diffusion to be at least roughly proportional to the binding energy, in which case the diffusion coefficient at constant temperature should

[*] C. Matano, *Japan J. Phys.*, 1933, **8**, 109.
[†] F. N. Rhines and R. F. Mehl, *Trans. Amer. Inst. Min. Met. Eng.*, 1938, **128**, 185.

decrease as the nickel content increases. Evidence for a correlation with other measures of the binding energy is provided by a comparison of ΔH for *self-diffusion* (i.e. for the diffusion in a pure substance of a radio-active isotope of that substance) with the absolute melting point, as is given in Table 7.

TABLE 7.—COMPARISON OF HEATS OF ACTIVATION FOR SELF-DIFFUSION (ΔH) AND ABSOLUTE MELTING POINTS (T_m) OF METALS*

Metal				ΔH, kcal./mol.	$T_m°$ K.	$\Delta H/T_m$
Pb	.	.	.	27	600	45
Ag	.	.	.	46	1234	37
Au	.	.	.	53	1336	40
Cu	.	.	.	47	1356	35
Co	.	.	.	67	1760	38
γ-Fe	.	.	.	68	1810	38
a-Fe	.	.	.	60	1810	33
W	.	.	.	142†	3680	39

The second factor which influences the value of D is that, in a non-ideal solution, the directions of migration of the atoms are not completely random. They migrate preferentially in the direction which will cause the internal energy to be lowered. This preferred direction may, according to the nature of the cohesive forces present, be either down or up the concentration gradient. In the first of these cases the rate at which the concentration becomes uniform is increased and the effective value of D is raised. In the second case D appears smaller. In extreme cases, where there is a substantial lowering of internal energy when similar atoms cluster together in the solution, the effect can even lead to 'uphill diffusion', in which atoms move against the concentration gradient towards regions of highest concentration. This clustering of atoms, if formed in an initially homogeneous solution, usually takes place on a fine scale and indicates a tendency towards separation into a phase mixture.

To incorporate the effect of non-random migrations in the equations of diffusion, it is customary to take the flux of atoms (see equation 73) as being proportional, not to the concentration gradient, but to the gradient of a quantity called the *chemical potential* of the diffusing species. The chemical potential μ_A of a component A in a system is the free energy required to take an atom of A from some standard state and place it in the system. Taking the flow of A as proportional to the gradient of μ_A thus recognises that the 'driving force' directing the motion of a migrating atom originates from the change in the free energy of the system as the atom moves through it.

12.4 The Kirkendall Effect

We have seen in the above section that in, e.g., copper-nickel alloys the atoms migrate more quickly in copper-rich regions than in nickel-rich ones. This raises a question; is it possible that a given region of the alloy

---

* Data collected in the paper by A. D. Le Claire, *Acta Metallurgica*, 1953, **1**, 438.
† Strictly, not self-diffusion but diffusion of Fe in dilute solution in W.

the copper atoms migrate more quickly than the nickel atoms? An intuitive reaction is to reject this idea on the grounds that the atoms are mounted on a fixed background lattice so that, for every atom taken away from a site, another one is eventually put in its place. In fact, for many years it was taken as axiomatic that an equal number of atoms must move in either direction across any reference plane fixed in the lattice.

The surprising fact that this is not so rests on an effect observed by Kirkendall.* The type of experiment used to demonstrate the *Kirkendall Effect* is as shown in Fig. 94. Here a block of α-brass has mounted along

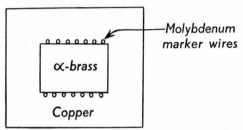

FIG. 94.—A Specimen for Demonstrating the Kirkendall Effect.

its faces a series of inert 'markers' (e.g. fine molybdenum wires) the sole function of which is to mark the position of the original interface. The block is then mounted within a larger copper block and an annealing treatment is given. It is observed that, concurrently with the interdiffusion of zinc and copper across the copper/brass interface, the two sets of markers move together by a greater amount than can be accounted for by changes of lattice parameter. The implication is that more atoms have moved out of the centre block than have moved in, i.e. that the zinc atoms migrate faster than the copper atoms. The original observations of Kirkendall were actually made with the brass/copper system, but subsequent work has confirmed the effect in other systems based on the face centred cubic lattice; it appears that in binary systems of this type the component with the lower melting point generally has the greater mobility.

Darken† first proposed a generalisation of the laws of diffusion to include the Kirkendall effect. He suggested that each component element, say A and B, in a binary solution of A and B must be given its own diffusion coefficient, D_A and D_B, and that these coefficients are not necessarily equal. Assuming also that, when an excess of atoms diffuses out of a given region of the specimen, the remaining atoms readjust themselves so that no porosity is formed (and vice versa if an excess of atoms enters the region), a Kirkendall effect occurs whenever $D_A \neq D_B$. Darken concluded that, under these conditions, the overall chemical diffusion coefficient D can be written as

$$D = c_B D_A + c_A D_B \quad . . . . (82)$$

* E. O. Kirkendall, *Trans. Amer. Inst. Met. Eng.*, 1942, **143**, 104; A. D. Smigelskas and E. O. Kirkendall, *ibid.*, 1947, **171**, 130.
† L. S. Darken, *Trans. Amer. Inst. Min. Met. Eng.*, 1948, **175**, 184.

where c_A and c_B are the atomic concentrations of A and B. If the solution examined is sufficiently dilute, i.e. if $c_A \ll 1$, then $D \simeq D_A$. Although equation 82 is usually accepted as a basis for discussing diffusion in systems which show the Kirkendall effect, it cannot be strictly valid because experiments have shown that porosity is in fact produced in such cases. Barnes,* for example, showed that holes, visible under a microscope, develop in copper/brass and copper/nickel systems on that side of the interface from which there is a net loss of atoms; moreover, the volume of these holes is a substantial part of the volume change associated with the Kirkendall effect; such that, if these holes were to collapse, the movement of the markers would be roughly doubled.

12.5   Atomic Movements in Diffusion

In the case of atoms which dissolve interstitially, such as carbon in iron, there is no doubt about the nature of the elementary atomic jumps which produce diffusion, and a theory of the type outlined in section 12.2 can be applied with precision. In self-diffusion and diffusion in substitutional solutions, however, the nature of the unit process which enables the atoms to reshuffle themselves in the lattice is by no means obvious. The various ideas proposed for this process have gradually crystallised into three main theories, based on (a) migration of vacancies, (b) migration of interstitialcies (see section 8.3), and (c) place exchange, respectively.

We have seen in section 8.3 that a crystal contains an appreciable number of vacancies in equilibrium at high temperature. These vacancies

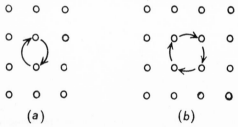

(a)   (b)

Fig. 95.—Place Exchange Mechanisms: (a) Simple Two-Atom Interchange, and (b) Interchange on a Four-Atom Ring.

wander continually through the crystal, each one displacing each atom along its path from one site to the next, so producing over a period of time the large-scale concentration changes which we observe as diffusion. Interstitialcies, by wandering through the crystal, can also produce diffusion in this manner. The place exchange mechanisms of diffusion are, however, quite different. They involve the direct interchange of two or more neighbouring atoms in their sites. Fig. 95 illustrates examples of such mechanisms. For many years only the simple two-atom process of diagram (a) was considered, but more recently Zener†

* R. S. Barnes, *Proc. Phys. Soc.*, 1952, **65B**, 512.
† C. Zener, *Acta Cryst.*, 1950, **3**, 346.

has pointed out interesting possibilities in *ring* processes of the type of diagram (*b*).

Evidence concerning the operation of these various processes can be grouped under the following headings:—

(*a*) *The Magnitude of* ΔH. Calculations of the heat of activation have been made by various authors.* For copper, Huntington and Seitz obtained the values, in kcal./mol., 64 for vacancy migration, 230 for interstitialcy migration, and 240 for two-atom interchange. The experimental value, 47, clearly favours the vacancy mechanism. The main factor contributing to the calculated values is the repulsion between the closed shells of the copper ions (see section 6.3); this raises several interesting points: (i) The much higher energies belonging to the interstitialcy and exchange mechanisms are due to the fact that, in these, the atoms have to be squeezed together against the ion-ion repulsion. (ii) The severe distortion round an interstitialcy makes it possible to move this defect through the lattice much more easily than a vacancy. Interstitialcies created in copper by cold-work or fast particle bombardment (see section 8.3) may thus enable diffusion to occur at considerably lower temperatures than those at which vacancies are mobile; there is some evidence for this effect.† (iii) As Zener has pointed out, the ion-ion energy is reduced if a ring of four atoms rotates (Fig. 95 (*b*)); his estimate of ΔH for this process in copper is 90 kcal./mol. (iv) Since copper is a full metal (see section 6.3) the ion-ion interactions are exceptionally large. It may be expected, therefore, that the heats of activation for the interstitialcy and place exchange mechanisms are less forbiddingly large in more open structures. Paneth, in fact, has calculated that the energy to form a certain kind of interstitialcy (a *crowdion*) in sodium is only about 5 kcal./mol.

(*b*) *The Magnitude of* D_0. Calculations of D_0 by refinements of the method described in section 12.2 have been made for the various processes by Zener and Le Claire.‡ It has been concluded by Le Claire, for example, that the observed values of D_0 are consistent with vacancy migration in F.C.C. metals, but in B.C.C. metals the observed values of D_0 and ΔH can be satisfactorily correlated only on the assumption that diffusion occurs by four-atom ring rotation.§

(*c*) *The Kirkendall Effect*. The Kirkendall effect, generally established in F.C.C. alloys, clearly cannot be produced by place exchange mechanisms.¶ In vacancy (or interstitialcy) diffusion, however, the way is open for the atomic defects to interchange places more often with atoms of

* H. B. Huntington and F. Seitz, *Phys. Rev.*, 1942, **61**, 315, 325; 1949, **76**, 1728; H. B. Huntington, 1953, **91**, 1092; C. Zener, *loc. cit.*; H. R. Paneth, *Phys. Rev.*, 1950, **80**, 708.

† T. Broom, *Advances in Physics*, 1954, **3**, 26.

‡ A. D. Le Claire, *Acta Met.*, 1953, **1**, 438.

§ But see, however, the recent paper by F. S. Buffington and M. Cohen, *Acta Met.*, 1954, **2**, 660.

¶ A Kirkendall effect has recently been observed in β-brass (B.C.C.) by U. S. Landergren and R. F. Mehl, *J. Metals*, 1953, **5**, 153.

one component than with those of the other one, so that the flow of rapidly moving atoms of the one component is balanced against the combined counterflows of defects and slowly moving atoms of the other component. If features are available in the material, such as grain boundaries (or dislocations), where the defects can be created freely to maintain the supply of those diffusing away, or to absorb those arriving in the reception areas, a Kirkendall shift will result. Admittedly, it is also possible to explain the Kirkendall effect by the flow of atoms along grain boundaries (and dislocation lines) but this is not a likely explanation because the effect has been observed in experiments in which the diffusion coefficient is not structure-sensitive* (see section 12.6).

(d) *Other Experiments.* Evidence in favour of the vacancy (and interstitialcy) mechanisms of diffusion is provided by experiments of the type made by Nowick (see section 8.3) in which the rate of diffusion is shown to be greater in a quenched alloy than in a slowly cooled one; the inference is that the quenched alloy contains more vacancies, these being retained from those in thermal equilibrium at the quenching temperature.

12.6 Structure-Sensitive Diffusion

It has often been observed in studies of diffusion in substitutional alloys that D_0 is smaller, sometimes by many orders of magnitude, than the theoretical value. These anomalously low values are always accompanied by low values of ΔH (e.g. as compared with that for self-diffusion in the pure solvent). This tendency is particularly pronounced at low temperatures. A small D_0 and ΔH both suggest that here diffusion is taking place along a small number of special channels in the material, which act as 'short-circuiting' paths in which the atomic structure is such as to allow atoms to move easily, with small activation energies.† The smallness of D_0 is then explainable on the basis that only a very small fraction of all the various paths through the material which are available to a migrating atom are of this highly conducting nature.

At high temperatures, where migration is rapid even in the 'normal' paths (i.e. those through perfect regions of the lattice), the main stream of migrating atoms flows through these channels, simply because there are so many of them, and the contribution of the still more rapid flow along the relatively few highly conducting channels appears small by comparison. Thus diffusion at high temperatures is not appreciably structure-sensitive. But at lower temperatures the flow in the normal channels becomes 'frozen in', because the thermal fluctuations are too weak to supply the large activation energy to move atoms in them, whereas flow along the anomalous channels is still possible because the activation energy is smaller there. The diffusion process at such temperatures

---

* L. C. Correa da Silva and R. F. Mehl, *Trans. Amer. Inst. Min. Met. Eng.*, 1951, **191**, 155.

† C. Zener, Chapter XI, 'Imperfections in Nearly Perfect Crystals' (Ed. W. Shockley), Wiley, 1952; A. S. Nowick, *J. Appl. Phys.*, 1951, **22**, 1182.

depends almost entirely upon the existence of these anomalous channels, and the rate of diffusion is directly proportional to the number present. Under these circumstances diffusion is a structure-sensitive process. This is shown by the fact that cold-working, which introduces imperfections such as dislocations and small-angle boundaries (see sections 3.7, 3.8, and 15.4) into the crystals, also speeds up diffusion at low temperatures. Admittedly, part of the increase in the diffusion rate may be due to the creation of vacancies and interstitialcies by plastic deformation,[*] but nevertheless the breakdown of the crystal structure should increase the number of highly conducting channels through the lattice.

Three possibilities have been considered for the highly conducting channels: grain boundaries, dislocation lines, and chemical inhomogeneities. Regarding the latter, Zener[†] has suggested that in, say, α-brass a vacancy interchanges places more readily with zinc atoms than with copper atoms and, as a consequence, the motion of vacancies will then be essentially confined to the network formed by the zinc atoms.

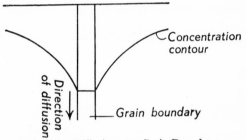

FIG. 96.—Diffusion at a Grain Boundary.

Most attention has been paid to grain boundaries. A mathematical analysis of simultaneous diffusion along grain boundaries and in the adjoining grains has been made by Fisher,[‡] which provides a method for determining the ratio D_{gb}/D_e, of the diffusion coefficients in the grain boundary and lattice. Fisher considers the situation shown in Fig. 96 and treats the grain boundary as a uniform sheet of definite thickness (e.g. 5×10^{-8} cm.) in which the diffusion coefficient is much higher than that in the neighbouring lattice. An important feature is that, although the diffusing atoms travel down the boundary at great speed, the concentration in the nearby lattice rises almost as fast as that in the boundary itself. The reason is that most of the atoms travelling down the boundary sooner or later wander off the boundary into the neighbouring crystal. The boundary thus acts as an irrigation channel which feeds the surrounding lattice with a stream of diffusing atoms, and so increases the concentration of such atoms in parts of the lattice which are quite inaccessible to direct lattice diffusion.

* F. Seitz, *Advances in Physics*, 1952, **1**, 43; N. F. Mott, *Proc. Phys. Soc.*, 1951, **64B**, 729.

† C. Zener, *loc. cit.*   ‡ J. C. Fisher, *J. Appl. Phys.*, 1951, **22**, 74.

Hoffman and Turnbull[*] have used the analysis to determine D_{gb} for self-diffusion in silver. They find, for this metal, that

$$D_e = 0.895 exp(-45,950) \text{ cm.}^2 \text{ sec.}^{-1},$$

and
$$D_{gb} = 0.03 exp(-20,200) \text{ cm.}^2 \text{ sec.}^{-1}.$$

Thus $D_{gb}/D_e \simeq 10^5$ at 500° C. More recently, Le Claire[†] has shown that D_{gb}/D_e can be determined rather simply from the angle at which a concentration contour meets the grain boundary, and this idea has been used by Barnes[‡] in a study of the penetration of copper along the grain boundaries of nickel.

Arguing on the basis that a grain boundary is a thin transition layer between adjoining grains (see section 3.8), it has been suggested that the rate of grain boundary diffusion should depend on the difference in orientation between the grains. Achter and Smoluchowski[§] confirmed this for copper, showing that diffusion is faster in large-angle boundaries than in small-angle ones. More recently, Turnbull,[¶] studying diffusion along small-angle boundaries in silver, has shown that in the formula $D_{gb} = D_{0gb} exp(-\Delta H_{gb}/RT)$ the factor D_{0gb} increases with increasing difference of orientation, but that ΔH_{gb} stays constant at about 20 kcal./mol. Turnbull emphasises that this suggests that diffusion takes place along certain channels in such boundaries, and that, as the boundary angle increases, the number of such channels also increases but the atomic structure in each channel (which determines ΔH for the channel) stays constant. Simple small-angle boundaries can be regarded as rows of parallel dislocation lines (see section 15.4), and Turnbull interprets the highly distorted centres of these dislocation lines as the channels or 'pipes' along which the atoms move rapidly.

FURTHER READING

In addition to the references given in the chapter, the following are recommended for further reading on diffusion:

A. D. Le Claire, Chapter 7 in 'Progress in Metal Physics, I' (Ed. B. Chalmers), Butterworth, 1949; Chapter 6 in 'Progress in Metal Physics, IV', Pergamon Press, 1953; *J. Iron and Steel Inst.*, 1953, **174**, 229.

'Diffusion in and through Solids.' R. M. Barrer, Cambridge University Press, 1941.

'Diffusion in Solids, Liquids and Gases.' W. Jost, Academic Press, New York, 1952.

'Transformations in Solids', p. 77. F. Seitz, Wiley, New York, 1951.

J. Bardeen and C. Herring, Chapter 10 in 'Imperfections in Nearly Perfect Crystals', Wiley, 1952.

'Physical Chemistry of Metals.' L. S. Darken and R. W. Gurry, McGraw-Hill, 1953.

Seminar on 'Atom Movements.' American Society for Metals, 1951.

* R. E. Hoffman and D. Turnbull, *J. Appl. Phys.*, 1951, **22**, 634.
† A. D. Le Claire, *Phil. Mag.*, 1951, **42**, 468.
‡ R. S. Barnes, *Nature*, 1950, **166**, 1032.
§ M. R. Achter and R. Smoluchowski, *Phys. Rev.*, 1949, **76**, 470.
¶ D. Turnbull, Report of 1954 Bristol Conference (London: Physical Society).

CHAPTER XIII

THE ORDER–DISORDER CHANGE IN ALLOYS

Several alloys of critical compositions, e.g. CuZn, CuAu, Cu_3Au, exist as ordered solid solutions at low temperatures and as disordered ones at high temperatures. The change from order to disorder which these undergo on heating, and the reverse change on cooling, show some interesting features. In many phase changes, e.g. melting and polymorphic changes in pure materials, the transition occurs sharply at a critical temperature (called *changes of the first order*). But in certain cases (*changes of the second order*) the transition takes place over a range of temperature, and the two states which mark the beginning and end of the change are the two extremes of a continuous series of intermediate states, all of which are realised at intermediate temperatures. The demagnetisation of a ferromagnet by heating (see section 8.5) is one such example. Another example, strikingly similar to the magnetic one in its thermodynamical aspects, is the order-disorder change in certain systems.

13.1 The Theoretical Basis of the Order-Disorder Change

According to the nearest neighbour bond energy approximation (see section 10.1) the condition for ordering at low temperatures is that $2V_{AB} < V_{AA} + V_{BB}$, for this gives a lowering of internal energy when the proportion of AB neighbours is increased at the expense of AA and BB neighbours. Then, at low temperatures there will be a preponderance of AB neighbours, since the free energy at such temperatures is practically the same as the internal energy, whereas at high temperatures the increased importance of the entropy factor will incline the equilibrium towards a purely random distribution of neighbours.

Practically all theoretical treatments of the order-disorder change make use of the nearest neighbour bond approximation. In systems where there is a distinct electrical difference between the participating atoms there is some justification for interpreting $2V_{AB} - V_{AA} - V_{BB}$ in terms of the energies of interaction between neighbouring atoms. In CuZn, for example, it is reasonable to expect the zinc atom to make a slightly larger donation of electronic charge to the free electron cloud than the copper atom, in which case the zinc and copper ions will carry small opposite electrical charges.* The binding forces in the alloy then have a slightly ionic character and the electrostatic interactions between the oppositely charged ions are then partially interpretable in terms of the parameter $2V_{AB} - V_{AA} - V_{BB}$.

In certain other cases, however, this parameter has no such direct

---

* N. F. Mott, *Proc. Camb. Phil. Soc.*, 1936, **32**, 281; *Proc. Phys. Soc.*, 1937, **49**, 258.

physical interpretation, even though it may still be used to denote the ordering energy in the alloy. The comparison of the systems Cu-Au and Cu-Ag, where ordering occurs in one case and phase separation in the other, and which involve atoms whose main difference lies in their sizes, raises the possibility that ordering may be a means of reducing strain energy in solid solutions involving atoms of different sizes, a suggestion that has been made from time to time.* Another case where long-range effects may be important, rather than nearest neighbour bonds, is that where the Fermi energy of the free electrons alters on ordering through a change in the Brillouin zone structure. It has been pointed out that when a superlattice is formed in a crystal, new Brillouin zone boundaries must also be formed due to electron reflections off the superlattice, and if the Fermi surface lies near to a superlattice zone boundary the energy of electrons in the surface will be altered.†

Experiment has shown that two distinct types of order can exist. In *long-range* order the lattice can be regarded as being composed of two (or more) interpenetrating *sub-lattices* one (or some) of which contains most of the atoms of one kind and the other(s) contains most of the atoms of the other kind. There is thus a long-range correlation in the distribution of the atoms on the sub-lattices, i.e. a coherent scheme of order extending over a large region of the lattice, even though the separation of the different components on to the different sub-lattices may not be completely achieved. Above the critical ordering temperature long-range order is destroyed, for the ordering force is no longer strong enough to maintain the coherent scheme in the face of intense thermal agitation. Although the long-range correlation in atomic distribution no longer exists at such temperatures, nevertheless the ordering force still acts on the atoms and prevents their distribution on the lattice from becoming completely random. Thus a *short-range* order exists in which small ordered groups of atoms continually form, break up and form again, so giving a greater number of unlike nearest neighbours than is present in a fully random solution. These states of *short-range* and *long-range* order are very reminiscent of the structure of a liquid near its freezing point and the structure of the corresponding solid. In each case a coherent ordered scheme, involving correlated atomic positions over large distances, is stable below the critical point, whereas above this point only small, dispersed, ordered groups are formed.

13.2 The Theory of Long-Range Order‡

The theory of order is greatly simplified if one deals with the case where long-range order is already present in the material. The only

* W. Hume-Rothery and H. M. Powell, *Zeit. Krist.*, 1935, **91**, 23; C. S. Barrett, 'Structure of Metals', 2nd Edition, McGraw-Hill, 1952 (p. 282).

† H. Lipson, Chapter I in 'Progress in Metal Physics, II' (Ed. B. Chalmers), Butterworths, 1950; J. C. Slater, *Phys. Rev.*, 1951, **82**, 538; 1951, **84**, 179.

‡ The theory presented in this section, although cast in a slightly different form, is in all essentials the same as that originally proposed by W. L. Bragg and E. J. Williams, *Proc. Roy. Soc.*, 1934, **A145**, 699.

question to be settled then is the extent to which the two kinds of atoms separate out on to their respective sub-lattices, and this can be treated by a rather simple theory, as we shall see below. The much more difficult problem of analysing how the atoms change, on cooling, from short-range order (where the sub-lattices are not defined) to long-range order (where the atoms have chosen their respective sub-lattices) will be discussed in section 13.4.

Let us consider in particular the alloy CuZn, or β-brass, in which the pattern of atomic sites is B.C.C. Suppose that there are N atomic sites, $N/2$ copper atoms and $N/2$ zinc atoms. As shown in Fig. 97, the B.C.C. lattice is composed of two interpenetrating simple cubic sub-lattices,

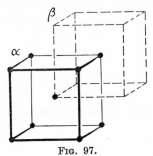

Fig. 97.

α and β respectively, each of which has $N/2$ sites. We define the *degree of long-range order*, W, by the statement:—

$$\text{Number of } A \text{ atoms in } \alpha \text{ sites} = (1+W)N/4,$$

which of course implies that

$$\text{Number of } A \text{ atoms in } \beta \text{ sites} = (1-W)N/4,$$
$$\text{,,} \quad \text{,,} \ B \quad \text{,,} \quad \text{,, ,,} \quad \text{,,} \ = (1+W)N/4,$$
$$\text{,,} \quad \text{,, ,,} \quad \text{,,} \quad \text{,, } \alpha \quad \text{,,} \ = (1-W)N/4.$$

Then all possible states of long-range order are included by letting W range in value from $+1$ to -1. When $W=0$ there is no long-range order. When $W=\pm 1$ the copper atoms are all situated on either the α lattice or the β lattice; these states are equivalent and both correspond to perfect long-range order. Intermediate values of W between 0 and 1 define intermediate amounts of separation on the two sub-lattices.

To find the equilibrium degree of order at any temperature we set up a function for the free energy F, in terms of W, and then find the value of W which gives $dF/dW=0$. This locates the minimum in the curve of F as a function of W and hence the equilibrium value of W. Since

$$dF/dW = dE/dW - T(dS/dW),$$

we have to find dE/dW and dS/dW.

For the internal energy term we assume that

$$E = N_{AA}V_{AA} + N_{BB}V_{BB} + N_{AB}V_{AB},$$

as in Chapter X. To find N_{AA}, etc., we notice that the eight nearest neighbours to an atom in one of the sub-lattices all belong to the other sub-lattice. Thus the number of AA bonds associated with an A atom in an α site is given by n_{AA}, where

$n_{AA} = 8 \times$ fraction of nearest neighbours (in β sites) which are A atoms.

To obtain this fraction we assume, for simplicity, that it is equal to the atomic concentration of A atoms in β sites, i.e. to

$$\frac{(1-W)N/4}{N/2},$$

so that $n_{AA} = 4(1-W)$. It must be emphasised that this assumption, although very convenient mathematically, is distinctly weak. For it implies that, once the atoms have sorted themselves out on the two sub-lattices, the internal distribution of atoms within each sub-lattice is quite indifferent to that on the other one, and is purely random. We have thus assumed that, in spite of the ordering force, every copper atom on an α site will gather round itself in the neighbouring β sites a strictly average proportion of the copper and zinc atoms that belong to the β sub-lattice. The tendency towards short-range order is thus ignored, and the theory is limited, by this approximation, to the treatment of long-range order only.

The total number of AA pairs is given by

$$N_{AA} = n_{AA} \times \text{number of } A \text{ atoms in } \alpha \text{ sites} = N(1-W^2).$$

Similarly we find that

$$N_{BB} = N(1-W^2), \quad N_{AB} = 2N(1+W^2).$$

The internal energy is thus given by

$$\begin{aligned} E &= N(1-W^2)(V_{AA}+V_{BB}) + 2N(1+W^2)V_{AB} \\ &= N(V_{AA}+V_{BB}+2V_{AB}) + NW^2V \quad \ldots \ldots \quad (83) \end{aligned}$$

where $V = 2V_{AB} - V_{AA} - V_{BB}$. Strictly a vibrational specific heat term should also be included in this expression, but, unless this varies appreciably with the degree of order, its contribution to dE/dW can be neglected. We thus have

$$dE/dW = 2NWV \quad \ldots \ldots \ldots \ldots \quad (84)$$

We now have to find dS/dW. Again we confine our attention to the configurational term, and ignore any effect of order on the vibrational entropy. Each sub-lattice consists of a random solid solution containing $N/2$ sites and components with atomic concentrations of $c = (1+W)/2$ and $(1-c) = (1-W)/2$ respectively. The total entropy of mixing is twice that for each sub-lattice. Applying the usual formula (equation 44), we obtain

$$S = -Nk\left[\left(\frac{1+W}{2}\right)\log_e\left(\frac{1+W}{2}\right) + \left(\frac{1-W}{2}\right)\log_e\left(\frac{1-W}{2}\right)\right],$$

and hence

$$\frac{dS}{dW} = -\frac{Nk}{2} \log_e\left(\frac{1+W}{1-W}\right) \quad \cdots\cdots\cdots\cdots\cdots \quad (85)$$

We have then for the equilibrium degree of order

$$\frac{dF}{dW} = 2NWV + \frac{NkT}{2} \log_e\left(\frac{1+W}{1-W}\right) = 0 \quad \cdots\cdots\cdots \quad (86)$$

It is convenient to express this relation in terms of T_c, the critical temperature at which $W=0$. A direct substitution of $W=0$ in the relation fails to give a value for T_c, however, since $W=0$ is also satisfied by any temperature above T_c. To find T_c we consider heating the ordered alloy towards its critical temperature, i.e. we observe what value of T is approached as W diminishes towards the value $W=0$. From the usual formula for the series expansion of a logarithm we find that $\log_e[(1+W)/(1-W)]$ approaches the value $2W$ as $W \to 0$. Hence, in the limit, T_c is defined by

$$2NWV + NWkT = 0,$$

i.e.
$$T_c = -2V/k \quad \cdots\cdots\cdots\cdots \quad (87)$$

Since V is negative for a solution with a tendency towards ordering, T_c is of course positive. The equation of equilibrium thus becomes

$$2W\frac{T_c}{T} = \log_e\left(\frac{1+W}{1-W}\right) \quad \cdots\cdots\cdots\cdots \quad (88)$$

To show the way that W varies with T we choose a set of values of W, substitute them in this equation and then find the corresponding values of T/T_c. The result is as shown in Fig. 98. We notice that the

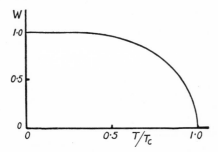

FIG. 98.—The Degree of Long-Range Order (W) as a Function of Temperature.

order is nearly perfect at low temperatures, that it decreases slowly with rising temperature at first, and that it decreases ever more rapidly until the critical temperature is reached, where the order completely disappears. These features are due to the *co-operative* nature of the order-disorder change (see section 8.5). It is difficult to start disorder in the perfectly ordered alloy, i.e. to place the first few atoms in 'wrong' positions, since each such move is resisted by all the neighbours of the atom concerned. However, the more atoms there are already in 'wrong' positions, the more these attract other atoms into 'wrong' positions, and the easier it becomes for further disordering to take place—indeed, a typical social phenomenon.

To test the theory against experiment we shall examine three property changes which result from disordering. First, the increase in configurational entropy is easily deduced. In the fully ordered alloy the configurational entropy is zero. In the fully disordered alloy it is that of a random solution of equiatomic composition; as we saw in section 7.5, this is 1·38 cal./degree/mol. An experimental value for the configurational entropy change due to disordering in β-brass can be deduced from observed specific heat measurements, and in this way has been found by Sykes and Wilkinson* to be 1·01 cal./degree/mol. This value is comparable with the theoretical one, although some 30 per cent. smaller. The origin of the difference is the assumption that the solution becomes completely random when the long-range order disappears. Actually this does not happen, since short-range order persists at temperatures above the critical point and this reduces the change in configurational entropy associated with the destruction of long-range order.

The change in configurational energy can also be deduced quite simply. From equation 84 we have $dE=2NWVdW$. Thus the total configurational entropy change, ΔE, is given by

$$\Delta E=2NV\int_{W=1}^{W=0} WdW=-NV$$

Since V is negative this is positive. Introducing $T_c=-2V/k$, we have

$$\Delta E=\tfrac{1}{2}NkT_c=\tfrac{1}{2}RT_c \quad . \quad . \quad . \quad . \quad . \quad . \quad . \quad . \quad (89)$$

when the number of atoms, N, in the alloy is equal to Avogadro's number. The observed value of T_c is 743° K. for β-brass, so that the theoretical value of ΔE is 740 calories. By subtracting the vibrational specific heat from the observed specific heat curve for β-brass, Sykes and Wilkinson (*op. cit.*) obtain an experimental value, $\Delta E=630$ calories. As with the entropy, this is in fair agreement with the theory, although distinctly lower. Again, this is due to the fact that the alloy does not become fully disordered when T_c is exceeded.

Thirdly, we can make a comparison with the observed specific heat due to disordering. In addition to the usual vibrational specific heat there exists also an extra specific heat which is accounted for by the increase in configurational energy as the material becomes disordered. If the entire change occurred at a single temperature, as in a polymorphic change, this extra specific heat would be replaced by a latent heat equal to ΔE, at the transformation temperature; but in the present case the energy ΔE is absorbed gradually over a range of temperature. Defining E as in equation 83, the extra specific heat is given by

* C. Sykes and H. Wilkinson, *J. Inst. Metals*, 1937, 61, 223.

$$dE/dT = (dE/dW)(dW/dT) = 2NWV(dW/dT).$$

Introducing $T_c = -2V/k$, this becomes

$$dE/dT = -NkW[dW/d(T/T_c)] \quad \ldots \ldots \ldots \ldots \quad (90)$$

For each value of T/T_c we can determine both W and $dW/d(T/T_c)$ from Fig. 98 or equation 88. Taking $Nk=R$, the curve of extra specific heat as a function of temperature is as shown in Fig. 99, curve (a). As a comparison we show an experimental curve, from the work of Sykes and Wilkinson, obtained by deducting the vibrational specific heat from the total specific heat. The curves agree in so far as they both show that the excess specific heat rises to a peak and then falls sharply. Beyond this, however, the agreement is poor, and it is clear that in practice the order-disorder change takes place within a much narrower range of

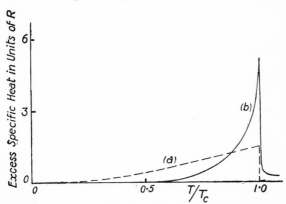

FIG. 99.—The Extra Specific Heat as a Function of Temperature for CuZn:
(a) Theoretical (Bragg-Williams Approximation), (b) Experimental (Sykes and Wilkinson).

temperature than is predicted by the theory. Several refinements of the theory have been directed towards explaining this sharpness of the peak. It must be emphasised, however, that the shape of the specific heat curve is extremely sensitive to the shape of the ordering curve (Fig. 98), so that this third comparison with experiment should be regarded as a searching test of the fine details of the theory rather than a broad check of its essential soundness.

It should be noticed that in the experimental curve the extra specific heat does not fall completely to zero above T_c. This is further evidence for short-range order, since extra energy will be needed to break this down as the temperature rises above T_c.

It is not difficult to repeat the theoretical method developed above for the case where the alloy has a composition of the A_3B type (e.g. Cu_3Au). The new feature which emerges then, which is absent in the CuZn case, is that the degree of long-range order changes discontinuously at the critical temperature. On heating, the alloy arrives at

T_c with a fairly high degree of long-range order, and the latter then drops sharply to zero as soon as T_c is exceeded, as shown in Fig. 100. This effect, which originates in a more complicated variation of F with W than is given by equation 86, has been confirmed experimentally. The order-disorder change in this case partly takes on the character of a first-order change, and a *latent heat* is observed at the critical temperature.

In certain cases it is possible for an alloy to split on ordering into a two-phase structure, consisting of separate regions with ordered and disordered structures, an effect which has been observed in the CoPt system.* This state of affairs is favoured if the alloy changes its structure on ordering (e.g. CoPt becomes F.C. tetragonal, instead of F.C.C.,

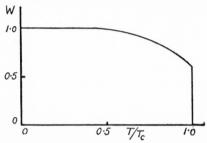

FIG. 100.—The Dependence of Long-Range Order on Temperature for a System of the Type Cu_3Au.

on ordering), or if the composition of the alloy deviates from the ideal one for the superlattice concerned. The tendency in this case, the theory of which has been worked out by Shockley,† is for an ordered phase to separate out with a composition closer to the ideal one than is the average composition of the alloy.

13.3   The Rate of Approach to Equilibrium

Since a definite time is required for atoms to rearrange themselves, the degree of order does not respond instantly to a change in temperature. At temperatures where diffusion is very slow it is possible for non-equilibrium states of order to persist for indefinitely long periods of time. Some possibilities have been discussed by Bragg and Williams,‡ based on the various cases shown in Fig. 101. These show some different positions of the critical temperature, T_c, relative to three important temperatures, T_m, T_a, and T_q, for the alloy. T_m is the melting point. T_a is the temperature below which equilibrium is never obtained, however slow the rate of cooling, for all practical cooling rates. An alloy can never obtain a degree of order greater than the equilibrium value

* J. W. Newkirk, A. H. Geisler, and D. L. Martin, *J. Appl. Phys.*, 1949, **20**, 816. See also F. N. Rhines and J. B. Newkirk, *Trans. Amer. Soc. Met.*, 1953, **45**, 1029.
  † W. Shockley, *J. Chem. Phys.*, 1938, **6**, 130.
  ‡ *Proc. Roy. Soc.*, 1935, **A151**, 540.

corresponding to T_a, since no appreciable change occurs at lower temperatures than this. T_q is the temperature above which equilibrium is established so quickly that it is always obtained in practice, no matter how fast the alloy is cooled. The most rapid quench cannot prevent the establishment of a degree of order equal to the equilibrium value at T_q.

The behaviour of an alloy depends on the position of T_c relative to T_a, T_q and T_m. In diagram a, T_a and T_q are low compared with T_c, so that the alloy will quickly assume the equilibrium state over the greater part of the temperature range where the state of order changes. It is impossible to preserve the disordered state by quenching, since the

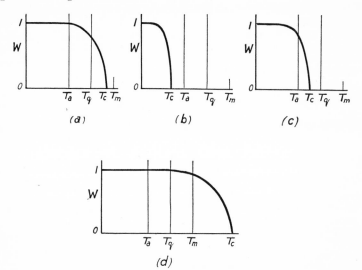

FIG. 101.—Conditions Governing the Degree of Order (W) Obtained after Slow or Fast Rates of Cooling.

fastest quench gives an extensively ordered alloy. In case b the ordered state cannot be observed since T_a is higher than T_c, so that the slowest possible cooling preserves the disordered state; such alloys will be known to us only as disordered solutions. The alloy AgAu may be of this type. In diagram c, T_c lies between T_a and T_q, and a variety of states of order are therefore possible by varying the rate of cooling. In the last diagram T_c lies well above the melting point, and in this case the alloy *freezes* directly into the fully ordered state; such an alloy resembles an intermetallic compound.

13.4 Short-Range Order and Anti-Phase Domains

The weak point in the theory of section 13.2 is the assumption that the only effect of the inequality $2V_{AB} < V_{AA} + V_{BB}$ is to cause the two kinds of atoms to separate on to two sub-lattices, in each of which the distribution is random. This assumption is mathematically convenient and is certainly consistent with the most prominent feature of the order-ing phenomenon, the existence of long-range order at low temperatures. On the other hand, it precludes the existence of short-range order. Basically, the condition for order is that dissimilar atoms should attract each other preferentially, and this can be satisfied to a high degree without having any long-range order present, but only groups or *domains* of local order. This is illustrated by Fig. 102 which shows two such domains. Within each of these the order is complete, so that the pro-portion of AB bonds is very high, but the two are out-of-step, or *anti-phase*, in that the sub-lattice chosen by the A atoms in one domain is the same as that chosen by the B atoms in the other one. Since the domains contain equal numbers of atoms the degree of long-range order is strictly zero, even though the only AA and BB bonds present are those across the domain boundary.

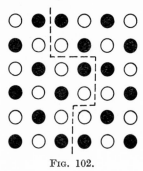

FIG. 102.

Bethe[*] developed the theory of short-range order by focusing atten-tion on the nearest neighbours to any atom in the alloy. A *degree of short-range order*, δ, is defined such that the proportion of the nearest neighbours to an A atom which are B atoms is given by $\frac{1}{2}(1+\delta)$; similarly, the proportion of the neighbours which are themselves A atoms is $\frac{1}{2}(1-\delta)$. Bethe shows that there is no critical temperature at which δ becomes zero, for the tendency for unlike atoms to become nearest neighbours is always present, in spite of the thermal agitation, so that although δ decreases with increasing temperature it does not reach zero at any finite temperature.

The second main result of the theory concerns the prediction of long-range order. In section 3.2 we assumed that the atoms would neces-sarily assemble into long-range order provided that $2V_{AB} < V_{AA} + V_{BB}$ and that the temperature was favourable. Although this assumption is prompted by direct X-ray evidence for the existence of superlattices, nevertheless the above discussion makes it far from obvious that it is a logical assumption. Since a large number of AB pairs can be formed by arrangements of the type of Fig. 102, in which the degree of long-range order is zero, why is it that long-range order is obtained at all?

[*] H. A. Bethe, *Proc. Roy. Soc.*, 1935, **A150**, 552.

The answer lies in the fact that the domain boundaries are unstable at low temperatures because the AA and BB bonds across them give them high internal energy. There is thus a tendency for neighbouring domains to grow and absorb each other, thereby reducing the total area of domain boundaries in the alloy and also converting the short-range order into long-range order. The process is analogous to grain growth in poly-crystals. At high temperatures, on the other hand, the presence of a domain boundary in a crystal can lower the free energy, since the boundary is also a source of entropy, and the negative contribution of this to the free energy must always outweigh the (positive) contribution of the internal energy at sufficiently high temperatures.

We can thus picture the sequence of changes on cooling in the following way. At high temperatures small ordered groups are continually forming and dispersing in the crystal lattice. As the alloy cools, this short-range order becomes more intense. When the critical temperature is reached the groups grow into clearly defined domains by absorbing each other and nearby disordered material until coherent schemes of order are established over large regions of the crystal. From a practical point of view, by the time that the domains exceed some 10^4 atoms in diameter the material may be described as possessing long-range order, for the X-ray superlattice reflections from domains of this size are sharp. The definition of long-range order introduced in section 13.1 is then, from this point of view, too exacting; the correlation of atomic positions on the sub-lattices need persist only over distances large enough to give coherent X-ray reflections from the superlattice.

Experimentally, the measurement of short-range order is far more difficult than that of long-range order, because short-range order does not reveal itself by means of sharp X-ray superlattice reflections. It has an effect, however, on the scattering of X-rays into the background between the main X-ray lattice reflections, and techniques have been developed and used successfully for studying short-range order by means of these diffuse reflections.* Methods have also been developed† for detecting short-range order from the measurement of thermodynamic properties, such as the vapour pressures of the components of the vapour in equilibrium with the alloy.

An excellent study of anti-phase domains in Cu_3Au has been made by Sykes and Jones.‡ Long-range order develops in this alloy much more slowly than the consideration of rates of diffusion leads one to expect. Copper and gold interdiffuse fairly readily at $250°$ C., and the critical temperature for long-range order is much higher than this (i.e. $390°$ C.), so that consideration of diffusion alone leads one to expect long-range order to develop even if the alloy is quenched. Sykes and

---

* A review of this work is given in C. S. Barrett's 'Structure of Metals', McGraw-Hill, 1952.

† See, for example, C. E. Birchenall, *Trans. Amer. Inst. Min. Met. Eng.*, 1947, **171**, 166.

‡ C. Sykes and F. W. Jones, *Proc. Roy. Soc.*, 1936, **A157**, 213; 1938, **A166**, 376.

Jones account for the slowness of ordering as an effect of the anti-phase domains in Cu_3Au. The lattice of atomic sites in this alloy is F.C.C., and can be regarded as being composed of four interpenetrating simple-cubic sub-lattices, three of which are occupied by copper atoms and one by gold atoms, in the fully ordered state. Above the critical temperature, groups of local order can form in any one of four different schemes, according as one or other of the four sub-lattices is chosen for the gold atoms. As the alloy is cooled below T_c these groups grow into an interlocking mesh of anti-phase domains which meet at change-step boundaries across which the order changes from one scheme to another. Jones and Sykes were able to measure the thickness of these boundaries experimentally and, by using methods based on X-ray diffraction and calorimetry, showed clearly that the boundaries are only about two atomic spacings thick. They also showed that the coalescence of the anti-phase domains into a single scheme of long-range order is a very slow process except at temperatures near the critical one.

The growth of a domain is analogous to the growth of a grain, and may be expected to be correspondingly slow. Bragg* has suggested that a state of affairs similar to that of a stable foam is produced in Cu_3Au, the domain boundaries being the counterparts of the bubble films in the foam. This state is reached when the domains have grown into equal regular polyhedra, such that any small displacement of any part of a domain boundary would cause the free energy to increase. For this to be possible certain topological conditions have to be satisfied. There must be a sufficient number of different schemes of order to enable three domains of different schemes to meet along a line, or four different domains to meet at a point. Since there are four different schemes in Cu_3Au this condition is satisfied and a persistent foam structure is possible. In CuZn, on the other hand, there are only two different schemes of order possible (corresponding to the two sub-lattices) and the essential condition for a stable foam structure is absent. It is significant that in this alloy long-range order forms very rapidly, showing that coalescence of the domains can occur easily.

REFERENCES

Accounts of the order-disorder change from both the theoretical and experimental points of view are given in the following articles and books:

F. C. Nix and W. Shockley, Reviews of Modern Physics, 1938, **10**, 2.

C. S. Barrett, 'Structure of Metals', 2nd Edition, McGraw-Hill, 1952.

H. Lipson, Chapter I in 'Progress in Metal Physics, II' (Ed. B. Chalmers), Butterworth, 1950.

S. Siegel, Chapter 14 in 'Phase Transformations in Solids' (Ed. R. Smoluchowski), Wiley, 1951.

C. E. Birchenhall, Chapter 7 in 'Thermodynamics in Physical Metallurgy', Amer. Soc. Metals, 1950.

* W. L. Bragg, *Proc. Phys. Soc.*, 1940, **52**, 105.

CHAPTER XIV

KINETICS OF PHASE CHANGES

Many important metallurgical phenomena are concerned with the following situation. A homogeneous metal or alloy phase enters on heating or cooling into a temperature range where some other phase is stable. To form the new phase certain movements of the atoms must take place. What is the nature of these movements, and what controls the rate of the process and the form of the new phase? These are the questions we shall take up in this chapter. Their practical importance is obvious since, for example, the industrial processes of the casting of metals and the heat-treatment of alloys make direct use of the phase change from liquid to solid and of phase changes in solid solutions.

14.1 Processes of Nucleation and Growth

In a few cases the rearrangement of atoms takes place homogeneously throughout the system. An example is the somewhat idealised order-disorder change of section 13.2. But in the typical phase change this does not happen. Instead, the change begins in certain small regions in the system, forming *nuclei* of the new phase, and then grows outwards from these by the advancement of sharp interfaces separating the nuclei from the old phase. The reason why the change takes place in this manner is closely connected with the notions of phase and phase interface, discussed in sections 10.2 and 10.5. When the system has to pass, while changing from the initial state to the final one, through intermediate configurations of higher free energy it minimises its total free energy by separating into distinct phases. Each of these phases is homogeneous and has low free energy, and the intermediate configurations of high free energy are localised in atomically thin layers at the interfaces between the phases. Most of the attempts of atoms in homogeneous regions of the old phase to change to the new state fail because they are unable to surmount the free energy barrier through which they have to pass to reach the new state. The few attempts that manage to succeed thus become of great importance, for once a nucleus has been formed, further change can take place easily in the material round it by means of the outward movement of its interface, a process which minimises the amount of material in the intermediate configurations.

14.2 Thermodynamical Theory of Nucleation

To develop the above ideas critically we need first a method for calculating the number of nuclei in the system. A simple argument, which gives a formula very near to that of the more rigorous treatments,* treats the nuclei by the same general procedure as that we have already used for estimating the density of vacancies; from this point of view, a vacancy could be regarded as a special form of nucleus, one atom in size, which forms in the crystalline phase. Let w be the work required to make one nucleus of specified type (i.e. specified in size, structure, composition, surface energy, etc.) at some particular place in the old phase, and let N be the number of such places available. To set against the work of forming the nucleus there will be an entropy of mixing, due to the numerous places in which the nucleus can be formed in the system. Following directly the method of section 8.3, we obtain for n, the number of such nuclei present in the system,

$$n = N exp(-w/kT) \qquad \ldots \ldots \ldots \ldots \quad (91)$$

If the nucleus is very small and if it can form with equal facility at every place in the system, then N is of the order of magnitude of the number of atoms in the system. When the probability of forming a nucleus is the same at every place a state suitable for *homogeneous nucleation* is said to exist in the system. Unless specially sought after, however, this state of affairs is rarely experienced in practice. In most large systems, e.g. in a crucible of molten metal or a block of quenched steel, there are numerous special places where the work to form a nucleus is much smaller than average. In casting, these places exist at the surface of the mould and around included particles of foreign substances in the melt. In the heat-treatment of alloys, they exist at grain boundaries, at dislocations, and on the surfaces of included particles of other phases. Because w is small at these places, nucleation occurs preferentially on them and a state suitable for *heterogeneous nucleation* is said to exist. Were it not for heterogeneous nucleation, it is doubtful if the casting of metals would be a practical proposition for, as we shall see below, homogeneous nucleation does not begin in a liquid until this is cooled far below its thermodynamical freezing point. If a nucleus were to form in a large mass of liquid supercooled so extensively as this, the growth process on the nucleus would occur with such violent speed as to distort severely, and probably shatter, the resulting solid.

When considering the factors which determine w it is usual to denote the latter by ΔF, the total free energy change involved in forming the nucleus at a specified place in the system, and to write it thus,

$$\Delta F = \Delta F_V + \Delta F_S + \Delta F_E \qquad \ldots \ldots \ldots \ldots \quad (92)$$

Here ΔF_V is the *bulk* or *chemical* free energy change, omitting all contributions due to *surface* energy or *elastic* energy. The increase in total surface free energy due to the interface between the nucleus and the

* A method was first introduced by A. Einstein, *Ann. Physik*, 1910, **33**, 1275, for the nucleation of liquid droplets in a vapour phase. A clear account of the application of this method to precipitation in solid solutions has been given by C. Zener, Chapter 2 in 'Thermodynamics in Physical Metallurgy', Amer. Soc. Metals, 1950.

parent phase is denoted by ΔF_S. In changes in the solid state there may be accompanying changes in the volume and shape of the region enclosing the nucleus, or alternatively the nucleus may be so constrained by the surrounding lattice that it cannot pull its atoms into the equilibrium structure of the new phase; in either case, the system acquires elastic energy due to the change, and this is represented by the term ΔF_E.

14.3 Freezing of Liquids

Perhaps the simplest phase change of interest in metallurgy is the freezing of a liquid metal. Because the solid has the same composition as the liquid there is no complication due to the separation of solute and solvent atoms. Moreover, the elastic energy factor is small, because the liquid in general accommodates all volume and shape changes, and it can be neglected at the nucleation stage at least. The only factors involved are the difference in chemical free energy between the solid and liquid phases, and the surface energy of the solid/liquid interface.

Consider the formation of a cubically shaped nucleus of solid, having sides of length a. This assumption about the shape is not critical and other simple shapes can be dealt with by making appropriate small alterations to the numerical factors in the formulae. Let ΔF_V denote the bulk free energy change involved in the creation of a nucleus of unit volume. Let γ be the surface free energy of unit area of the interface between the nucleus and the parent phase, and for simplicity suppose that the value of γ is the same for all crystal faces of the solid phase. Then we can write

$$\Delta F = a^3 \Delta F_V + 6a^2 \gamma \quad \ldots \ldots \ldots \ldots (93)$$

The important feature here is that the surface energy term varies as the square of the linear size of the nucleus, whereas the bulk free energy term varies as the cube. This introduces a *size effect* into the problem.*
Remembering that ΔF_V is necessarily negative, since the melt is cooled below its thermodynamical freezing point, we see that ΔF in equation 93 varies as shown in Fig. 103. When the nuclei are very small the positive surface term predominates, but when they are large the negative volume term predominates, so that the curve rises to a maximum at a critical nucleus size given by an edge length a_0. A nucleus is only stable when its edge length is not smaller than a_0, since for any smaller value the free energy *increases* if the nucleus begins to grow. There is thus a lower limiting size for a permanent nucleus, and a corresponding critical value, A, of the work of nucleus formation. The nucleus of critical size, a_0, is in *unstable* equilibrium with the parent phase, since any alteration in its size provides it with the tendency either to disappear or to grow larger.

* The general principles of size effects in nucleation processes were laid down by M. Volmer and A. Weber, *Zeit. Phys. Chem.*, 1925, **119**, 277, and R. Becker and W. Döring, *Ann. Phys.*, 1935, **24**, 719.

To calculate A we note that, at the critical size where $a=a_0$,

$$d(\Delta F)/da=3a^2\Delta F_V+12a\gamma=0,$$

which gives

$$a_0=-4\gamma/\Delta F_V \dots \dots \dots \dots (94)$$

Substituting this in equation 93 gives

$$\begin{aligned}
A&=\Delta F \text{ at } a=a_0\\
&=-(4\gamma/\Delta F_V)^3\Delta F_V+6(4\gamma/\Delta F_V)^2\gamma\\
&=a\gamma^3/(\Delta F_V)^2 \dots \dots \dots \dots (95)
\end{aligned}$$

where $a=32$; if the nucleus were spherical we should find that $a=16\pi/3$.

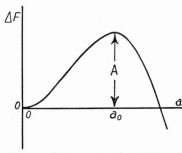

FIG. 103.—The Free Energy of Formation of a Cubical Nucleus as a Function of the Size of the Nucleus.

We must now consider the way in which A varies with temperature. The important point here is that ΔF_V is zero at the equilibrium freezing point and increases with increasing undercooling; the effect of a temperature variation of γ is small by comparison, and in a simplified treatment we can take γ to be constant. If we regard the phases A and B in Fig. 50 as solid and liquid, respectively, then ΔF_V at any given temperature is the vertical distance between the two curves at the temperature concerned. Clearly, for small degrees of undercooling, ΔF_V is directly proportional to the undercooling. To find this variation of ΔF_V the relations of section 8.2 are useful. From equation 55 we see that the free energy of a phase varies with temperature according to the relation $dF/dT=-S$, where S is its entropy. It follows then that

$$d(\Delta F_V)/dT=d(F_A-F_B)/dT=-(S_A-S_B)=\Delta S,$$

where F_A and F_B are the free energies of the solid and liquid at the temperature concerned, and ΔS is their difference in entropy. In a simplified treatment we can regard ΔS as independent of temperature and equal to the value it has at the true melting point, T_m. Equation 57 shows that $\Delta S=\Delta Q/T_m$, where ΔQ is the latent heat (per unit volume). Let M be the volume of a gram. molecule, L_m the latent heat per gram. molecule, and let $\theta(=T_m-T$, where T is the temperature of nucleation) be the *degree of undercooling*. Then we have

$$\Delta F_V=\theta d(\Delta F_V)/dT=\theta L_m/MT_m \dots \dots \dots (96)$$

and

$$A=a\gamma^3(MT_m/\theta L_m)^2 \dots \dots \dots \dots (97)$$

We notice that, if $\theta=0$, A is infinite and no nucleation can occur. For small degrees of undercooling, A is large and nucleation is slow. As the undercooling increases, the rate of nucleation must also increase. When the undercooling becomes sufficiently large, however, the diminution in the intensity of thermal fluctuations and the increased sluggishness in the movements of the atoms slow down the nucleation; this range of conditions can be reached with glasses, which can be retained in the form of supercooled liquids of very high viscosity for long periods of time, but apparently not with metals.

A detailed calculation of the rate of nucleation for various degrees of undercooling has been given by Turnbull and Fisher.* A simplified treatment is as follows. For freezing to begin, at least one nucleus must be formed in the liquid. Hence, taking $n=1$ in equation 91, the work of nucleation cannot have a value greater than $kT \log_e N$. For homogeneous nucleation $N \simeq 10^{23}$ (i.e. the number of atoms in a system of 'reasonable' size) and $kT \log_e N \simeq 50kT$. Freezing should take place when, with increasing undercooling, A diminishes to the value of $50kT$. Combining this with equation 97 then gives

$$\alpha\gamma^3(MT_m/\theta L_m)^2 = 50kT \quad \ldots \quad \ldots \quad (98)$$

If we knew values of the surface energy γ, this relation could be used to predict the degree of undercooling. These are not available, however, and so instead we must examine what values of γ are implied by the observed degrees of undercooling. Experiments to be described below† have shown that for a large number of materials $\theta \simeq 0.2T_m$. We shall use this observed value and also take (since $\theta = T_m - T$) $T = 0.8T_m$. For typical metals melting in the range 1000 to 2000° K. we take $L_m/M \simeq 1.5 \times 10^{10}$ erg per c.c. and $kT_m \simeq 2.5 \times 10^{-13}$ erg. These values give a surface energy for the solid/liquid interface of 150 to 200 erg/cm.², which seems reasonable in view of the fact that for such metals the energies of large-angle grain boundaries, which might crudely be regarded as two solid-liquid interfaces placed back to back, are of the order of 500 erg/cm.²; moreover, as Smith‡ has pointed out, the liquid in a metal 'wets' the grains of the solid with which it is in equilibrium, which implies that the energy of the solid/liquid interface is less than half that of a large-angle grain boundary. Turnbull's§ values of θ and γ for a number of metals are given in Table 8.

TABLE 8.—SOLID-LIQUID INTERFACIAL ENERGIES OF PURE METALS, DEDUCED FROM SUPERCOOLING EXPERIMENTS

Metal	Hg	Ga	Sn	Bi	Pb	Sb	Ge	Ag	Au	Cu	Mn	Ni	Co	Fe	Pd	Pt
θ, °K.	58	76	105		90	80	135	227	227	230	236	308	319	330	295	332	370
γ, erg/cm.²	24·4	56	54·5	54	33	101	181	126	132	177	206	255	234	204	209	240

* D. Turnbull and J. C. Fisher, *J. Chem. Phys.*, 1949, **17**, 71.

† In these experiments the number of atoms in the system was much less than 10^{23}. However, the value of γ is very insensitive to that of N.

‡ C. S. Smith, *Trans. Amer. Inst. Min. Met. Eng.*, 1948, **175**, 15.

§ D. Turnbull, *J. Chem. Phys.*, 1950, **18**, 769.

Equation 98 shows γ^3 as proportional to $L_m^2 T / T_m^2$. Since T is proportional to T_m and hence, approximately, to L_m (see section 8.4), this means that γ should be proportional to L_m. Turnbull has emphasised that this proportionality is observed in practice for many metals; he concludes that the total surface free energy of a number of atoms, if spread into a monatomic solid/liquid interface, is very nearly equal to one-half of the latent heat needed to melt this number.

The method used by Turnbull to measure the degrees of supercooling reported in Table 8 is based on a technique first used by Vonnegut for studying the solidification of metals.* The problem is to prevent heterogeneous nucleation on foreign particles suspended in the liquid. This is overcome by breaking the liquid up into a large number of very small droplets, 10 to 50 microns in diameter, which are separated from each other by being suspended in some other liquid, e.g. oil or slag, or by being spread out on a supporting plate. The aim is to break up the liquid into a number of droplets greater than the number of foreign particles present. Then, although some droplets contain particles which catalyse freezing immediately, others are free from them and do not freeze until the temperature range of homogeneous nucleation is reached.

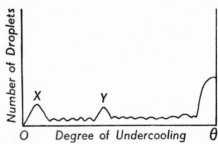

Fig. 104.—The Number of Droplets which Freeze at a Given Degree of Undercooling: Specific catalysing particles cause freezing at X and Y of those droplets which contain them; homogeneous nucleation of the remaining droplets occurs when the degree of undercooling is θ.

The freezing points of individual droplets were found to be sharply defined and reproducible in repeated cycles of melting and freezing. It was observed, for example, in lead that one droplet would always freeze at a temperature near the equilibrium freezing point, another would supercool to about $\theta/2$, and another one would supercool to θ. Thus, each particle appeared to possess its own characteristic undercooling temperature, and one could construct a 'spectrum' of such temperatures from observations on a large number of droplets, as shown diagrammatically in Fig. 104. Such regularity of behaviour suggests that foreign particles present in droplets nucleate freezing at certain definite degrees of supercooling, which are determined by the extent to which their surfaces form suitable substrates for the nucleated crystals. The importance

* B. Vonnegut, *J. Colloid Science*, 1948, **3**, 563.

of a good 'match' between the lattice of the substrate and that of the nucleated crystal is recognised in the development of materials used as nucleating agents in commercial cast metals.*

The theory of heterogeneous nucleation can be developed from that of homogeneous nucleation by taking account of the interface energies, γ_{PL} and γ_{PS}, respectively, between the catalysing particle (P) and the liquid (L) and solid (S) phases.† Heterogeneous nucleation takes place in preference to homogeneous nucleation when $\gamma_{PS} < \gamma_{PL}$. If we have

Liquid

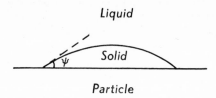

Particle

FIG. 105.—Nucleation of Solid from Liquid on the Surface of a Foreign Particle.

nucleation on a flat particle, as in Fig. 105, then the relation between the interfacial energies is

$$\gamma_{PL} = \gamma_{PS} + \gamma \cos \psi \quad . \quad . \quad . \quad . \quad . \quad . \quad . \quad . \quad . \quad (99)$$

where γ is the liquid/solid interfacial energy and ψ is the contact angle. A calculation of the critical nucleus size, following the method used above for homogeneous nucleation, then gives the result

$$A = a\gamma^3[(2 + \cos \psi)(1 - \cos \psi)^2/4]/(\Delta F_V)^2 \quad . \quad . \quad . \quad . \quad (100)$$

which is the same as equation 95 except for the function involving ψ. When ψ is zero freezing should occur almost without supercooling, since the original liquid/particle interface can then be replaced by solid/particle and solid/liquid interfaces without increase in surface energy (i.e. $\gamma_{PS} + \gamma \ll \gamma_{PL}$).

Turnbull observes that once nucleation occurs in a drastically supercooled droplet the rate of freezing is then extremely rapid. In the casting of metals under practical conditions, however, heterogeneous nucleation occurs at temperatures near the thermodynamic freezing point and in such cases the rate of growth of the solid phase is much smaller, being limited by the rate of removal of the latent heat of solidification liberated at the solid/liquid interface. If not removed, this heat warms up the system and stops further freezing. The theory of crystal growth from a melt under these conditions has been developed by Chalmers‡ and his associates.

Various features are discussed by Chalmers. Since the interface is the place where the latent heat is liberated, it should be slightly hotter

* See, for example, A. Cibula, *J. Inst. Metals*, 1949-50, 76, 321.

† J. H. Hollomon, 'Thermodynamics in Physical Metallurgy', pp. 161-77, Amer. Soc. Metals (1950).

‡ B. Chalmers, *Trans. Amer. Inst. Min. Met. Eng.*, in press (1954).

than neighbouring regions. The condition for freezing, however, is that the interface temperature should be equal to, or slightly lower than, the thermodynamic freezing point. It follows that the liquid just ahead of the interface must have a still lower temperature, i.e. it must be in a supercooled state. As in the case of constitutional supercooling discussed in section 11.5, this leads to an *instability* in the growth and a tendency to form dendrites, the solid/liquid interface taking on a corrugated form. These corrugations are frequently associated with a columnar sub-structure in the growing crystal, and a crystal grown in this manner usually has the form of a bundle of parallel rods joined together by small-angle boundaries (see section 15.4) in which impurities are concentrated. This substructure is thought to originate from the condensation of vacancies, created in large numbers at the solid/liquid interface, into flat sheet-like cavities which subsequently collapse. Once a misalignment is formed in such a manner as this between two pieces of the crystal in contact with the liquid, it continues between those parts of the crystal which subsequently grow on them.

14.4 Precipitation of a Phase from a Solution

If the parent phase is not a pure metal but a solution, the new phase which nucleates and grows in it generally has a different composition. In this section we shall consider how this affects the processes of nucleation and growth. We shall consider the surface energy at the interface between the phases, but neglect any effects of strain energy. The discussion is thus applicable to the freezing of liquid solutions and to precipitation in solid solutions at high temperatures where the material cannot support large stresses.

Although the composition in a homogeneous disordered solution is usually described as 'uniform' this term is strictly applicable on a macroscopic scale only. If samples containing, say, 100 atoms only could be taken from the solution we should find that the composition varied strongly from one sample to another. Fink and Smith* have given an instructive example based on the precipitation of $CuAl_2$ from a solution of 2 at. per cent. copper in aluminium. They considered an ideally random solution of this composition and calculated, from the statistics of random distributions, that 22,500 groups of 48 atoms in 1 mm.^{3} of alloy would have a suitable composition (16 copper and 32 aluminium atoms) for forming particles of $CuAl_2$; in addition there would be many more groups lacking but one or two copper atoms. Thus, accidental fluctuations in distribution can provide many small groups of atoms which have suitable compositions for nuclei before the system is even taken into the temperature range where the new phase is stable.

This calculation, although illuminating, cannot of course be applied generally since in real solutions, as opposed to ideal ones, the forces between the various kinds of atoms present favour one type of group-

* W. L. Fink and D. W. Smith, *Trans. Amer. Inst. Min. Met. Eng.*, 1940, **137**, 95.

ing more than another. In such cases we have to proceed in the following way: (1) calculate the work w required to form a nucleus of specified composition, size, structure, and surface energy, in a particular place in the system; (2) use equation 91 to find the number of such nuclei in the system. This procedure is a direct generalisation, bringing in the effect of composition, of that described at the beginning of section 14.2 for nucleation in pure materials; having included the effect of composition in w the theory can then be developed in the same way as in section 14.2.

Consider the free energy curves of Fig. 106. If the curves α and β do in fact join, the diagram represents a system of the type of Fig. 61 (c). If, on the other hand, they are separate curves which cross, they can represent a system with two phases of different structures. For

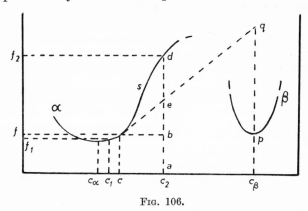

FIG. 106.

example, in the freezing of a solution, α and β represent liquid and solid respectively; applied to a precipitation-hardening alloy, α represents the parent solid solution (e.g. copper in aluminium) and β the precipitating phase (e.g. $CuAl_2$). Suppose that we have initially a homogeneous solution of composition c, with a free energy f per atom, and containing a total of N_1+N_2 atoms. Let it split into a nucleus (N_2 atoms, composition c_2, free energy per atom f_2) and a matrix (N_1 atoms, composition c_1, free energy per atom f_1). Then the free energy of the system, neglecting surface energy, changes by

$$\Delta F_V = N_1(f_1-f) + N_2(f_2-f).$$

Since $N_1(c-c_1) = N_2(c_2-c)$ this can be written as

$$\Delta F_V = N_2[f_2-f+\{(f_1-f)(c_2-c)/(c-c_1)\}].$$

Since the nucleus is very small compared with the matrix then $N_1 \gg N_2$ and c_1 is very close to c, so that

$$(f_1-f)/(c-c_1) = -df/dc,$$

where the slope df/dc is measured at the composition c. This gives

$$\Delta F_V = N_2[f_2-f-(c_2-c)(df/dc)].$$

In Fig. 106 we have $f_2=ad$, $f=ab$, and $(c_2-c)(df/dc)=be$, so that $\Delta F_V/N_2=ed$. At the actual composition shown for c_2, ΔF_V is positive, but it is clear that for more intense fluctuations of composition, ΔF_V can be negative. For a nucleus of composition c_β we have $\Delta F_V/N_2=-pq$. Unless the surface energy of the nucleus varies sensitively with composition, the work of nucleation is least for nuclei of compositions near c_β, and according to equation 91 these nuclei will be formed by thermal fluctuations more abundantly than any others.

The degree of supersaturation of the solution is determined by the position of c relative to c_α. The 'driving force' for forming nuclei is greatest when the degree of supersaturation is such that the initial composition c of the solution coincides with that of the *spinodal point, s* (see section 10.7). Here the slope df/dc is a maximum so that q is as high as possible in Fig. 106, and hence the greatest possible amount of chemical free energy is released on forming a nucleus of composition c_β. Another special feature of the spinodal point, emphasised by Borelius,[*] is that when the initial solution has this composition, small finite fluctuations in composition *reduce* the chemical free energy, whereas for initial compositions to the left of the spinodal point in Fig. 106, i.e. in the region where the a free energy curve has positive curvature, only large fluctuations in composition lower the chemical free energy; small ones raise it.

The fact that the 'driving force' (measured by the length pq) for nucleation is greatest when the initial composition is the spinodal one is consistent with the observations by Borelius[†] and his associates that the rate of precipitation in certain supersaturated solid solutions increases rapidly when the system is cooled to the temperature where the composition of the initial solution crosses the spinodal line in the equilibrium diagram (see Fig. 72).

14.5   Coherent and Incoherent Nucleation

There is much evidence[‡] that precipitation from solid solutions becomes 'anomalous' at sufficiently low temperatures, in the sense that various effects occur which do not appear consistent with a simple theory of the nucleation and growth of particles of the expected new phase; the alloy may show two or more age-hardening peaks, the electrical resistivity and lattice parameter may not change in the manner anticipated, and X-ray diffraction effects from the particles of precipitate may show them to have a crystal structure which is not the stable one for the new phase, or even to consist of segregates of solute atoms in the parent solution, rather than distinct particles with their own crystal structure and a definite interface. This has led to theories which envisage the first stage of precipitation at such temperatures as

---

[*] G. Borelius, *Ann. Physik*, 1937, **28**, 507; 1938, **33**, 517.

[†] A summary of this work has been given by G. Borelius, *Trans. Amer. Inst. Min. Met. Eng.*, 1951, **191**, 477.

[‡] Discussed in the references given at the end of this chapter.

a clustering of solute atoms in the solvent lattice, followed by a second stage in which some of these clusters 'break away' to form particles with a characteristic crystal structure of their own.

Something of the kind is to be expected from the theory of nucleation developed above. The surface energy term in equation 92 dominates the process of nucleation when the interfacial energy is large, i.e. when there is a discontinuity in atomic structure, at the interface between the nucleus and the matrix, somewhat similar to that at a large-angle grain boundary in a polycrystal. Such nuclei are said to be of the *incoherent* type. As we have seen, an incoherent particle must exceed a certain minimum size if it is to nucleate the new phase. The time needed for assembling atoms in sufficient numbers to create such nuclei becomes long at low temperatures, and the alloy may seek a faster mode of precipitation which avoids this nucleation difficulty.

Such modes of precipitation become possible when the degree of supercooling (or, what is equivalent, the degree of supersaturation) is large. The initial solution then has enough surplus free energy to enable it to form nuclei of metastable structures, which have higher free energies than the equilibrium structure of the new phase, but which also have smaller interfacial energies and smaller critical nucleus sizes. In the extreme case where the degree of supercooling is sufficient to bring the alloy below the spinodal line (see Fig. 72) the initial solution is even unstable against small fluctuations of composition within itself and a process of segregation can take place on the solvent lattice with an accompanying reduction in free energy.*

A small surface energy is not possible if the precipitated particle is joined to the matrix by an incoherent interface similar to a large-angle grain boundary. What is needed instead is some *coherence* in atomic structure across the interface (see section 10.5). Precipitates of this kind are described as being *coherent* or *semi-coherent* according to the closeness of matching in the atomic positions across the interface.

In general the condition for coherence requires the precipitate to adopt a metastable lattice, or to strain its equilibrium lattice to fit that of the matrix. In either case the free energy of the precipitate is increased by a certain amount per atom which, apart from a small contribution from surface energy, is essentially independent of the number of atoms in the precipitated particle. The size effect, so important in incoherent precipitation, has a minor significance in coherent precipitation and can to a first approximation be ignored. The free energy relations between the parent solid solution α, the equilibrium precipitate β (neglecting surface energy) and the coherent metastable precipitate β', are of the form shown in Fig. 107. The higher free energy of β', relative to β, can be interpreted as a result of the non-equilibrium structure or of the strain energy needed to distort the equilibrium structure of the precipitate

---

* The conditions for this segregation have been discussed by R. Becker, *Zeit. Metallkunde*, 1937, **29**, 245, and H. K. Hardy, *J. Inst. Metals*, 1950, **77**, 457.

into coherence with the matrix. As a result, the solubility limit c' of the α phase in equilibrium with the coherent precipitate is higher than that, c, for equilibrium with the β phase.* Thus a second solubility line can be entered in the equilibrium diagram, below that for equilibrium with β, to denote the temperatures and compositions at which

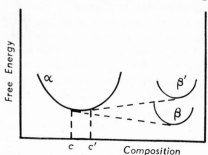

FIG. 107.—Free Energies of a Parent Solid Solution α, an Equilibrium Precipitate β, and a Coherent Precipitate β'; c and c' denote the respective solubility limits.

the α phase becomes supersaturated with respect to precipitation of the coherent β', as shown in Fig. 108.

If an alloy in this system is cooled into the temperature range between AB and $A'B'$, only the incoherent precipitation of β is possible, but as

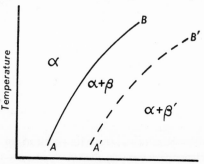

FIG. 108.—Solubility Limits in the System of Fig. 107. AB is the solubility limit with respect to precipitation of β, and $A'B'$ is the corresponding one for β'.

soon as it is cooled below $A'B'$ the coherent precipitate β' can form. In the limiting case where the surface energy of the latter is negligible there is no size effect and no nucleation problem for forming β'. Once the line $A'B'$ is crossed, particles of this precipitate can form as fast as the necessary atoms can migrate together.

Even in an incoherent precipitate the system will tend to reduce its

* F. R. N. Nabarro, *Proc. Phys. Soc.*, 1940, **52**, 90; *Proc. Roy. Soc.*, 1940, **A175**, 519; C. S. Barrett, 'Phase Transformations in Solids' (p. 536), Wiley, 1951; J. C. Fisher, J. H. Hollomon, and J. G. Leschen, *Ind. Eng. Chem.*, 1952, **44**, 1324.

surface energy as much as possible by arranging that the crystal planes of matrix and precipitate that form the boundaries of the interface have very similar atom spacings and patterns. As Barrett* has pointed out, this principle appears to govern the *orientation relationships* and *habit planes* of many precipitates in alloys. These crystallographic features of the precipitate are specified by two pieces of information:—

(1) A statement of the orientations of the principal crystallographic axes in the precipitate relative to those of the matrix. It is often observed that these orientation relationships are very simple, certain important crystallographic planes and directions in the two structures being parallel to one another. For example, when β-brass precipitates α-brass in the Cu-Zn system, a (110) plane of β is parallel to a (111) of α, and a [111] direction of β is parallel to a [110] of α. These relations are usually stated in the form: $(110)_{\beta}//(111)_{\alpha}$ and $[111]_{\beta}//[110]_{\alpha}$.

(2) A statement of the *habit* of the precipitate, i.e. the shape of the particle, and also, in the case of plate-shaped or needle-shaped particles, of the crystallographic plane or direction in the matrix which is parallel to the plane of the plate or axis of the needle. In many, but not all, precipitates the particle is plate-shaped and the regular pattern of such plates on certain crystallographic planes of the matrix crystal gives rise to forms of the well-known *Widmanstätten structure*.

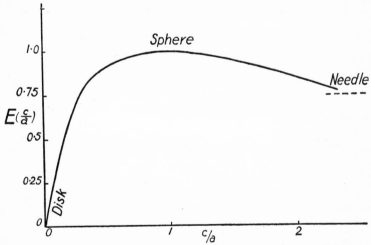

FIG. 109.—The Strain Energy E of an Ellipsoidal Particle of Precipitate as a Function of its Shape; a is the equatorial diameter, and c is the polar diameter of the ellipsoid.

A theory of the influence of strain energy on the shape of certain precipitates has been developed by Nabarro.† He considers a given region which has the shape of an ellipsoid with semi-axes a, a, and c, and which eventually becomes the site of a precipitate and thereby

* C. S. Barrett, 'Structure of Metals', McGraw-Hill, 1952.   † *Loc. cit.*

alters its volume. The amount of precipitate and the volume change on precipitation are held constant, and the effect of the ratio c/a upon the strain energy created by the volume change is studied. When $c/a \ll 1$ the precipitate has the form of a flat disc, when $c/a = 1$ it is spherical, and when $c/a \gg 1$ it is needle-shaped. The results of Nabarro's calculations are summarised in Fig. 109, which gives the strain energy E as a function of c/a. The strain energy factor clearly favours the formation of plate-shaped precipitates.

14.6 Heterogeneous Nucleation in Solids

The great importance of heterogeneous nucleation in promoting the crystallisation of liquids, clearly demonstrated by the experiments of Turnbull, leads us to expect it to play a similar role in solid-state reactions. There is in fact much evidence that this is the case. When a 0·9 per cent. carbon steel is cooled from the austenitic region (see Fig. 85) to temperatures of about 600° C., the eutectoid structure (*pearlite*) grows from nuclei which form at grain boundaries in the austenite or on particles of undissolved carbides; the important effect of austenitic grain size upon the hardenability of steel originates here. Comprehensive studies of the nucleation of pearlite at austenitic grain boundaries have been made by Mehl and his associates.* In precipitation-hardening systems it is commonly observed that precipitation takes place discontinuously, in the vicinity of grain boundaries and along slip planes on which plastic deformation has taken place. Measurements of rates of precipitation also point to heterogeneous nucleation. For example, Wert and Zener,† analysing the rate of precipitation of iron carbide from ferrite, were led to the conclusion that all the nuclei were present at the beginning of the ageing period, which suggests that nucleation was heterogeneous. Turnbull‡ has recently obtained the same result in a lead-tin alloy and also observed that the number of nuclei formed is independent of the quenching temperature, which leads him to the view that the centres of heterogeneous nucleation in this case are dislocations in the grains.

As regards incoherent precipitates, where surface energy is of prime importance, grain boundaries and the surfaces of foreign particles in the crystals are of course excellent sites for heterogeneous nucleation, since new phases can form there with a minimum increase in surface energy; the ideas of Smith regarding the distribution of second phases in alloys, discussed in section 10.5, are directly applicable here. In the case of coherent precipitates we expect the sites suitable for heterogeneous nucleation to be those where the particles can reduce their strain energy as much as possible. If the lattice contains internal strains, so that the lattice constants vary from place to place, then in some

---

* R. F. Mehl, *Trans. Amer. Soc. Met.*, 1941, **29**, 813; *J. Iron and Steel Inst.*, 1948, **159**, 113. See also A. Hultgren, *Trans. Amer. Soc. Met.*, 1947, **39**, 915.

† C. A. Wert and C. Zener, *J. Appl. Phys.*, 1950, **21**, 5.

‡ D. Turnbull, Report of 1954 Bristol Conference (London: Physical Society).

places the lattice will more closely match that of the precipitate than others, and coherent precipitation will take place more readily there. Dislocations are centres of internal strain in crystals and so should be favourable sites for coherent precipitation, in agreement with the observation that precipitation at low ageing temperatures occurs readily on planes along which slip has taken place. The localised precipitation observed on small-angle boundaries* is further evidence of this, since such boundaries consist in fact of rows of dislocations (see section 15.4). An entirely different effect of grain boundaries and dislocations has been suggested recently.† When these migrate through a solid solution they encounter solute atoms. A solute atom caught in this way can then migrate very quickly along the boundary, or the dislocations, until it finds a nucleus of precipitate. This process can speed up precipitation at low temperatures, where normal lattice diffusion is very slow. A high temperatures the free energy released by the process can provide a driving force for grain boundary migration.

14.7 Growth of New Phases in Solutions

As the precipitated nuclei increase in size and number, more and more solute atoms are removed from the parent solution and the concentration of the solute steadily falls towards that degree of dilution at which it reaches equilibrium with the precipitated phase. If the new phase is precipitated as massive incoherent particles, with surface and strain energies that are negligible in comparison with their chemical free energies, equilibrium is not reached until the concentration in the matrix reaches the ideal solubility limit (e.g. AB in Fig. 108). But if the precipitate has an appreciable surface energy (e.g. small incoherent particles) or strain energy (e.g. coherent particles), the effective solubility limit lies at a higher solute concentration (e.g. $A'B'$ in Fig. 108) and the precipitation reaction will come to rest while the parent solution is still, according to the equilibrium diagram, supersaturated. Premature end-points to low-temperature precipitation reactions have in fact often been observed. Another feature often observed in such reactions is that they proceed in two or three distinct stages, leading to the so-called 'double' and 'multiple ageing peaks'. It is reasonable to suppose, in such cases, that a fast reaction takes the system to a preliminary metastable equilibrium (e.g. by forming a fine coherent precipitate) and that then a slower reaction, involving a different type of nucleus, takes the system on a further stage towards its final equilibrium, and so on.

Closely allied to these effects is the process of *coarsening*, in which an initially fine precipitate is gradually replaced by a coarse one. The reason for this lies in the fact that the free energy per atom cannot be exactly the same in all particles of the precipitate. Some particles may

---

* P. Lacombe and A. Berghezan, *Comptes Rendus Acad. Sci. Paris*, 1949, **228**, 95; A. Castaing and A. Guinier, *ibid.*, 1949, **228**, 2033.

† D. Turnbull, J. C. Fisher and J. H. Hollomon, private communication, 1954.

be better situated (e.g. at grain boundaries) than others. Furthermore, due to local variations in the conditions of growth, particles may differ in other ways. There may, for example, be a mixture of coarse incoherent particles and fine coherent ones, or a mixture of both coarse and fine incoherent particles. When the free energy per atom differs in this manner from particle to particle, a parent solution of one definite concentration cannot be simultaneously in equilibrium with all of them. If it is in equilibrium with an 'average' particle, then it must be supersaturated with respect to those particles of lower free energy and undersaturated with respect to those of higher free energy; the former particles will grow and the latter will redissolve. Since the free energy per atom is lowest for coarse incoherent particles, it is these that ultimately win this competition for the excess atoms originally dissolved in the parent solution, and all other types of particles which were precipitated at earlier stages in the reaction are eventually forced to redissolve in order to feed them.

Another closely related phenomenon is *retrogression*, or *restoration*. An alloy which has been hardened by ageing at a low temperature can be made temporarily softer if subsequently heated to a higher temperature within the precipitation range. Clearly, if the alloy of Fig. 108 is first aged below the line $A'B'$, to bring down the precipitate stable below it, and is then reheated into the range between $A'B'$ and AB, the particles of this precipitate must dissolve again. Furthermore, by repeated cooling and heating across the line $A'B'$ the cycle of precipitation and re-solution can be repeated, as is observed in the retrogression phenomenon. This cycle is broken only when the alloy is held in the range from $A'B'$ to AB for long enough to bring down the precipitate that is stable in this range; once formed, this precipitate persists at all lower temperatures. Although Fig. 108 refers specifically to the precipitation of coherent particles below the line $A'B'$, essentially the same argument applies if we regard this line as the limit below which fine incoherent particles are precipitated and above which they return to solution.

We turn now to consider the factors which govern the rate of precipitation in a supersaturated solution once the nuclei have been formed. There are two main ones:—

(1) The rate of transport of atoms to the nuclei; this is determined by the rate of diffusion of solute atoms in the solution.

(2) *Impingement*; the growing particles, by claiming solute atoms from further and further out in the solution, begin to encroach upon each other's 'spheres of influence'. This effect, which has been analysed mathematically by several writers,* slows down the rate of reaction.

A calculation of the rates at which particles of certain shapes can

---

* W. A. Johnson and R. F. Mehl, *Trans. Amer. Inst. Min. Met. Eng.*, 1939 **135**, 416; M. Avrami, *J. Chem. Phys.*, 1939, **7**, 1103; 1940, **8**, 212; 1941, **9**, 177; U. R. Evans, *Trans. Faraday Soc.*, 1945, **41**, 365; J. E. Burke and D. Turnbull, 'Progress in Metal Physics, III' (Ed. B. Chalmers), Pergamon Press, 1952; J. L. Meijering, *Philips Research Reports*, 1953, **8**, 270.

grow has been made by Zener and Wert,* on the basis (i) that the effect of the surface energy of the particles on the equilibrium concentration is negligible, i.e. that the nuclei are well above the critical size, (ii) that the diffusion coefficient D of the solute in the parent solution is independent of concentration, and (iii) that the rate of growth is limited solely by diffusion, i.e. that each part of the interface of a particle advances just as rapidly as the transport by diffusion of atoms to it will allow.

Spherical particles grow most slowly, for the area of contact they make with the solution, for a given volume of particle, is a minimum. Each such particle is surrounded by a sphere of influence in the solution, from which it has drawn the atoms necessary for its growth. As the particle expands, so also does its sphere of influence spread further out into the solution. Since the process is controlled by diffusion, the radius of this sphere increases as $(Dt)^{1/2}$, where t is the time of growth. Because the particle absorbs a constant proportion of the atoms in this sphere, its own radius also increases as $(Dt)^{1/2}$. The volume of the spherical particle thus increases as $t^{3/2}$ until the stage is reached where its sphere of influence begins to overlap those of its neighbours, after which the growth slows down.

Particles having the shape of long thin rods or thin flat discs can grow faster than spherical ones (provided that an atom can attach itself with equal facility to any point on any face of the particle) because they have greater ratios of surface area to volume. In other words, the ends of a rod-shaped particle or the rim of a disc-shaped one are continually advancing outwards, as they grow, into new and untapped regions of the solution, regions not yet depleted of atoms (assuming, of course, that impingement has not occurred). The speed of advance of these ends or rims is constant, since they advance into material of constant composition. Hence the length of a rod, or the radius of a disc, increases linearly with time. The growth of the side faces, however, i.e. the cylindrical faces of the rod, or the flat faces of the disc, is faced with the same difficulty as in the case of the spherical particle. Regions of the solution near such faces are drained of atoms and, to allow the faces to grow further, atoms have to be brought in from further away. Thus the radius of the rod, or the thickness of the disc, increases as $t^{1/2}$. It follows, allowing also for the linear growth of the ends and rims, that the volume of the rod increases as t^2, and that of the disc as $t^{5/2}$. An experimental study by Wert† of precipitation of carbides and nitrides in iron showed that the amount of carbon precipitated increases initially as $t^{3/2}$, suggesting spherical precipitates, and that of nitrogen as $t^{5/2}$, suggesting disc-shaped precipitates. In cold-worked iron,‡ by contrast, the amount of precipitate of both elements

* C. Zener, *J. Appl. Phys.*, 1949, **20**, 950; C. Wert and C. Zener, *ibid.*, 1950, **21**, 5.
† C. Wert, *J. Appl. Phys.*, 1949, **20**, 943.
‡ S. Harper, *Phys. Rev.*, 1951, **83**, 709.

increases as $t^{2/3}$, in confirmation of a predicted formula for precipitation on dislocations.*

A theory of the growth of lamellar eutectic structures, which refers particularly to the growth of pearlite (the eutectoid mixture of ferrite and cementite) from austenite in carbon steel, has been developed by Brandt,† Zener‡ and Fisher.§ Fig. 110 shows the growth of a pearlite nodule. The common interface that the ferrite and cementite lamellae make with the austenite advances into the latter, and it is observed that, at constant temperature and with homogeneous austenite, the growth process reaches a steady-state in which both the velocity of the interface and the interlamellar spacing remain constant. The process of growth involves two distinct steps: (i) a redistribution of carbon at the interface, since the carbon concentrates in the cementite (Fe_3C) and

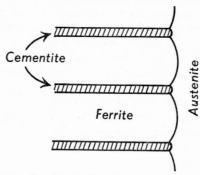

FIG. 110.—Growth of a Pearlite Nodule in Austenite.

avoids the ferrite; thus the austenite just ahead of a ferrite lamella is enriched by the carbon rejected from the ferrite, while that ahead of a cementite lamella is correspondingly impoverished; (ii) a change in crystal structure, from that of austenite to those of ferrite and cementite.

It is generally agreed that the rate of growth is controlled by the rate of diffusion of carbon in the vicinity of the interface, and that the accompanying crystallographic changes occur as fast as the necessary redistribution of carbon will allow. The constant velocity of growth is explained by the fact that the pearlite nodule advances into austenite of constant composition and temperature. Zener explains the factors governing the interlamellar spacing in the following manner. If the spacing is unduly large the distance L over which the carbon atoms have to travel in order to concentrate in the cementite is correspondingly large, and the rate of redistribution is slow. If the spacing is unduly small the area, and hence energy, of the ferrite/cementite interfaces

* A. H. Cottrell and B. A. Bilby, *Proc. Phys. Soc.*, 1949, **62**, 19.
† W. H. Brandt, *J. Appl. Phys.*, 1945, **16**, 139.
‡ C. Zener, *Trans. Amer. Inst. Min. Met. Eng.*, 1946, **167**, 550.
§ J. C. Fisher, 'Thermodynamics in Physical Metallurgy' (p. 201), Amer. Soc. Metals, 1950.

become large, with the result that so much of the free energy released in the austenite→pearlite transformation is absorbed as ferrite/cementite interfacial energy that little is left to provide a 'driving force' ΔF for the change. A balance between these opposing effects is struck at an intermediate spacing which maximises the quantity $\Delta F/L$. Since the free energy released in the austenite→pearlite transformation increases with increasing degree of undercooling, the optimum interlamellar spacing decreases as the temperature of transformation is lowered.

REFERENCES FOR FURTHER READING

'Kinetic Theory of Liquids.' J. Frenkel, Oxford, 1946.

'Progress in Metal Physics, IV'. J. H. Hollomon and D. Turnbull (Ed. B. Chalmers), Pergamon Press, 1953.

G. Borelius, *Trans. Amer. Inst. Min. Met. Eng.*, 1951, **191**, 477.

H. K. Hardy, *J. Inst. Metals*, 1948-49, **75**, 707; 1950, **77**, 457.

'Structure of Metals.' C. S. Barrett, McGraw-Hill, 1952.

M. L. V. Gayler, *J. Inst. Metals*, 1937, **60**, 249.

J. N. Hobstetter, *Trans. Amer. Inst. Min. Met. Eng.*, 1949, **180**, 121.

S. T. Konobeevski, *J. Inst. Metals*, 1943, **69**, 397.

'Progress in Metal Physics, I'. G. C. Smith (Ed. B. Chalmers), Butterworth, 1949.

'Phase Transformations in Solids' (Ed. R. Smoluchowski), Wiley, 1951.

'Thermodynamics in Physical Metallurgy', Amer. Soc. Metals, 1950.

CHAPTER XV

SHEAR PROCESSES IN METAL CRYSTALS

15.1 Types of Shear Processes

Let us consider a crystal and imagine that, by applying a suitable set of forces to it, we cause one half of the crystal to begin sliding over the other half on some chosen surface and along some chosen direction in the crystal. At first, since the atoms on the one side of the surface are pulled past their neighbours on the other side, their energy must increase, this increase being responsible for the elastic rigidity of the crystal. If the direction of shear is suitably chosen (i.e. a simple crystallographic direction), however, a stage will be reached with increasing shear where the atoms in the sheared region begin to fit neatly again. Their energy then begins to fall and reaches a new minimum as the increasing shear takes them forward into the new set of equilibrium positions. The elastic rigidity of the crystal is regained when the atoms reach these positions. If, for example, the applied forces are reduced, the atoms in these new positions do not slip back to their original ones; at this stage, therefore, the shear deformation differs from a purely elastic one (which is reversible on unloading), and to emphasise this difference it is described as a *permanent deformation*. This deformation can be detected, when sufficiently large, in various ways; e.g. by the change in the shape of the crystal, by the displacement of the halves of an initially straight line scribed across the region of the shear, and by the appearance of steps or tilted regions at places where the sheared region emerges at the surface of the crystal.

Some of the most important changes in metal and alloy crystals occur by such shear processes. They may be classified according to the relation of the lattice in the sheared region to the coherent surrounding lattice, as follows:—

(1) *Slip*. In this case the lattice generated in the sheared region is identical in all respects with the surrounding lattice, i.e. each atom in the slipped region makes the same movement, and this takes it forward by a whole number of lattice vectors (see section 3.3). This is the common mode of plastic deformation in metal crystals and the sheared regions it produces are often confined to surfaces one atom thick, called *slip planes*, which are parallel to a prominent crystallographic plane.

(2) *Deformation Twinning*. Here the lattice generated in the sheared region is the same as the parent lattice but is oriented in *twin* relationship to it, i.e. the lattices of the twinned and untwinned parts of the crystal are mirror images of each other by reflection in some simple crystal plane. This difference between slip and twinning is illustrated in Fig. 111. The vectors describing the atomic movements in twinning

are not lattice vectors, since they generate a new configuration of the atoms. A sheared region in twinning encloses many atomic layers, the atoms in each layer being sheared by the same amount with respect to those of the layer below them; this difference from slip occurs because the characteristic twinning shear can be applied only once to any given atomic layer so that, if a large displacement is to be produced by twinning, each repetition of the shear must occur on a new atomic layer. The *mechanical shear* of a twinned region can be measured by the methods mentioned above; the *crystallographic shear*, i.e. the change in crystal orientation, can be measured by the usual crystallographic methods. In certain simple kinds of deformation twinning (e.g. that in α-iron) of the type envisaged in Fig. 111, the mechanical and crystallographic shears are equal. In other kinds, however (e.g. that in zinc),

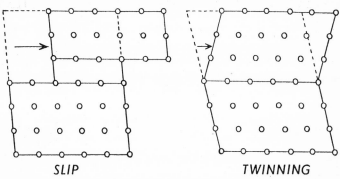

SLIP   TWINNING

FIG. 111.—Slip and Twinning in a Crystal.

localised inhomogeneous movements of the atoms occur, in addition to the overall mechanical shear, and in such cases the two shears are not equal.

(3) *Shear Transformations.* These are similar to deformation twinning in many respects, but differ in that a *new* lattice is generated in the sheared region. The sheared region then contains a new phase and its boundary with the parent material is a phase interface. Although these are called shear transformations, a name which is justified because a mechanical shear of the transformed region takes place, the deformation is usually of a more general kind than a simple shear; for example, if the new phase has a different specific volume from the old one, a *dilatation* must occur as well as a shear. The best-known example of a shear transformation occurs in the decomposition of austenite to *martensite* (see section 9.5) in steel, and in recognition of this, the name *martensitic transformation* is often used in place of shear transformation.

In slip, in twinning, and in many shear transformations, the composition of the sheared region is the same as that of the parent material; no diffusion of solute atoms in or out of the sheared region occurs. Such transformations are described as being *diffusionless*. It is characteristic of them that, since the growth of the sheared region does not have to wait for diffusion and since the region is joined coherently to its matrix, they are capable of spreading at great speed, comparable with the speed of sound, through the crystal. Not all shear transformations are of this kind, however. At temperatures a little higher than those at which martensite forms, austenite decomposes to *bainite* by a shear transformation which appears to be very similar to that which produces martensite, but the rate of growth is slow because a redistribution of carbon, which is dissolved in austenite but precipitated in bainite, has also to occur.*

15.2 Mechanics of a Simple Shear Process

Many of the features of the shear processes described above can be understood with the aid of the simple example shown in Fig. 112. Two

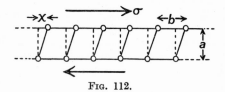

FIG. 112.

rows of atoms are subjected to a shear along their length by the application of a shear stress σ. For sufficiently small stresses the displacement x from the initial equilibrium positions is so small compared with the atomic spacing b, along the shear direction, that *Hooke's law* is obeyed; i.e. $\sigma = \mu(x/a)$, where x/a is the *shear strain*, μ is the *shear modulus*, and

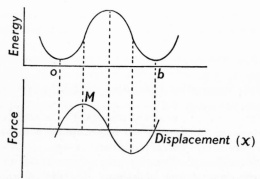

FIG. 113.

a is the spacing of the layers. At large strains, however, this law breaks down because, as x increases, the atoms in the upper layer begin to approach the next set of equilibrium positions along the row.

In terms of an energy diagram the situation is as shown in Fig. 113. The energy of the interatomic bonds is a minimum at the equilibrium

---

* See, for example, T. Ko and S. A. Cottrell, *J. Iron and Steel Inst.*, 1952, **172**, 307.

positions, $x=0$, b, $2b$, . . . , nb, etc., and rises symmetrically between them. The precise shape of the curve depends of course on the law of interatomic force, but in the very simplest case we can assume a sinusoidal shape, as shown. The force (or stress) necessary to hold the lattice at each stage in its shear is measured by the slope of the energy curve at the point concerned, and varies in the manner shown in Fig. 113.

When the crystal is subjected to the applied stress σ its equilibrium state can be decided only by including the *source* of the applied stress within the thermodynamic system. This means, in fact, that we must include the energy of the source with that of the crystal. The source, for example, may be a stretched elastic spring which contracts and lowers its strain energy as the crystal shears; or it may be a suspended weight which falls and lowers its gravitational energy as the crystal shears. The inclusion of this energy thus modifies the energy diagram to the type shown in Fig. 114.

The state of the system represented by the minimum A now has higher energy than that represented by B, and there is a thermodynamic tendency for the transition $A \rightarrow B$ to occur. In discussing the

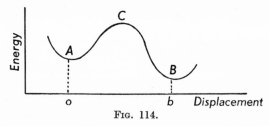

FIG. 114.

mechanism of this transition we can reapply the arguments already developed for other types of transition governed by energy curves of the shape of Fig. 114 (see, for example, Fig. 54 and sections 10.5, 14.1 and 14.2). These lead us to conclude that the transition will not occur simultaneously over the whole of the sheared region. Instead, in order to minimise the amount of material in the high-energy configuration C at any instant during the transition, a process of nucleation and growth will occur, with part of the material in the fully sheared state B, with part in the initial state A, and with these separated by an interfacial region in the state C, as shown in Fig. 115. As in the previous examples of nucleation and growth processes, the process of growth consists of the advance of the interfacial region into the untransformed region. Furthermore, by analogy with previous examples (see section 10.5), we expect that the interfacial region will be very narrow, i.e. of atomic dimensions only, in order to minimise the amount of material in the high-energy state C.

This interfacial region is a simple example of a *dislocation*. In this particular case the dislocation is a *slip dislocation* since it forms the boundary in the plane of slip between slipped and unslipped regions.

If, on the other hand, the material in region *B* had sheared into a twin orientation or into a new crystal structure, the dislocation would have been a *twinning dislocation* or a *transformation dislocation*, respectively.

The thickness of the interfacial region (i.e. *C* in Fig. 115) is called the *width* of the dislocation, and is of great importance. The factor

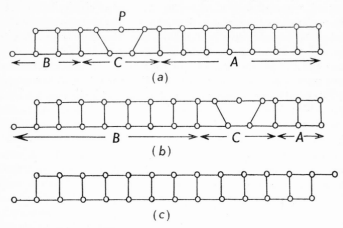

FIG. 115.—(*a*), (*b*) and (*c*) Stages in the Nucleation and Growth of a Unit of Slip Deformation; *A* denotes the unslipped region, *B* the slipped region, and *C* the interfacial region.

tending to reduce the width, or *contract* the dislocation, is the interfacial energy, as discussed above, and that which opposes the contraction is the elastic energy of the dislocation, discussed in section 15.4. The elastic energy is proportional to the elastic constants of the material and hence to the curvature of the energy function in the region of its minima, *A* and *B* in Fig. 114. It follows that the width of the dislocation depends on the height of the maximum, *C*, relative to the curvature

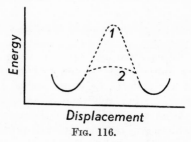

FIG. 116.

at the minimum. For example, a dislocation in a structure represented by curve 1 in Fig. 116 would be narrow, since the interfacial energy is high, whereas that represented by curve 2 would be wide.

The main factor influencing the width is the type of interatomic bonding in the material. If the bonds are of a *directional* nature (see section

2.3), so that the energy is increased when the *angle* of the bond is changed, as well as when its length is changed, the interfacial energy is high and a narrow dislocation results; this state of affairs is to be expected in homopolar crystals such as diamond. On the other hand, if the bond energy is insensitive to angle and depends mainly on its length, as in metals (see section 6.3), the energy will not be so greatly increased for large shear strains, and the dislocation will be wider. A dislocation in copper, for example, is considered to be at least six atoms wide.*

The reason why the width of a dislocation is important is that it determines the *mobility* of the dislocation, that is, the ability of the dislocation to glide along its slip plane, under a given driving force, so causing the slipped region to grow at the expense of the unslipped region. Simplified arguments lead to the conclusion that the minimum force needed to move the dislocation is arbitrarily small. For example, consider the central atom P in the dislocation of Fig. 115. What interatomic forces act on it? By symmetry, the horizontal components of force acting on it from both rows of atoms vanish, because for every atom in a given position ahead of the dislocation there is another one in the equivalent position behind it. The applied force needed to start atom P moving in the slip direction is thus zero. More exact calculations show that the force needed to make the dislocation glide is not zero, because the atoms have to pass through unsymmetrical configurations at other stages during the glide of the dislocation.† This effect of unsymmetry is, however, extremely sensitive to the width of the dislocation, and becomes negligible when the dislocation is wide. The stress needed to cause a dislocation to glide through an otherwise perfect metal lattice should thus be small, whereas the corresponding one for a lattice with directed bonds should be large. This aspect of dislocation theory therefore provides a basis for understanding the characteristic ductility of metals and the brittleness of certain non-metallic solids.

To nucleate slip in an initially *perfect* crystal, it would be necessary first to strain the intended nuclear region to the point, M in Fig. 113, beyond which the lattice forces resisting the shear begin to decrease; the atoms will then slide forward to the next equilibrium position. If the force-displacement relation is sinusoidal, as in Fig. 113, this critical displacement is given by $x=b/4$, corresponding to a critical shear strain $1/4(b/a)$. For the planes and directions of slip in actual crystals, a is a little larger than b. Also, with a realistic law of interatomic force the critical displacement is a little smaller than $b/4$. After allowing for these

---

* W. L. Bragg and W. M. Lomer, *Proc. Roy. Soc.*, 1949, **A196**, 171; W. M. Lomer, *ibid.*, 1949, **A196**, 182; A. J. Foreman, M. A. Jaswon, and J. K. Wood, *Proc. Phys. Soc.*, 1951, **A64**, 156. Note that, if the dislocation dissociates, as suggested in section 15.3, its width increases still further.

† R. V. Peierls, *Proc. Phys. Soc.*, 1940, **52**, 34; F. R. N. Nabarro, *ibid.*, 1947, **59**, 256.

and other small effects the critical strain for nucleating slip in a perfect crystal is deduced to be about 0·1. If a state suitable for homogeneous nucleation exists (see section 14.2), i.e. if the applied stress is distributed evenly over the crystal, and if there are no irregularities in the crystal that can promote nucleation, then the macroscopic elastic strain of the crystal must reach the order of magnitude of 0·1 before slip begins.

In practice the behaviour is reminiscent of that observed in the freezing of liquids and described in section 14.3. Herring and Galt* first showed, with tin 'whiskers' about 10^{-4} cm. diameter and several mm. long, that when the diameter of the crystal is sufficiently small, plastic deformation does not begin until a strain of about 0·1 is applied. Thus the full theoretical strength of the metal is realised in these very small specimens.

In larger specimens, even when these are commercial materials hardened by cold-working, alloying and heat-treatment, the observed limiting elastic strain is much smaller than 0·1, and we conclude that in these slip is nucleated heterogeneously at stresses smaller than are needed to reach the theoretical elastic limit; in hard commercial materials, for example, the observed limiting elastic strain is of order 10^{-2}, and in large soft single crystals it is only of order 10^{-5}.

Experience has shown that the only reasonable conclusion from these facts is that the nuclei for slip are always present in large crystals; in other words, that slip in these is produced by dislocations which are already present before the load is applied. Certainly, the processes of crystal growth favour the formation of dislocations during crystallisation. The misalignments formed during growth from a melt, as described at the end of section 14.3, can be resolved into groups of dislocations. In growth from dilute vapours and solutions the presence of dislocations is essential (see section 15.3). Experimental methods for locating dislocations in crystals by means of localised precipitation on them have been developed recently; in this manner Hedges and Mitchell† have recently been able to render dislocations visible in crystals of silver bromide by delineating them with precipitates of silver.

15.3 Geometrical Properties of Dislocations

The most important property of a dislocation is its *Burgers vector*. When the dislocation glides through a crystal, the atoms in its wake are sheared past their neighbours in a certain definite direction and by a certain definite amount; the vector which defines this atomic displacement is called the Burgers vector of the dislocation. In Fig. 115, for example, the Burgers vector is one atom long and points along the row of atoms.

Clearly, an arbitrary Burgers vector would not produce a mechanically stable crystal structure in the wake of the dislocation. The characteristic

---

* C. Herring and J. K. Galt, *Phys. Rev.*, 1952, **85**, 1060.
† J. M. Hedges and J. W. Mitchell, *Phil. Mag.*, 1953, **44**, 223.

dislocations of crystals must therefore possess Burgers vectors that are fixed in magnitude and direction by the crystal structure. These dislocations are classified into various types according to their vectors. A *unit* dislocation has a Burgers vector equal to one lattice vector (see section 3.3); the dislocation of Fig. 115 is an example. A *large* (or *multiple*, or *super*) dislocation has a Burgers vector that is greater than one lattice vector. The internal boundary of a microscopically visible slip band which extends partly across the crystal is a large dislocation with a vector some hundreds or thousands of atom spacings long. It is preferable to regard such a dislocation as a group of unit dislocations (see section 15.4).

A *perfect* dislocation has a Burgers vector equal to a whole number

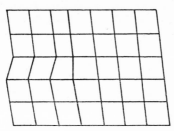

FIG. 117.—A Partial Dislocation.

of lattice vectors. The important feature here is that the lattice reconstructed in the wake of the dislocation is identical with that ahead of it. The dislocation of Fig. 115 is perfect. An *imperfect* dislocation has a Burgers vector not equal to a whole number of lattice vectors. Because of this it creates a new configuration of atoms in its wake. An example is shown in Fig. 117. Twinning and transformation dislocations are of this type. An imperfect dislocation is said to be a *partial*

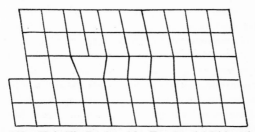

FIG. 118.—Unit Slip Produced by Two Partial Dislocations.

one when, as in Fig. 117, its Burgers vector is shorter than a unit lattice vector. It is clearly possible, as Fig. 118 shows, for two or more partial dislocations with suitable Burgers vectors to form collectively a unit dislocation. This unit dislocation is called an *extended* dislocation, or is said to have *dissociated* into a *pair* of partial dislocations (sometimes called a pair of *half* dislocations). It is believed that the slip dislocations in many crystals consist of closely-spaced pairs of partial dislocations.

Some types of imperfect dislocations are unable to glide and are thus described as being *sessile*. The simplest example of one of these is shown in Fig. 119. We have here a face-centred cubic lattice which is seen from a side view as a stack of horizontal (111) planes. On the left hand side the stacking follows its correct *ABC ABC* . . . order (see section 3.1), but on the other side part of an extra *B* layer has been inserted, producing the faulted sequence *ABC B ABC* . . . The edge of this extra layer is a partial dislocation with a Burgers vector perpendicular to the plane of the layers. This dislocation should glide along the direction of its Burgers vector, but it cannot do so because this does not lie in a proper slip plane for this lattice.

Although it cannot glide, the sessile dislocation of Fig. 119 can move slowly by what is called a *climbing* process. Suppose that there is a flow of vacant atomic sites in the crystal to the dislocation, and that these

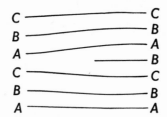

FIG. 119.—A Sessile Dislocation in the F.C.C. Lattice.

vacancies attach themselves on the edge of the extra half-sheet of atoms. There must then be a compensating outward flow of atoms from the half-sheet, i.e. the extra layer becomes gradually eaten away by the vacancies and its edge, which defines the centre of the dislocation, gradually moves (*climbs*) along the plane of the fault.

Sessile dislocations are believed to be able to form in various ways, e.g. as a result of faulty crystal growth, or by the collapse of cavities formed by the aggregation of vacancies, or as a result of collisions between slip dislocations moving on intersecting slip planes. They are important because, being unable to move by glide, they act as obstacles to mobile dislocations and make the crystal harder to deform plastically.

A dislocation is a *line defect* since it lies along the line forming the boundary of a sheared surface in the crystal. From this point of view the above diagrams of dislocations are all sections, cut across the line of the dislocation. We must now consider the orientation of a dislocation line in relation to its Burgers vector. There are three main classifications: (1) the *edge* dislocation, in which the line is perpendicular to the Burgers vector, (2) the *screw* dislocation, in which the line is parallel to the vector, and (3) the *mixed* or *compound* dislocation, in which the line is obliquely inclined to the vector.

Diagrams of edge and screw dislocations are shown in Figs. 120 and

121. In each case the plane of slip is *ABCD*, and the dislocation line *EF* marks the boundary between the slipped region *ABEF* and the unslipped one *FECD*. The structure of a mixed dislocation can be described in terms of those of edge and screw dislocations by resolving

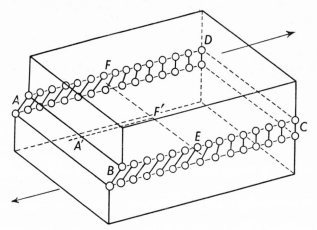

Fig. 120. An Edge Dislocation (along *EF*) in a Crystal.

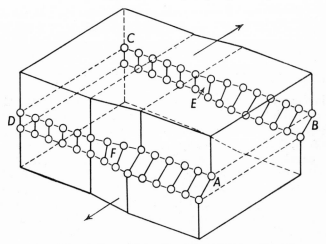

Fig. 121.—A Screw Dislocation (along *EF*) in a Crystal.

its Burgers vector into two components, an *edge* component perpendicular to the line, and a *screw* component parallel to the line; in this way we can regard the mixed dislocation as two superposed dislocations, edge and screw, with Burgers vectors of appropriate lengths.

An extremely important property of a dislocation line is the following one. Suppose that we have a family of parallel planes and project through them a dislocation line with a suitable Burgers vector which also

projects through them. Then the structure is changed by the dislocation from a family of parallel planes into a single spiral surface, or
helicoid. This property is true of edge, screw and mixed dislocations,
but can be seen most easily in the case of screw dislocations which
project vertically through the family of planes. Fig. 122 illustrates the
effect. If we begin on the top face, at the bottom of the cliff *BC*, and
then make one complete circuit round the dislocation line *AB*, always
remaining on this layer of the crystal, we arrive at the top of the cliff,
i.e. one layer *above* that where we began. The same is true of every

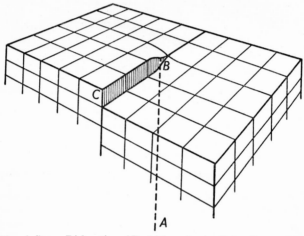

Fig. 122.—A Screw Dislocation *AB* which ends at a Point *B* on a Crystal Face.

layer in the crystal; the dislocation has converted the horizontal layers
of the crystal into a single screw-like surface.

This property is important in the growth of crystals. As Frank* has
emphasised, it is practically impossible to grow a crystal from a dilute
vapour or solution unless it contains dislocations, for the atoms deposit-
ing on the crystal need a ledge, such as *BC* in Fig. 122, against which
to attach themselves permanently to the crystal. Such ledges serve as
'growth steps' on the faces of the crystal. The actual observation of
these growth steps emanating from dislocations, on various types of
crystals including metal crystals grown from their vapours, has provided a striking confirmation of Frank's theory.

The spiral crystal structure round a dislocation is also likely to be
important in the growth of deformation twins and in shear transformations. Suppose in Fig. 123 that two crystals are joined coherently, and
that the interface between them makes a vertical step at *P*. Then *P*
is the site of a transformation dislocation. When this moves along the
interface, one of the crystals grows at the expense of the other one. This
transformation dislocation is thus analogous to the surface step in the

* F. C. Frank, *Advances in Physics*, 1952, **1**, 91.

growth of a crystal from a vapour. If the interface is pierced by the line of a screw dislocation, running from the one crystal into the other, then the spiral layer structure round the screw will ensure that there is always a transformation dislocation on the interface, available for use by the growing crystal. Theories of twinning and shear transformations based on this idea have been developed.*

What arrangement of the dislocation lines is to be expected in an

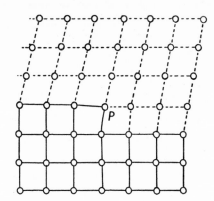

FIG. 123.—A Transformation Dislocation, *P*, on a Coherent Interface.

unworked crystal? Frank suggested, by analogy with foam structures, that the dislocation lines would link up into a three-dimensional network, as shown in Fig. 124. The average length of a link is thought to lie in the range 10^{-2} to 10^{-4} cm. for most crystals. Confirmation of the existence of such networks has been obtained by Hedges and Mitchell (*loc. cit.*) in their silver bromide crystals.

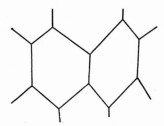

FIG. 124.—A Dislocation Network.

One would expect in such a network that most of the dislocation lines would not lie in planes favourable for slip, so that the mobile ones which happened to lie in good slip planes would be anchored at their ends (called *nodes*) by the immobile dislocations linked with them.

This is the basis of an important concept in the theory, called the

* A. H. Cottrell and B. A. Bilby, *Phil. Mag.*, 1951, **42**, 573; N. Thompson and D. J. Millard, *ibid.*, 1952, **43**, 422; B. A. Bilby, *ibid.*, 1953, **44**, 782.

Frank-Read source.* In Fig. 125 we consider a Frank-Read source which joins the nodes A and B, and has its slip plane in the plane of the diagram. When a shear stress is applied to the plane (or, in the case of a transformation dislocation, when the free energies of the phases are different) the dislocation line bends into a loop (stage *b*) which spreads round the nodes (stage *c*). The opposite arms of the dislocation line coalesce as the loop sweeps across the slip plane behind the source, with the result that a complete dislocation ring is formed, which is

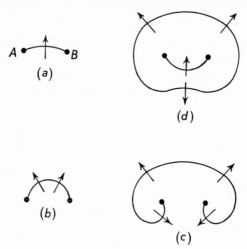

FIG. 125.—Stages in the Formation of a Dislocation Ring from a Frank-Read Source.

free to expand outwards across the slip plane, together with a new dislocation line bridging the nodes (*d*). The Frank-Read source is thus reconstituted after each revolution of the dislocation line and is capable of generating a virtually unlimited number of dislocation rings in its slip plane. This is thought to be the reason why very large amounts of slip, giving displacements of, for example, 1000 atomic spacings, occur on certain slip planes in plastically deformed crystals.

15.4 Elastic Properties of Dislocations

A dislocation in a crystal is the centre of a field of internal strain. At the centre of the dislocation the strains between the atoms are too intense to be treated accurately by the methods of the theory of elasticity. The strains diminish with increasing distance from the dislocation, however, and beyond a distance of a few atom spacings from the centre they become small enough to be treated by elasticity theory. Fortunately, many of the important elastic properties of dislocations depend on their strain fields at large distances from their centres and so can be

---

* F. C. Frank and W. T. Read, *Phys. Rev.*, 1950, **79**, 722.

evaluated accurately; the *energy* of the dislocation is such a property.

The strain field of a screw dislocation in an elastically isotropic crystal can be deduced by means of a very simple argument. Consider, in Fig. 126 (*a*), a thin ring of material of radius r and width b round a screw dislocation AB with a Burgers vector of length b. Then the ring will be distorted into a screw as shown. If we open out this strained ring, as in Fig. 126 (*b*), we see that a strip of length $2\pi r$ has been sheared to a displacement b at one end. Hence the shear strain at a distance r from the screw dislocation is given by

$$\theta = b/2\pi r \quad \ldots \ldots \ldots \ldots \quad (101)$$

The corresponding shear stress at this distance is $\mu\theta$, where μ is the elastic modulus of shear for the material.

To find the strain energy of this dislocation we use the result, from Hooke's law, that this energy is one-half of the product of stress and

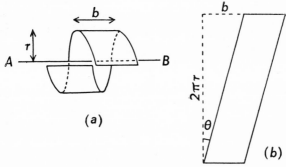

FIG. 126.

strain. Consider a cylinder round the dislocation, of length L and inner and outer radii r and $r+dr$, respectively. The strain in this cylinder is $b/2\pi r$, so that the strain energy *density* (i.e. the strain energy per unit volume) in it is $\frac{1}{2}\mu(b/2\pi r)^2$. The volume of the cylinder is $2\pi r\,dr.L$, and hence the strain energy in it is $(\mu b^2 L/4\pi)(dr/r)$. The total strain energy, U, of the whole field of the dislocation is the integral of this over all values of r, i.e.

$$U = (\mu b^2 L/4\pi)\log_e (r_1/r_0) \quad \ldots \ldots \ldots \quad (102)$$

where r_1 and r_0 are the outer and inner limits of integration. For a single dislocation at the centre of the crystal, r_1 is the radius of the crystal. It is more difficult to decide on a value of r_0 since this depends on conditions at the centre of the dislocation where elasticity theory breaks down. However, r_0 must be of the order of the interatomic spacing, and since it enters only logarithmically in the formula, no great error in U will be made by assuming such a value for r_0. To see the general magnitude of U consider a crystal for which $L = r_1 = 1$ cm. With $b = 3 \times 10^{-8}$ cm. and $r_0 = 10^{-7}$ cm. the strain energy is about $5 \times 10^7 \mu b^3$.

For most metals $\mu b^3 \simeq 5$ electron volts, so that the total strain energy is about $2 \cdot 5 \times 10^8$ electron volts. Clearly there can be no thermal creation of defects with such large energies as this. The largeness is due essentially to the long length of the dislocation; expressed in terms of the energy per atom of length along the dislocation line, it is only about 7 electron volts.

The logarithmic function in formula 102 should be noted. It implies that the energy of the dislocation is not concentrated at the centre. For example, the total strain energy within the radius $r=10^{-4}$ cm. is somewhat smaller than that which lies beyond this radius. This is a consequence of the *long-range* character of the strain field. For example, from formula 101, the elastic strain even at a distance 10^{-4} cm. from the dislocation is as large as the applied elastic strain at which soft crystals begin to deform plastically. This means that the movements of dislocations in crystals are strongly influenced by each other's presence.

The formula 102 also shows that the strain energy is proportional to the square of the length of the Burgers vector. Thus, a large dislocation

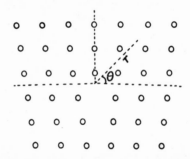

Fig. 127.—Strain Field Round an Edge Dislocation.

with a vector of length $2b$ has an energy $4b^2$, but if this splits into two unit dislocations, which move well apart from each other, the energy falls to $2b^2$. This is why large dislocations tend to dissociate into smaller ones. It also shows that two dislocations with the same Burgers vectors repel one another, since the further they move apart, the more their energy changes from $4b^2$ to $2b^2$. Conversely, two dislocations with parallel Burgers vectors of opposite signs are attracted towards each other; if they coalesce they cancel one another out and the strain energy falls to zero.

The elasticity theory of edge dislocations is similar to the above but more complicated. The strain field round an edge does not have such simple symmetry as that round the screw, because the atoms on one side of the dislocation are compressed (see Fig. 127) and those on the other side are expanded. The effect of this is to introduce a trigonometric factor into the formula (101) for the strain. For example, the *dilatation strain*, Δ, at a point with co-ordinates r and θ relative to the edge is given by

$$\Delta = -\frac{b}{2\pi r}\left[\frac{(1-2\nu)}{(1-\nu)}\sin\theta\right] \quad\ldots\ldots\ldots (103)$$

where r and θ are defined as in Fig. 127, and where $\nu(\simeq 1/3)$ is Poisson's ratio; positive and negative values of Δ indicate expansion and compression, respectively.

The angular dependence of the strain field does not appreciably affect the strain energy, which is given by a formula similar to equation 102, but it does affect the forces acting between edge dislocations. Although the rule that two dislocations repel if they have the same sign (i.e. parallel Burgers vectors) and attract if they have opposite signs (i.e. anti-parallel vectors) remains true, the resolved component of the force in the direction of slip behaves in a somewhat complicated manner. If, in Fig. 128

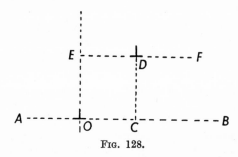

FIG. 128.

(using an obvious symbol to represent an edge dislocation), one dislocation lies at O on the slip plane AB, and another at D on the plane EF, then D is attracted towards the point E when $OC<CD$, and repelled from it when $OC>CD$. The force in the latter case is mainly due to the repulsion along the line between the centres of the dislocations which, when $OC>OD$, has a large component along the slip planes. The attraction which occurs when $OC<CD$ is a different effect, however, due to the lower symmetry of the strain field round an edge.

It can be understood with the aid of Fig. 129, which shows edge dislocations in crystal strips. As diagram a shows, the extra half-sheet of atoms on the upper side of the dislocation bends the crystal into the shape shown. To make a crystal which contains two dislocations we can join together two of these strips. Obviously they fit together more neatly, with less expenditure of strain energy, if the bends occur in the same places in each strip. Crystals (a) and (b) would join with less distortion than crystals (b) and (c), for example, so that there is a tendency for parallel edge dislocations to align themselves vertically, one above the other. When a large number of edges align themselves like this they are said to form a dislocation *wall* (Fig. 129 d).

Many observations have been made of such walls, and, according to the nature of the experimental conditions in each case, these walls have been called *polygonisation boundaries, small-angle boundaries, bend planes*, and *kink planes*. Because they can be seen with the aid of a microscope, and because the difference in orientation between the crystals they separate is measurable, they form an excellent testing ground for the theory of dislocations. The main things that have been studied are as

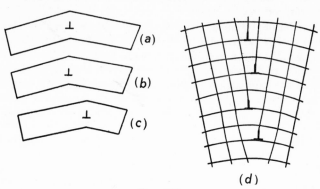

FIG. 129.

follows: (1) the formation of the walls (*polygonisation*) during the annealing of plastically bent crystals; (2) the measurement of the spacing of the dislocations along a wall, as revealed by the spacing of etch-pits formed at the ends of the dislocations; (3) the measurement of the energy of the boundary (which can be predicted from the strain energies of its dislocations) as a function of the orientation difference between the grains; (4) the observation of the movement of the boundaries under

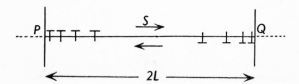

FIG. 130.—The Piling-up of Dislocations at Barriers.

stress, caused by the gliding in their slip planes of the dislocations forming the boundaries.

These boundaries can be described as 'vertical' groupings of dislocations, since the latter are aligned above one another. The other important grouping of dislocations observed in crystals is the 'horizontal' one, a simple example of which is illustrated in Fig. 130. Here a Frank-Read source S creates dislocations which run along their slip plane until they are held up by obstacles (e.g. grain boundaries) at P and Q. The mutual elastic repulsion of the dislocations piled up at each obstacle spreads them out into a distribution of the type shown in the diagram.

Furthermore, their stress fields combine to exert a 'back-stress' at the source S which opposes the externally applied stress and eventually stops the source acting. The number of dislocations needed to do this can be estimated roughly in the following way. Let the applied stress be σ and the shear modulus be μ. Then, before slip takes place, the elastic strain over the whole region between P and Q is σ/μ. When slip occurs the elastic strain between P and Q relaxes to some lower value, being exchanged for plastic strain in the slip band PQ. If the stress needed to operate the source is sufficiently small compared with σ, the surface PQ can be regarded as similar to a *shear crack*, i.e. a surface across which no shear stress can be sustained. This means that all the original elastic strain in a roughly circular region with PQ as its dia-meter is relaxed. Since the original elastic strain is σ/μ and the diameter is $2L$, this relaxation requires a slip displacement of $2L(\sigma/\mu)$ to occur at S. Let n dislocation rings be created at S. Then the displacement they produce at S is nb, where b is the length of the unit Burgers vector; equating these displacements, we obtain

$$n = 2L\sigma/\mu b \ . \ . \ . \ . \ . \ . \ . \ . \ . \ . \ (104)$$

In a long slip band, e.g. $L \simeq 10^{-2}$ cm., the number of dislocations piled up at the ends can become very large, e.g. $n \simeq 1000$. A piled-up group of n dislocations is, as mentioned in section 15.3, effectively the same as a large dislocation with a Burgers vector nb, and its total stress field will reach n times as far, for the same intensity, as that of a single unit dislocation. Thus there will be large highly-stressed regions of the crystal round such groups, and it is believed that the eventual fracture of plastically strained crystals originates in them.*

These intense stresses round piled-up groups are also believed to play a major part in strain-hardening, since they have such a strong effect on the motion of other dislocations in nearby slip planes. From this point of view, the process of softening by annealing, after cold work, is thought to involve the redistribution of the dislocations, by climbing out of their slip planes with the aid of vacancies (see section 15.3), from these highly stressed 'horizontal' distributions into comparatively un-stressed 'vertical' ones. This is probably most important during the *recovery* stage of annealing. The *recrystallisation* stage, which appears later, involves the formation of incoherent *large-angle* boundaries which sweep through the whole crystal structure and replace it by less distorted material.

In both the vertical and horizontal groupings of dislocations the group extends preferentially along some plane in the material. A similar effect appears to govern the shapes of deformation twins, regions of shear transformation, and kink bands, in crystals. A 'horizontal' grouping of dislocations round a twinned or sheared region, allowing for the fact

* N. F. Mott, *Phil. Mag.*, 1952, **43**, 1151; *ibid.*, 1953, **44**, 187, 742; *Proc. Roy. Soc.*, 1953, **A220**, 1.

that each dislocation must lie on a different atomic layer, should appear as in Fig. 131 (*a*), which is otherwise similar to Fig. 130. The alternative is the vertical group, shown in diagram (*b*), which is constructed essentially of two parallel dislocation walls. Deformation twins in a-iron appear to be of the horizontal type, since the plane of the twin (112) contains the twinning direction [11Ī] and is also the plane of shear. In shear transformations on the other hand the groupings are usually vertical, and the *habit plane* (see section 14.5) in such cases is often not a simple crystal plane. Various theories* have been proposed to explain these habit planes in terms of the fitting together of the atoms of the two crystals at their common interface.

In their theory of the formation of martensite from austenite in steel, Jaswon and Wheeler assumed that the new lattice is produced by a

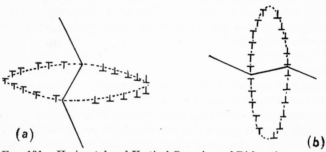

FIG. 131.—Horizontal and Vertical Groupings of Dislocations round Sheared Regions in a Crystal.

homogeneous deformation of the parent lattice. They deduced, from this deformation, that three non-parallel planes in the parent lattice remain unrotated during the transformation of the new lattice, and they identified one of these, the (225) plane, as a habit plane of martensite. Subsequently, Bowles pointed out that the criterion of non-rotation of the habit plane was not sufficient; there must also be no overall distortion *within* the habit plane. Only special types of homogeneous deformations can provide planes of this type and in general the observed lattice relations cannot be described by them.

As a result, Bowles returned to an ealier theory of Greninger and Troiano, in which two distinct shear deformations were postulated to occur. The first is a homogeneous shear on the habit plane, which remains unrotated and undistorted. The second, which completes the

* M. A. Jaswon and J. A. Wheeler, *Acta Cryst.*, 1948, **1**, 216; J. S. Bowles, *Acta Cryst.*, 1951, **4**, 162; A. B. Greninger and A. R. Troiano, *Trans. A.I.M.E.*, 1940, **140**, 307; 1949, **185**, 590; J. S. Bowles, C. S. Barrett, and L. Guttman, *Trans. A.I.M.E.*, 1950, **188**, 1478; M. S. Wheeler, D. S. Lieberman and T. A. Read, *Trans. A.I.M.E.*, 1953, **197**, 1503; E. C. Bain, *Trans. A.I.M.E.*, 1924, **70**, 25; E. S. Machlin and M. Cohen, *Trans. A.I.M.E.*, 1951, **191**, 1019; J. S. Bowles and J. K. Mackenzie, *Acta Met.*, 1954, **2**, 129, 138, 224; F. C. Frank, *Acta Met.*, 1953, **1**, 15; L. C. Chang and T. A. Read, *Trans. A.I.M.E.*, 1951, **191**, 47; Z. S. Basinski and J. W. Christian, *Acta Met.*, 1954, **2**, 148.

crystallographic change, occurs obliquely *across* the habit plane (actually along the twinning plane and direction in martensite); it is homogeneous on a microscopic scale (within lamellae not less than 18 atomic planes in thickness) but is macroscopically *heterogeneous*, such that over large distances in the habit plane it gives no overall distortion. Bowles developed this theory by replacing the first shear by the most general type of homogeneous deformation (an invariant plane strain) capable of providing an undistorted and unrotated plane, and a theory of the same type was applied by Bowles, Barrett and Guttman to the transformation in indium-thallium alloys.

Another approach was made by Wechsler, Lieberman and Read. Starting from an early suggestion by Bain, they proposed that microscopically small regions of austenite transform by homogeneous deformation to the final structure, and they examined the conditions under which such deformations, differently oriented, in neighbouring regions may together produce a macroscopically undistorted plane. The observed deformation is then that part of the two different strains which does not cancel. This theory can be regarded as an alternative formulation of a 'two-distortions' type of theory, such as that of Bowles, in which the first and second distortions occur simultaneously.

Other generalizations are possible. The second shear need not necessarily be on both the twinning plane and the twinning direction of the martensite lattice, a point which is brought out in the analysis given by Machlin and Cohen. Bowles and Mackenzie emphasize in their treatment that the concept of the habit plane should be generalized, while retaining the notion of zero macroscopic distortion, to include the possibility of a small uniform dilatation of the transformed lattice.

Frank's treatment of the martensite problem is based directly on dislocation theory. He shows that the second, and inhomogeneous, distortion can be produced by a row of screw dislocations moving in the transformation interface, situated one in every sixth pair of (011) planes. These dislocations shear blocks of six planes by one atomic spacing past one another. Within each block a homogeneous shear occurs such that neighbouring planes slide past one another by one-sixth of a spacing, so that the total 'Burgers vector' of the second shear is zero when measured over groups of six layers. The concept of transformation interfaces as rows of dislocations has received strong support from the observations of Chang and Read, and Basinski and Christian, of the movements of such interfaces through gold-cadmium and indium-thallium alloys, and by analyses of the deformations produced in the wake of such interfaces.

15.5 Obstacles to the Movement of Dislocations

What determines the stress at which a metal or alloy begins to deform plastically? Two points are important here: (1) the calculated stress for moving a dislocation through a slip plane in an otherwise perfect metal crystal is far smaller than the lowest observed yield stress; (2) the yield stress is very *structure-sensitive*, i.e. its value is affected greatly by the presence of foreign atoms, precipitates and grain boundaries in the material. These lead to the conclusion, on which the whole theory of the yield strength rests, that the observed hardness of the material is caused by imperfections in the structure which obstruct the dislocations. Various kinds of obstacles may be encountered, and these can obstruct it in various ways. In polycrystals, for example, a dislocation which reaches the boundary of its own grain cannot continue its glide motion into another grain, when the plane and direction of slip change from one grain to another, and it sticks at the grain boundary and obstructs the other dislocations following it in the slip plane. In work-hardened metals the evidence suggests that the main obstacles to dislocations are other dislocations moving on intersecting slip planes.

Foreign atoms in a metal, either in solution or grouped into second phases in various states of dispersion, interact with dislocations in several ways. The importance of these interactions is shown by the fact that the most common method of improving the mechanical properties of metals is by alloying. A simple but important interaction of a dislocation and a solute atom can be appreciated with the aid of Fig. 127. The form of the dilatation field round the dislocation should be noticed; those atoms above the dislocation are squeezed into holes too small for them and those below are stretched to fit large holes. The energy of the dislocation would be reduced if the *natural* sizes of these atoms could be altered to fit those of their sites round the dislocation. This is possible in a solid solution containing atoms of different sizes, and there is a tendency for such solute atoms to migrate to dislocations, those which expand the lattice collecting in the expanded side of the slip plane and vice versa.

A dislocation which becomes surrounded in this way by an *atmosphere* of solute atoms (which in a more concentrated solution may condense into a precipitate on the dislocation) cannot glide easily at temperatures where diffusion is slow since it is held back by them. A large force is needed to break the bond between the dislocation and its atmosphere, but once the dislocation does break away into cleaner regions of the crystal it can then move easily under smaller forces, as shown in Fig. 132. This has several practical consequences:—

(1) When plastic yielding begins, the specimen gives way suddenly to the applied stress, showing that it has become softer. This is the phenomenon of the *sharp yield point*, observed in many metals and alloys, and notably in soft iron containing carbon and nitrogen.

(2) Once yielding has occurred no yield point is seen (provided the temperature is too low for diffusion) during a second loading of the specimen applied immediately after the first one. This is because the dislocations have been pulled away from their atmospheres and the large break-away force no longer has to be applied. The material is then said to be in the *overstrained* condition.

(3) On resting the overstrained specimen, the solute atoms are given a chance to diffuse to the new positions of the dislocations, and this causes a return of the yield point. The material is then said to become *strain aged*.

Making an obvious military analogy, we can say that the atmosphere provides a 'defensive line' resisting the advance of the dislocation. This defensive line can be overcome only with difficulty, but once a 'break-through' occurs in one part of it, further resistance is small and a rapid advance follows. A 'defence in depth', on the other hand, is provided by other distributions of solute atoms in the crystal, not localised in dislocations but dispersed either as individuals in homogeneous solution or clustered together in randomly distributed precipitates; these

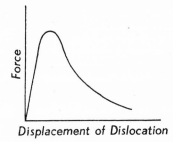

FIG. 132.—The Force Needed to Pull a Dislocation away from an Atmosphere of Foreign Atoms.

offer a resistance to the dislocation that is statistically independent of its position in the slip plane. Once the dislocation overcomes one obstacle the section of its line which has surmounted it moves on a little way to the next obstacle, and so on. No 'break-through' is possible and, in consequence, no yield point is observed; there is instead a hardening which persists during plastic flow.

The theory of dislocations is able to provide an explanation for the critical size of dispersion of a precipitate at which the hardening is a maximum. If the precipitate is dispersed on too fine a scale the random internal stresses acting on the dislocation line from nearby precipitates largely cancel one another and the net obstruction from them is small. If the dispersion is on too coarse a scale, on the other hand, so that there are large regions of 'clean' crystal between isolated massive particles of precipitate, the dislocation line can, by bending, curl its way through the spaces between the particles and so 'by-pass' them; again the hardening is small. Between these two extremes there is a critical stage where the internal stresses acting on the dislocation do not cancel and where the particles are too close for the dislocation line to spread between them; the material is then hard.

References for Further Reading

General texts on crystal plasticity are the following:

'Plasticity of Crystals.' E. Schmid and W. Boas, F. A. Hughes, 1950.
'An Introduction to the Physics of Metals and Alloys.' W. Boas, Wiley, 1947.
'The Distortion of Metal Crystals.' C. F. Elam, Oxford, 1936.

For the theory of dislocations:

'Dislocations in Crystals.' W. T. Read, McGraw-Hill, 1953.
'Dislocations and Plastic Flow in Crystals.' A. H. Cottrell, Oxford, 1953.
'Progress in Metal Physics, I', A. H. Cottrell (Ed. B. Chalmers), 1949; IV, 1953.

For crystal growth and experimental observations of dislocations:

F. C. Frank, *Advances in Physics*, 1952, **1**, 91.
A. J. Forty, *Advances in Physics*, 1954, **3**, 1.
'Crystal Growth and Dislocations.' A. R. Verma, Butterworth, 1953.

For Twinning and Strain Transformations:

'Structure of Metals.' C. S. Barrett, McGraw-Hill, 1952.
'Twinning and Diffusionless Transformations in Metals.' E. O. Hall, Butterworth, 1954.
'Progress in Metal Physics, III'. J. S. Bowles and C. S. Barrett (Ed. B. Chalmers), 1952.
'Progress in Metal Physics, IV'. D. Turnbull and J. Hollomon (Ed. B. Chalmers), 1953.
R. W. Cahn, *Advances in Physics*, 1954, **3**, 363.

INDEX